ᵗS-
ᵀⁿᴬ

WHITE MAN'S MEDICINE

WHITE MAN'S MEDICINE

Government Doctors and the Navajo, 1863–1955

ROBERT A. TRENNERT

University of New Mexico Press
Albuquerque

Library of Congress Cataloging-in-Publication Data

Trennert, Robert A.
White man's medicine: government doctors and the Navajo, 1863–1955
Robert A. Trennert. — 1st ed.
    p.   cm.
Includes bibliographical references and index.
ISBN 0-8263-1839-8
  1. Navajo Indians—Medical care—History.
  2. Navajo Indians—Health and hygiene.
  3. Navajo Indians—Medical care—Government policy—History.
  4. Public health administration—Arizona—History.
  5. Public health administration—New Mexico—History.
  6. United States. Office of Indian Affairs.
  I. Title.
RA448.5.I5T73 1998
362.1'089'972—dc21
97-36481
CIP

CONTENTS

ILLUSTRATIONS

PREFACE

Despite considerable interest in Indian history over the past three decades, there has been surprisingly little scholarship on federal efforts to provide health care to the reservation population. Yet between the mid-nineteenth century and 1955, when the U.S. Public Health Service took charge of Indian health care, the Indian Service developed an elaborate, if inadequate, system of doctors, nurses, hospitals, and even medical research activities related to specific Indian health issues. During the nineteenth century this effort was wholly insufficient, with a few poorly trained and underfunded doctors attempting to bring western medical technology to a native population wary of the "White Man's Medicine," yet suffering from many medical problems. Indeed, much of the early medical work was intended primarily to aid the assimilation process—to get the "uncivilized" Indians away from their reliance on native healers, who were viewed as obstacles to progress.

During the first half of the present century the Indian Service began to develop a more modern medical network. Hampered by a persistent lack of funding, the medical service nevertheless attempted to reach out to the reservation peoples with special physicians, field nurses, clinics, and educational programs. By the 1930s some success had been attained in treating such diseases as trachoma, yet many ailments, especially tuberculosis, still disproportionately affected the native population. The New Deal era also produced the first governmental efforts to accept the validity to native healing arts and to create a cross-cultural exchange. Further medical advances were retarded by the massive disruptions associated with World War II. The Indian medical service never recovered from the wartime emergency, and with the Termination movement of the 1950s opponents of the Indian Bureau seized on an unacceptable medical situation to remove medical responsibilities from the beleaguered agency.

I first became aware of the close relationship between medical matters and the operation of federal Indian policy while compiling a history of Phoenix Indian School. Issues related to disease, contagion, and prevention occupied a significant portion of official policy and personal interaction. Intrigued by the great amount of documentary materials available and the lack of prior interest in the subject, I soon began to collect information. How to compose and focus the study proved quite vexing. Realizing that an overview of federal medical activities would require an extraordinarily large study, I ultimately decided to focus on Navajo health care between 1863 and 1955 as a case study. The post-1955 activities of the Public Health Service (Indian Health Service) represent a different and more successful story, which is presently being compiled by other historians.

The Navajo offer a particularly good case study because of their large population, widespread experience with communicable diseases, and the presence of strong traditional healers. Government doctors have worked among the Diné since their arrival at the Bosque Redondo reservation in 1863. During the next ninety-two years the Navajo people accepted some aspects of western medicine, yet fiercely fought against pressure to abandon their own healers as the government desired. The result was a long and complicated period of cultural conflict, bureaucratic bungling, politics, bigotry, and good and bad white doctors molded together to battle an overwhelming array of medical difficulties.

This study focuses largely on the efforts of Indian Service doctors and nurses to deliver medical services to the Navajos. The result is thus an account of federal Indian policy, seen largely from the perspective of government employees. Wherever possible, however, I have attempted to include the reaction and viewpoint of the Navajo people. Unfortunately, the scarcity of recorded Indian commentary has made it difficult to secure the response of individuals. Yet the Navajo were far from silent and their reaction to medical issues appears in various ways—most often through their refusal to take advantage of government services, preferring to rely on traditional medicine. Much of the Navajo reaction was recorded by government officials, who neither appreciated nor respected Indian ways. Nevertheless, analysis of existing records sheds considerable light on Navajo concerns, fears, and beliefs.

Finally, it should be understood that this is not a medical history. I am by no means a medical specialist and it is not my desire to provide a detailed analysis and description of the ailments that pestered the tribe. Medical conditions and terminology are therefore presented in a very basic form. From this vantage point, the layman can understand some of the basic medical issues confronting government doctors without becoming bogged down in technical terms. For the purposes of this study it is much more important to understand the social, cultural, and policy issues involved as western medicine was introduced to the Navajo peoples of the Southwest. Issues related to specific disease histories are left to specialists with more medical knowledge.

I am indebted to many individuals and institutions for help and encouragement in preparing this book. First I wish to express my appreciation to Wilbur R. Jacobs, now retired from the University of California at Santa Barbara, for encouraging my scholarly pursuits across the many years since graduate school. It also would have been impossible to complete this study without the help of my colleague at ASU Peter Iverson, who offered sage advice and willingly read much of the manuscript. Thanks also go to Norman Bender and Gerald Thompson for reviewing early chapters and encouraging me to push forward.

Arizona State University has been exceedingly generous in providing me with the time and resources to complete the book. In particular, I received released time in 1992–93 as a recipient of a Graduate College Research and Creative Activity Award, and a sabbatical leave in the fall of 1995. In addition, small research grants were provided from time to time. Finally, the Department of History has been extremely supportive. I wish especially to thank Sharon Brockus, departmental administrative associate, and graduate students Elizabeth James, Karen Condon, and Wade Davies for their helpful assistance.

A number of libraries and archives have gladly helped me find materials for this study. I am particularly grateful to Patricia A. Etter of the Labriola National American Indian Data Center at ASU, Ann Cummings at the National Archives in Washington, D.C., and Suzanne Dewberry at the Regional Archives Branch at Laguna Niguel, California. These three women cheerfully provided me with guidance and information in my search to uncover the activities of government doctors. The staffs of a number of other archives also contributed to the project. Among them are the archivists and librarians at the Arizona Historical Society, the Arizona State Library and Archives, the New Mexico State Records Center and Archives, the University of Arizona Library (Special Collections), Norman Smith Memorial Library (Hinton, Oklahoma), Maine Historical Society, Fredonia Public Library (Fredonia, Kansas), The Presbyterian Historical Society, The Episcopal Diocese of Rochester (New York), the Episcopal Diocese of New York, and others.

All of these individuals and institutions have aided me in this project. To no one, however, am I more indebted than to my wife Linda, who put up with all my frustrations, and my children Anthony and Kristina, who chose not to pester their dad too much by going out on their own.

TEMPE, ARIZONA
JUNE 1996

CHAPTER ONE

WORLDS APART
Contrasting Medical Practices

The Indian medicine man, who through the traditions of the race, rules, and wields a powerful influence, through his practice of healing or attempting to heal is the most influential man of the tribe. They encourage and breed superstition.

E. H. PLUMMER, NAVAJO AGENT

Physicians working among the Navajo peoples during the nineteenth century were astonished to discover that their patients saw little advantage to western-style medicine, generally preferring to rely upon their own healers and remedies. To men and women steeped in modern theories of medicine, the Navajo preference for a centuries-old approach to treatment appeared superstitious and out of place in the contemporary world. For white doctors, however, Indian medicine represented more than just an antiquated relic of the past. Non-Indian medical specialists often opposed the continuation of traditional healing practices because their existence appeared to threaten the "civilization" program they represented. Thus the type of health care utilized by the Navajo peoples symbolized far more than their physical welfare; it became involved with the government's determination to destroy native culture and replace it with the values of white America.

The roots of this conflict reach far back into history. Originating from totally different traditions, Native American and European cultures developed contrasting concepts of medicine, health care, and healing. For the Navajo, these differences held no significance until the United States took possession of the American Southwest. Once under American jurisdiction, the Navajo were subjected to the dictates of federal Indian policy. Sometimes by force, the United States government imposed programs designed to establish peace and, ultimately, to end the "Indian problem" by assimilating the native population into American society. One aspect of this policy involved the effort to provide health care to the Indians, motivated as much by a desire to demonstrate the superiority of Anglo-European culture as to minister to the sick. For many years this effort met with marginal success as the Navajo clung to their traditional ways.

Before examining the details of federal medical efforts among the Navajo, it is necessary to offer some understanding of the medical condition of the tribe in the mid-nineteenth century, their traditional healing practices, and the contrasting theories of western medicine and Indian policy.

NAVAJO HEALTH PRIOR TO THE 1850S

When the ancestors of the modern Navajo people entered the American Southwest sometime in the dimly remembered past (most probably between the thirteenth and fifteenth centuries), they brought with them a system that satisfactorily dealt with their medical and health needs.[1] The exact status of Navajo health conditions is, of course, difficult to determine with any certainty before outside observers arrived on the scene. However, some assumptions about Navajo health and medical treatment may be ventured with a fair degree of assurance. Because the health of any prehistoric people depended on nutritional habits, sanitary practices, and the nature of the diseases to which they were susceptible, the remaining fragmentary evidence provides a few clues to health conditions. When these factors are placed in the context of other archaeological and historical information, it becomes possible to project a picture of Navajo well-being at a time when medical practices depended solely on custom and religion.

The Navajo are descendants of Athapaskan-speaking peoples who once resided in the Pacific Northwest and over a span of years migrated south along the western edge of the Great Plains and into the southwestern portion of the present United States, arriving in all likelihood well before the Spanish *entrada*. A nomadic and hunting people before taking up residence in the Southwest, the Navajo left little archaeological evidence of their lifeways. Once located in the Four Corners country, the scattered groups of Navajo continued to rely on hunting for their nutritional needs, procuring game animals ranging in size from bighorn sheep and deer to rabbits and squirrels, and by gathering natural plants and herbs. Residence in northern New Mexico and Arizona also introduced the Navajo bands to the agricultural economy of their Pueblo neighbors. From this source they learned to plant and harvest corn and other crops. Certainly by the time that Spanish explorers arrived in the late sixteenth century, the Navajo were cultivating a variety of plants, although they most likely continued to rely on hunting and gathering as their main source of food.[2]

On the basis of what is understood about Navajo groups prior to European contact, it is possible to make a few assumptions about their physical health.

It can be argued that in some important ways the Navajo were more healthy and robust than their European contemporaries, yet in other ways they were plagued with various ailments, some very simple, that made life difficult. Recent studies suggest that most of the contagious diseases that later decimated the American Indian (including the Navajo) were imported by the Europeans and did not affect pre-Columbian groups. Diseases such as smallpox, trachoma, measles, influenza, cholera, typhoid, and certain venereal diseases did not exist among the aboriginal population of North America prior to the arrival of Europeans. As a consequence, the Indians had developed no immunities to such diseases, making them extremely vulnerable to the so-called virgin soil epidemics that came along with the invading white population.[3]

Although most of the diseases that eventually took a fearful toll in Indian lives were alien, other common maladies were clearly present. These included such ailments as dysentery, pneumonia, various insect-born and viral fevers, round worms, non-venereal syphilis, a wide variety of nutritional diseases and bacterial pathogens, and food poisonings. Current evidence also suggests that tuberculosis existed among the prehistoric tribes of North America. Scholars disagree on the extent to which pre-Columbian peoples suffered from this disease, but general opinion today holds that tuberculosis was present in some form prior to 1492. Even so, the disease was unlikely to have played a significant role in native health conditions. Supporting this conclusion are the observations of early European visitors, who made little reference to the disease, and the paucity of native remedies to deal with the symptoms of tuberculosis.[4]

Other diseases, such as cancer, also existed, but were apparently rare. Pre-1700 Navajos existed on an austere diet. Depending primarily on gathering foods from the natural environment, they relied on such staples as cactus fruit, piñon nuts, wild cherries, and meat from the small game they killed, particularly deer and rabbits. They also grew an undetermined amount of corn and beans. Most meats and vegetables were cooked before consumption while ears of corn were baked in pits. As a result, native dietary intake usually ranked high in fiber and low in fat, significantly limiting the number and types of malignancies. On the other hand, because of the frequent scarcity of food and the fact that overeating often followed periods of famine, digestive problems were common. In addition, infections killed many infants, women died in childbirth, and degenerative arthritis seems to have crippled many adults. Because of the consumption of stone-ground grains, teeth wore out at a relatively young age, creating additional nutrition problems.[5]

During the pre-Columbian period, native mortality was high and life expectancy, on the whole, quite short by today's standards. Nonetheless, given the circumstances, the native population was comparatively healthy. As one early twentieth-century medical specialist noted, it could be logically assumed that the early Indians "lived a more natural and active life, were better inured to hardship, and, with the exception of particular localities and periods, were better provided with suitable food."[6]

The European conquest of New Mexico impacted Navajo health in several ways. Although the Navajo remained on the fringe of Spanish influence and were never brought under the direct control of either Spain or Mexico, events occurring nearby worked their way into Navajo life. Many of these changes came by way of the Pueblo Indians, who lived in more intimate contact with the Europeans. In this sense, the Pueblo served as unwitting culture brokers, especially following the Revolt of 1680, when many of them mixed with the Navajo, bringing revolutionary new goods, techniques, and cultural concepts to the Diné.

Two major health-related developments occurred as a result of European presence in New Mexico. Most important, the outsiders brought with them a variety of new foods, substantially modifying the Navajo diet. Meat from sheep and goats (and to a lesser extent cattle) transformed Navajo culture and subsistence patterns. Once they acquired the ability to herd and breed these hardy animals, their standard of living and population increased dramatically. Animal products became a primary source of food. The Navajo fully utilized this resource, including cheese and other basic dairy products available from goat's milk. Agricultural products, imported by the Spaniards, also enriched Navajo life. Such items as peaches, watermelons, and some varieties of wheat added nutritional variety and promoted a general state of well-being. The Navajo never became full-time agriculturalists like their Pueblo neighbors, but they knew enough about growing crops to provide a significant supplement for the high level of protein they ordinarily consumed. Although the care of large flocks forced them to migrate between summer and winter grazing camps, families frequently maintained agricultural fields.[7] Thus, from hunters and gatherers the Diné became a more pastoral and well-fed people, spread over a considerable area and healthier than ever before.

Although the Navajo people lived relatively well for the century and a half between 1700 and 1850, they were not immune to the impact of European diseases. Despite scant records, it is evident that alien diseases struck the Pueblo peoples of New Mexico, killing thousands. Early accounts also note the abandonment of nearly a hundred Pueblo villages, suggesting a precipitous population decline. Because some Pueblo groups intermarried with the Navajo, especially after the 1680 Revolt, it may be assumed that contagious diseases were transmitted from one group to the other. The extensive slave trade and livestock raiding that developed in the Southwest may also have spread infections.[8]

Alien diseases no doubt extracted a heavy toll on the Navajo, particularly in the early years of European presence. While there is no information to suggest the magnitude of the population decline, certain Navajo characteristics may have lessened the impact of some forms of contagion. The Navajo tradition of living in widely scattered locations rather than in villages (like the Pueblo), and the habit of abandoning or destroying any dwelling associated with death, may have retarded the spread of disease. Nevertheless, what Percy M. Ashburn has described as "crowd-type" European diseases, such as smallpox and measles, made occasional appearances among the Navajo. Other contagious diseases also left their mark. Some experts believe that trachoma, an eye infection that frequently caused blindness, entered the Southwest as early as the expedition of Francisco Vásquez de Coronado. Venereal diseases such as syphilis and gonorrhea most likely developed in the Old World and were imported into the Western Hemisphere shortly after the voyages of Columbus. There is little question that syphilis, in all its debilitating forms, spread among the American Indians during the early phases of European conquest, probably reaching the Navajo during the era of Spanish occupation.[9] Nevertheless, it appears that venereal diseases were not widespread among the Navajo prior to 1846. Although conclusive documentation is lacking, a comment that the Navajo were free of venereal diseases, attributed to a white man living with the tribe in the early 1840s, suggests that it was not a significant problem. Remarks by Charles Bent shortly after the American occupation of New Mexico, to the effect that the Navajo were the only Indians he knew whose population was actually on the increase, second that opinion.[10]

Thus, from the fragmentary evidence available, it appears that the Navajo people were relatively healthy and prosperous at the time of the American occupation of the Southwest. With a population of over ten thousand, they occupied an extensive area ranging from the mountainous area of northern New Mexico to the valleys west of Canyon de Chelly in eastern Arizona. Warfare with the Hispanic population continued to exact a toll, but from a medical standpoint they were generally a well-fed, robust people who experienced relatively modest physical adversity. Under these circumstances, traditional Navajo healing systems were able to cope with most health problems.

TRADITIONAL NAVAJO HEALING PRACTICES

Anthropologists such as Marshall T. Newman maintain that Native American systems of medical care were well enough advanced to offer competent treatment for most pre-Columbian health problems. It was therefore not until the arrival of European diseases that Indian practitioners were overwhelmed. In the case of the Navajo, their medical delivery system remained intact well into the twentieth century, and even today it plays a significant role among the reservation population. The persistence of Navajo medicine is explained by its unique character, and the ability to adapt to changing circumstances. Although traditional Navajo medical technology has been analyzed by many scholars, it is also true, as Newman states, that "only a small portion of native American Indian medical knowledge has come down to us, and all we have is an iceberg's tip."[11]

The traditional Navajo method of health care contrasts sharply with the scientific philosophy of western medicine. For most purposes, Navajo healing practices can be divided into two distinct spheres: the treatment of ordinary aches and pains, and the ceremonial system for handling more serious problems. Like all indigenous peoples prior to the twentieth century, the Diné relied upon a variety of herbs and other plant substances to treat common ailments. Over a hundred roots, seeds, leaves, and other natural products have been used historically by tribal members for both internal and external purposes. The resultant pharmacopeia provided substances that could be used as laxatives, purges, diuretics, poultices, and pain relievers. The Navajo used plant products to treat a wide variety of problems, ranging from spider bites and sores to headaches, cramps, gastro-intestinal problems, and even gunshot wounds. Another natural remedy was the sweat lodge, where heated stones sprinkled with water engulfed the patient in a cloud of steam. Sweat baths proved to be particularly effective in dealing with rheumatism and other problems of the joints. They also tended to produce a general sense of well-being.[12]

There have always been individuals among the Navajo especially skilled in the use of herbs and plants. Many of them also understand and treat other medical problems, such as setting broken bones and cauterizing wounds. These individuals might best be described as "herbalists," since they handle only ordinary ailments and do not resort to the supernatural or ceremonial cures. Stephen Kunitz makes a sharp distinction between herbalists and healers, remarking that "Navajos in the past have often equated [western] physicians with herbalists" because they both sought relief from basic symptoms, rather than attempting "to cure the underlying condition."[13]

When illness proves untreatable by ordinary means, the problem is relegated to the sphere of the supernatural, where psychotherapeutic treatment in the form of ceremonials, special prayers, and the ministrations of healers comes into play. The Navajo people believe that failure to observe various behavioral restrictions or taboos (bahadzid) can cause disease and illness. Once stricken, an individual is compelled to seek a cure through ceremonial cleansing. From the Navajo perspective, any number of activities or events might cause sickness. Among the most common are bad dreams, an excess of gambling or sexual activity, ignorance of proper ceremonies, contact with the dead, and sorcery or witchcraft. Avoidance of taboos becomes especially important at certain times in an individual's life. Pregnant women, for example, are beset with any number of taboos, the misinterpretation of which can lead to sickness in the mother, husband, or child. Another significant taboo involves the fear of anything connected with death or a corpse. Traditional Navajos believe that spirits of the dead are particularly detrimental, and they avoid hogans or other dwellings where someone has died, lest they too be stricken.[14]

Navajo medical and healing practices historically have been a combination of religious and moral beliefs. Religion is deeply embedded in Navajo life and permeates every activity. Unlike Christianity or many other Indian religions, Navajo religion focuses primarily on curing illness, which the Diné regard as a great source of insecurity. Their teachings and legends focus heavily on the relationship between ordinary human beings, *Earth Surface People*, and a set of supernatural beings, *Holy People*, empowered to intervene in times of crisis to restore nature's harmony. The Holy People are not regarded so much as virtuous as they are dangerous. They possess destructive powers, thereby necessitating that man understand and placate them. As Leland Wyman explains, "man has a place in the universal continuum and if he misbehaves with respect to the traditional restrictions on human behavior in relationship to the 'supernatural' there is a breakdown in the harmonious balance of things, resulting usually in illness of the transgressor or future illness of his or her unborn child."[15]

Because the Navajo religion tends to classify illnesses by cause, rather than symptom, the main object in healing is to discover and remove the cause. And because sickness and disease in the Navajo mind are not connected to what modern doctors classify as medical reasons, traditional cures have focused heavily on the psychological or emotional. As many scholars observe, the Navajo method of healing concentrates on making the patient feel better about his or her condition and creating a positive mind-set.[16]

Thus when an individual falls ill and needs the intervention of a ceremonial curing, a specific series of actions is required. The usual first step is to summon a "diagnostician." This individual is called in to determine the nature of the sickness. By means of hand trembling, stargazing, or other trancelike activities, the diagnostician is able to determine the cause of the ailment and thereby prescribe an appropriate ceremony. The diagnostician does not possess the ability to perform the required ceremony, however, and must be understood as playing a distinctly different role from that of the healer.[17]

Once a diagnosis is made, a Singer (*hatalii*, or medicine man in older usage) will be asked to perform the proper ritual, either a ceremony or a sing. These healers (male and female) are trained specialists possessing knowledge of hundreds of songs and prayers, sandpainting designs, herbal mixtures, and the use of proper paraphernalia and ritual actions. Because of the complexity of many ceremonies, healers generally specialize in only a few chantways which are designed to cure a specific health problem. Even so, it requires a long period of learning or apprenticeship for a Singer to gain enough proficiency to perform a proper ceremony. Most accomplished and talented healers have accordingly been older tribesmen and women. They ordinarily receive compensation for their services, which before the general use of money came in the form of animals and goods.[18]

Reliance on special ceremonies and Singers dates back to pre-Columbian times. Most ceremonial cures apparently came with the Navajo when they entered the Southwest, although some elements may have been acquired from the neighboring Pueblos. Nevertheless, Navajo healers are a unique group. Whereas some native societies treat shamans or medicine men as priests or high-ranking possessors of supernatural power, Navajo medicine men, although very influential, possess no such power. They function primarily as trained individuals who understand the proper way to conduct a healing ceremony, which if done correctly will produce the desired result. In this sense, the healer does not actually cure; he or she simply enables healing to happen. There is little question that ceremonial rites are frequently successful, especially when the patient is treated for a sickness primarily attributable to psychological circumstance.[19]

Chant ceremonies are the primary vehicle used to cure a patient. At one time as many as two dozen chantways existed, although the number is now considerably lower. A typical chant ceremony might last from two to nine nights, with the event following a carefully prescribed routine. At various points, sandpaintings representing the legend from which the ceremony has evolved might be completed with meticulous care as an aid in curing the diseased patient. Some ceremonies include the use of masked dancers and medicinal plants and herbs. Almost every ceremony involves a series of complicated songs. At the conclusion of the ceremony, the patient is expected to feel better about his or her illness, and perhaps even be cured.[20] Although in the past non-Indian doctors tended to discount such healing practices as superstition, healing ceremonies frequently produced the desired result, and are deeply embedded in Navajo culture.

Healing ceremonies, of course, do not always achieve the anticipated result. As a consequence, the Navajo have long been open to new songs and ceremonies which might be more effective. They generally reacted in the same adaptive way to the introduction of western medical ideas. It must be emphasized that the Diné have never been totally opposed to scientific medicine, nor were they hesitant to incorporate some concepts into their own practices. However, they expressed little or no desire to abandon their own healing practices and thus objected when western medicine was touted as a total replacement for traditional cures. As Robert L. Bergman has observed, "the elaborate and well-established methods of Navajo medicine were preferred by most patients to the foreign and seemingly whimsical techniques of the White doctors whose persons, tools, and hospitals were contaminated by contact with the dead."[21] They also demanded evidence that western medicine actually worked, something that could not effectively be demonstrated until well into the twentieth century.

NINETEENTH-CENTURY AMERICAN MEDICINE

Compared with modern advancements in scientific health care, medical practice in nineteenth-century America seems primitive indeed. Yet for all its lack of sophistication, American medicine rested on a philosophy and tradition totally different from that of the Navajo. The differences in western medical theories and practices as superimposed on the Indians require the reader to have some conception of the nature and philosophy of the medical profession at the time white doctors first began to practice among the Navajo. The gap in beliefs and techniques proved to be so wide that in most instances neither side appreciated nor understood what the other hoped to accomplish.

Western or scientific medical philosophy came to America with the first settlers. Based on traditions extending back to the classical era of Aristotle, Hippocrates, and Galen, medical theory developed and matured in Western Europe over the course of centuries. During the Renaissance, scholars in England, France, and Germany began to regard science as a key to understanding the mysteries of medicine. Following a continuing series of scientific developments, doctors increasingly came to view the human body in terms of anatomy, biology, and the effect of drugs and chemicals. Advanced scholarship also realized, if only dimly, that the human physic could be revealed through research, statistical record keeping, clinical observation, and examination of internal organs. As a consequence, laboratory work and experimentation produced an ever-expanding list of theories, some basically correct, others totally worthless. On the whole, however, the laws of physical and biological science increasingly formed the basis of medical theory. By the founding of Jamestown in 1607, the medical profession in Europe maintained a position of some respect, with the best university-educated practitioners holding the title of physician or Doctor of Medicine.[22]

Although medical theory came to rely more and more on science, practical benefits lagged behind. In most cases, only the most theoretical scholar understood even the most basic of concepts. Consequently, well into the eighteenth century a sick patient might be expected to endure the torture of bloodletting, purging, or worse, as these ineffective and dangerous procedures remained the stock and trade of most physicians. Richard Shryock remarks that "the general picture of early eighteenth-century therapeutics . . . is bizarre and somber, and presents an unfortunate contrast with the light already thrown by [scientific research] on sensible and humane practice."[23] Thus, although the course of modern medicine had been charted by the time of American colonization, age-old folk treatments and remedies held sway in general practice.

Medical care in the colonies required an unusually long time to mature. Although the earliest settlements suffered greatly from disease and illness, only a handful of European-trained physicians came to North America prior to the eighteenth century. With a robust European intellectual climate and the prospect of substantial hardship in America, physicians, mostly men of substance and status, saw little reason to migrate. A few notable individuals, such as Dr. Walter Russell at Jamestown, were of course present, but for the most part pioneer settlers accepted whatever services might be available. As a result, medical care frequently rested in the hands of men with little or no education. These individuals learned their trade by studying under a physician, sometimes working more as an indentured servant than a student. Such apprenticeships fell within the European tradition, yet a lack of defined standards meant that almost anyone could proclaim himself a doctor and put whatever rudimentary knowledge he might possess into practice, often with extremely unfortunate results.[24]

With little or no scientific training required or available and with an abundance of poorly trained doctors, the colonies suffered through a dark era. Scottish Dr. William Douglass reacted to some of the common American medical practices by remarking that "in general, the physical practice in our Colonies is so perniciously bad, that excepting in surgery and some acute cases, it is better to let nature take her course than to trust to the honesty and sagacity of the practitioner. . . . Frequently there is more danger from the Physician than from the distemper." Bleeding, vomiting, blistering, and pills were "the principal tools of our practitioners." If a treatment failed to work it was repeated until it finally resulted, as Douglass observed, in "murderandi."[25]

Not until the eighteenth century did European-educated physicians migrate to the colonies in significant numbers, bringing with them a demand for better medical training. In 1765 the College of Philadelphia (University of Pennsylvania) opened the first medical school in the English colonies. The moving force behind the establishment of this school, Dr. John Morgan, wanted American doctors to adopt European standards of professionalism. In particular, he suggested that schools separate general health care from such specialties as surgery and pharmacy. Additional medical schools came into existence following the Revolutionary War, but for some time graduates commonly traveled to Europe for advanced classes. Nonetheless, the number of individuals actually possessing an M.D. remained small. One interesting statistic shows that of the more than three thousand doctors known to have practiced in America prior to 1776, only four hundred possessed medical degrees. The remainder "either were trained by apprenticeship or were merely pretenders, men who 'suddenly' decided to abandon other pursuits in favor of medical practice."[26]

The American medical profession entered the nineteenth century suffering from considerable confusion. As early as 1760 laws appeared in New York City requiring that medical students be examined by a board of physicians. Although a number of states enacted similar legislation prior to 1830, and medical societies agitated for some form of licensing, medical standards actually declined as medical schools downgraded programs and scientific preparation lessened. Learning tools such as postmortem dissections were opposed by the public (who frequently viewed medical students as little more than grave robbers), hospitals for clinical observation seldom existed, and many potential students found extended medical education too expensive, preferring instead to enter practice without obtaining an advanced degree. Increasing competition among the rapidly expanding number of schools, all desirous of making a profit and attracting students, also impacted standards. Some rural colleges went so far was to eliminate basic examinations, and few administrators seemed concerned about the character of their students.[27]

The antebellum period has been described by medical historians as a disaster. Joseph Kett notes that medical schools were bad, the profession suffered from low public esteem, medical practice was opened to anyone, and charlatans abounded. In 1853 one observer remarked that a citizen rarely knew the qualifications of his physician. Instead of pulling a gun and robbing his victim, he suggested, "some unscrupulous horse doctor would set up his sign as 'Physician and Surgeon' and draw his lancet on you, or fire at random a box of pills into your bowels, with a vague chance of hitting some disease unknown to him, but with a better prospect of killing the patient."[28]

As late as the Civil War, many ailments remained misunderstood and epidemics of infectious diseases raged across the nation. Preventive medicine did not exist. In the absence of positive cures, worthless potions frequently served as remedies. Doctors commonly administered such toxic medicines as calomel (which contained mercury), laudanum (a mixture of opium and alcohol), and various combinations of salts and drugs. Many practitioners also relied on the wide variety of patent and "Indian" medicines peddled by hucksters and traveling salesmen.[29]

Despite a tragic cost in human life, the Civil War (1861–65) became something of a turning point in American medicine. As bloodshed and suffering overwhelmed the medical system, the need for change became acute. An estimated 60 percent of all fatalities during the conflict resulted from diseases such as dysentery, malaria, smallpox, tuberculosis, and pneumonia. Overburdened by the magnitude of the disaster, army physicians stood powerless as thousands of men died from unsanitary camp and hospital conditions. Hundreds of doctors entered national service, but their poor training did little more than confirm the faults of the medical system. Nonetheless, a few positive advancements came to light. Some military physicians recognized the connection between sanitation and fitness, and by war's end some progress had been made at improving personal hygiene. As the connection between sanitation, germs, and disease became more evident, treatment for some common ailments actually improved. On the whole, however, the Civil War illustrated the fact that American doctors required better preparation and a modern medical technology solidly based on research.[30]

The medical community after 1865 once again turned its attention to regulation and education. During the 1870s and 1880s physicians successfully pushed for new statutes setting minimal qualifications for medical practitioners. In many cases, however, these licensing programs were gradually phased in so as to permit existing doctors, many of them war veterans, to continue to practice. Moreover, standards in some states remained so lax that almost anyone might obtain a license. Even where higher standards prevailed, some physicians objected to the idea of regulation, frequently ignoring local restrictions. Not until the turn of the century, after medical societies successfully lobbied for better control of the profession, did licensing and regulatory standards become effective.[31]

The war also impacted medical education, and between 1865 and 1890 numerous reforms gained support. Simply stated, many physicians believed that standards should be tightened and the title of Medical Doctor restored to a position of respect. Changing the current system proved as difficult as licensing, however. Many colleges remained in business solely for profit, refusing to exclude inferior students. In fact, dozens of new medical schools opened their doors, thereby increasing competition. By 1900 some 150 medical schools (many little more than diploma mills) existed in the United States. Fortunately, at about the same time, advances in medical research found cures for such killer diseases as typhoid, malaria, and yellow fever. Wholesale immunizations and attention to sanitation began to reduce the death rate while such old remedies as bloodletting disappeared. The scientific revolution that produced these discoveries demanded that medical education emphasize proficiency in such basic fields as chemistry, pathology, biology, and physics. While it required many years for schools to incorporate the new science, by 1893 the trend had become visible with the establishment of the Johns Hopkins University Medical College, recognized as the first institution to adopt the higher standards of modern scientific medicine.[32]

The American medical system that came to the Navajo people in the latter half of the nineteenth century was thus in the process of change, of becoming more professional and scientific. Nevertheless, many of the old practices remained. "Doctors" might not be physicians, and remedies frequently remained worse than the disease. Moreover, a large number of individuals, some qualified and others decidedly not, eagerly sought an opportunity to find postwar employment by ministering to the Indians just as the government undertook the enormous task of providing health care to the reservation population.

Although the talents of doctors called to treat the Navajo varied, they uniformly viewed themselves as representing a superior society. From their perspective, western medical practices seemed the most advanced in the world. After all, mysterious diseases were being identified and conquered, the germ theory had been accepted, and science seemed to prevail.[33] These medical specialists thus viewed their Navajo patients in terms of sanitation, hygiene, germs, vaccinations, contagion, and surgery. None of these ideas made much sense to the Navajo.

NATIVE HEALTH AND INDIAN POLICY

Prior to the general adoption of the reservation system during the 1870s, a weak connection existed between health care and Indian policy. From the earliest European settlement, white leaders advocated bringing the "gift of civilization" to native peoples, often as a moral corollary to taking their lands. Over the years various plans for education, Christianization, and the end of tribalism were put forward as ways of resolving the so-called Indian problem. More often than not the native tribes resisted the destruction of their culture, avoiding the Europeans if possible, and going to war if necessary. Although warfare resulted in public demands for revenge and extermination, the hope of civilizing the native peoples continued to be a significant theme for white policymakers. Following the American Revolution, the United States government adopted an official goal of encouraging native assimilation, as much at first, perhaps, in the forlorn hope of keeping peace on the frontier as for any altruistic interest in Indian welfare. This policy continued into the 1860s, by which time it became accepted that the best way to civilize the still uncooperative tribes would be to place them on reservations, out of the reach of white contact, save for government agents, missionaries, farm instructors, and educators who would teach them the "white-man's way."[34]

Early European explorers and settlers clearly made a connection between health care and the accomplishment of colonial goals. As epidemics of imported diseases ravished the native population, often destroying entire bands and weakening armed resistance, the invaders realized that medical care could be an effective and useful tool. As early as 1534, French explorer Jacques Cartier attempted to heal ailing Indians through bloodletting and other folk remedies, hoping thereby to earn native favor. Although it is doubtful that these treatments provided much assistance, whites quickly capitalized on their own immunity from many diseases, proclaiming their way of life superior to tribal culture, which appeared incapable of dealing with such widespread and insidious destruction.[35]

French Jesuit missionaries used the prevalence of epidemic disease to destroy the influence of medicine men and shamans, an initial step in replacing traditional religions with Catholicism. Historian James Axtell remarks that the Jesuits eagerly nursed ill tribesmen: "The Jesuits' timely administration of some sugar or raisins or some elementary nursing might save the lives of natives suffering from infectious disease, apparently without jeopardizing their own health. When the Jesuits told the natives that native susceptibility to disease was directly attributable to pagan ignorance of Christianity and sinful ways, the natives had another powerful reason to convert." A major reason for Jesuit success rested with their ability to provide food, water, and basic care while entire villages were stricken, thus preventing mass starvation, a leading cause of death.[36] Ministering to sick natives as a way of convincing them of the superiority of white civilization thus dates back to the sixteenth and seventeenth centuries.

The English settlers in New England also took advantage of native illness. The Puritans moved into lands cleared by the great plague of 1616–1617. While regretting the great loss of Indian life, they accepted it as a sign of God's judgement in their favor. Although the state of European medical practice may have been incapable of much actual help, the practical value of offering medical assistance to the Indians became evident as early as 1623, when the Wampanoag leader Massasoit fell gravely ill. Hoping to assist their friend, Pilgrim leaders sent Edward Wilson to provide comfort. Wilson quickly administered "a liberal portion of English potage," and other remedies that brought the chief back to life. Much impressed by Wilson's doctoring, Massasoit repaid the English by alerting them to an uprising being planned by the Massachusetts tribe.[37]

English missionaries also offered medical assistance as part of an ongoing effort at conversion. Puritan pioneer Thomas Mayhew, Jr., treated a number of Indians on Martha's Vineyard, reportedly curing a tribal elder whom the traditional healers could not help and restoring a sachem's son to health through liberal bloodlettings. Mayhew attributed his success to God's intervention, which provided him with evidence that tribal shamans could not compete with Christianity. And this lesson was not lost on the Indians, some of whom became fast allies and converts, going so far as to help Mayhew discredit traditional religious and political opposition.[38] An interesting sidelight to the New England missionary effort was the almost total disdain for natural Indian remedies, which Virgil Vogel suggests stemmed from the Puritan concept of the chosen people of God, prompting them to dismiss as unimportant anything of Indian origin.[39]

Occasional efforts to treat Indians appeared throughout the remainder of the colonial period, usually with minimal results. Although colonists outside of New England took some interest in learning Indian medical secrets, knowledge of the diseases actually decimating the native population remained limited. Moreover, the few doctors in the colonies found more reward in treating their own kind. As a consequence, a significant commitment to improving Indian health care did not exist during the colonial era, although the advantages were evident. Following American Independence, the federal government attempted to define a new Indian policy. Civilization remained the preferred objective, but little practical advance in that direction occurred for years as wars and removal took center stage. Under such circumstances, provisions for Indian health care received practically no attention. When the issue did arise, the government left it to missionary societies, a large group of whom came into existence following 1783. To a minor extent at least, these organizations undertook to provide medical care as a means of keeping potential converts out of the hands of "conjurers and medicine men of native tradition and religion."[40]

During the first decades of the nineteenth century the federal government aided the civilization process only indirectly, adding treaty provisions calling for schools, and establishing the "Civilization Fund" in 1819, which authorized up to ten thousand dollars a year to subsidize Indian education. Although neither of these efforts directly provided health care, they stimulated missionary activity. With such encouragement, organizations like the American Board of Commissioners of Foreign Missions opened missionary training facilities. These schools not only prepared teachers, they offered other practical skills, including medicine. As one report stated, Christian men were being trained "to become useful Missionaries, Physicians, Surgeons, School-masters, or Interpreters; and to communicate to the Heathen nations such knowledge in agriculture and the arts, as may prove the means of promoting Christianity and civilization."[41] Although medical training may have been a useful tool for some missionaries, it seldom extended beyond a rudimentary level. The primary Christian responsibility focused on teaching the gospel; medicine remained only a means to an end. Most tribes, of course, stayed well beyond the reach of the civilization program.

A turning point came in the 1840s when continental expansion ended the possibility of maintaining a separate Indian Country. From this fact evolved the reservation system. By 1851 the federal government had concluded that the only alternative to extinction rested with concentrating the surviving tribes on small plots of land located away from the path of expansion. During the mid-1850s reservations began to appear on the western landscape. At these remote locations, government officials planned to protect the native population from the corruption of white society while their traditional ways were replaced with the values of white Christian civilization. By the late 1860s the reservation program was in full swing as the western tribes were confined to barren plots of land.[42]

The establishment of reservations forced the federal government to assume full responsibility for Indian welfare. It also became increasingly clear that if the Indians were going to be civilized, they had to be protected from the growing threat of disease and illness. In most cases, native health conditions declined dramatically as a result of confinement. Reservations usually represented an alien environment where old methods of nutrition and sanitation disappeared. Traditional means of food production, such as the buffalo hunt, vanished in the expectation that Indians would adopt farming. In reality, however, reservation agriculture seldom produced sufficient food, leaving the residents vulnerable to starvation and disease. As a consequence, the early reservation years witnessed an unacceptably high mortality rate, with old diseases flourishing and new ones taking hold. Under such circumstances, the government had no choice but to introduce some form of basic health care.[43]

But again, as had been the case with missionary efforts, the offer of medical care extended well beyond providing for physical well-being. If the assimilation goals of the government were to succeed, all vestiges of traditional Indian culture became obsolete. Thus native medical practices continued to be regarded as just another superstitious gimmick that must be proven fraudulent. In this sense, the age-old argument that demanded individualism, education, and Christianity applied as well to traditional healing activities.[44] Most of the white men—soldiers, government agents, and missionaries—who came to the Navajo country during the latter half of the nineteenth century expressed such ideas. The first manifestation of a clash between western medicine and traditional healing surfaced when the Diné were exiled to Fort Sumner, New Mexico, between 1863 and 1868.

CHAPTER TWO

ARMY DOCTORS
Western Medicine Comes to the Navajo

During the confinement at Fort Sumner a lot of people perished from diarrhea because of the change in diet and the poor quality of food. Also, various diseases had spread, and the people couldn't tolerate the situation any longer.

AKINABH BURBANK, NAVAJO

Most of the sick Indians prefer the attendance and treatment of their own doctors or charmers—These Indian doctors are the worse class of humbugs.

GENERAL M. M. CROCKER, FORT SUMNER

General Stephen Watts Kearny entered New Mexico in August 1846 keenly aware that he needed to establish peace with the Indians. Navajo and Apache raiders had long kept the Southwest in turmoil and now it became America's responsibility to provide a solution. Thus, with Kearny's army of occupation came a commitment to extend American Indian policy over the Navajo. During the subsequent fifteen years the United States government conducted a number of military expeditions against the Diné, established forts in their country, marked out tribal boundaries, negotiated treaties, and ordered out the first Indian agents. These events generally did little to alter Navajo ways. Nevertheless, the irritating presence of American soldiers kept the tribe on edge and anxious to be rid of their new neighbors. Although relations between the two groups stayed relatively calm during the 1850s, unanticipated events set the stage for a major conflict to erupt when American soldiers withdrew from the Navajo country in 1861.[1] The resulting Navajo War and subsequent Long Walk to Fort Sumner permanently changed tribal life, destroyed Navajo health, and brought the Diné into contact with white doctors for the first time.

INTERLUDE OF HEALTH AND PROSPERITY

The American government began to chart dramatic changes for the Navajo well before the outbreak of full-scale hostilities in 1862. As early as 1849 Indian

Agent James S. Calhoun proposed creating a reservation out of the Navajo homeland. Such a measure promised to prevent raiding, and to "restrict inter-course with them, and instruct them, and compel them to cultivate the soil." This vague policy went into effect in August 1851, when Colonel Edwin Sumner established Fort Defiance at Cañon Bonito in the heart of Navajo country. The first post commander, Major Electus Backus, received orders to treat the Navajo "with the utmost vigor, till they showed a desire to be at peace." Almost immediately thereafter the Office of Indian Affairs appointed Spruce M. Baird to the position of Navajo Indian agent. The agent's responsibility included distributing seeds and farm implements, communicating with Navajo leaders, and assuming limited responsibility for tribal welfare. This show of government force and determination surprised the tribe and encouraged them to settle down.[2]

The government's intrusion technically included an obligation to look after Navajo health. At the time, however, this hardly seemed necessary. As had the Mexicans before them, the first Americans to observe the tribe found them to be a hearty, well-fed people, many of whom owned large flocks of sheep and horses. Members of an 1849 military expedition into Navajo country, led by Colonel John M. Washington, had been quite impressed. Historian William A. Keleher writes that "poverty, as it was known in some American communities of the day, apparently did not exist in the Navajo country. Fairly good cattle grazed on the ranges; bands of fat sheep were seen in the draws and *canyons*. . . . There was every indication that all the people in the Navajo country were getting enough to eat, and everybody seemed to be fairly well clothed." David Meriwether, New Mexico Superintendent of Indian Affairs, seconded this opinion, writing in 1854 that the Navajo "have numerous herds of horses and sheep, and some horned cattle and mules, and, on the whole, live in a degree of comfort and plenty unknown to the other wild Indians in this section of the Union." While not all tribal members lived this well, little indication of serious medical problems existed, and no one expressed the slightest interest in taking over for traditional healers.[3]

Baird proved to be an ineffective and unconcerned agent. When Henry L. Dodge replaced him in April 1853, the Diné welcomed the first government representative to possess a sincere interest in their welfare. Dodge understood the Navajo, having lived among them and taken one of their women as a wife. Frank McNitt notes that Dodge "knew the Navajos as few men ever did, and his liking for them was returned in kind." Known to the Diné as "Red Shirt," he traveled extensively across the Four Corners country visiting clan leaders and individual hogans. Until 1855, when Dodge officially established agency headquarters at Fort Defiance, he resided with his Indian friends in a remote area of the Chuska Mountains.[4]

The new agent found ample opportunity to observe the Navajo. Given his interest in their welfare and the absence of any expression of concern about medical conditions, it may be assumed that Dodge found the Navajo healthy. He frequently attempted to enhance tribal self-sufficiency by distributing seeds and providing farming tips. As a result of these efforts, new foods were added to the Navajo diet. The richness of their agricultural production, combined with the half-million or so sheep in their possession, consistently presented a picture of prosperity. Peace with the Americans seemed to be especially beneficial. In 1855 Dodge wrote that "they are in full enjoyment of peace with all its blessings and have raised fine crops of corn, wheat, and vegetables, their flocks and herds are rapidly on the increase."[5]

The only significant medical issue concerning the Navajo during the mid-1850s related to an outbreak of smallpox. In late 1853, Major Henry L. Kendrick, commander at Fort Defiance, reported that the disease was raging among the Zuni and Hopi population to the south and west of the Navajo homeland. By this time, vaccination as a preventive against smallpox had achieved a considerable degree of reliability. Utilizing crusts commercially prepared from infected cattle (cowpox virus), nearly anyone could be trained to administer mass inoculations. Yet when representatives of the stricken tribes applied to Major Kendrick for vaccine matter and a physician, he refused the request because his surgeon did not have a sufficient supply of vaccine. After delaying for well over a month, the Indian Office finally hired the Reverend Lewis Smith to vaccinate the Pueblo tribes and prevent the spread of "this fatal disease." Although the subsequent vaccinations ended the epidemic, the delay took a heavy toll—both tribes "were almost totally destroyed by the small-pox."[6]

None of the correspondence regarding the 1853–54 smallpox epidemic specifically mentions the Navajo. Yet the Navajo were deathly afraid of the disease, and evidence suggests that Dodge made an attempt to have some of his wards vaccinated. In 1870, during another effort to inoculate the tribe, the surgeon in charge reported finding almost nine hundred Navajos who had been successfully vaccinated "at the time Mr. Dodge was agent for the Navajos."[7] Whatever the actual numbers involved, it seems that Dodge's action helped prevent a significant outbreak of smallpox among the Navajo and that no significant tribal opposition to his vaccinations surfaced.

Henry Dodge died in late 1856 and Major Kendrick left Fort Defiance six months later. These two individuals, along with several prominent Navajo headmen, had been largely responsible for the interlude of general peace, and relations quickly deteriorated in their absence. Part of the problem stemmed from a devastating drought in 1857, which caused the corn crop to fail and destroyed a large number of sheep, thereby creating a state of near starvation. Indian Superintendent James L. Collins rightly feared that hunger would drive the Navajo to resume raiding.[8]

It required more than drought to drive the Navajo to hostilities, however. By 1858 many Navajo leaders had lost patience with the Americans. They objected to the army's arrogance in ordering them about and in appropriating the best pastureland at Fort Defiance. When a black slave was killed at the post in July 1858, the army ordered punitive campaigns against the suspected perpetrators. Although inflicting few casualties, the army reprisals further disrupted tribal food production. New Mexico governor Abram Rencher observed in 1858 that "if the war continues, the inevitable result must be that, their flocks destroyed and their cornfields laid waste, they will become more dependent on us [New Mexicans] for support and more reckless in their marauding incursions upon our people."[9]

Rencher's prediction proved correct. Intermittent raids and army reprisals continued into 1861. Navajo raiding activities against Pueblo and Hispanic settlements created such anxiety and discontent that New Mexicans demanded increased levels of military action. As warfare became more general, New Mexican civilians also resumed slave raids against the tribe, taking an additional toll on tribal livelihood because they found it increasingly difficult to remain in fixed areas long enough for crops to mature. In the midst of the intensifying rounds of hostility, in April 1861, the army suddenly abandoned Fort Defiance. The soldiers, of course, withdrew in response to the outbreak of the Civil War, but the Navajo regarded it as a victory. While the Navajos did not immediately launch a wild binge of raiding, the absence of military restraints enabled them to refill their larders.[10] Yet, although they could not know it at the time, the era of plenty and good health had ended. In the next few years nutritional and medical problems came to dominate their life as Kit Carson launched a campaign to bring the Navajo under control.

THE LONG WALK

Confusion descended on New Mexico at the beginning of the Civil War. As Apache and Navajo raiding intensified, the Union army fell into disarray and the Confederates launched an invasion from the south. Until Union forces could reorganize and drive the Rebel soldiers back into Texas, Indian affairs received scant attention despite their devastating impact on the local economy.

Consequently, when General James H. Carleton's California Column restored federal control to New Mexico in September 1862, one of the first priorities involved putting an end to Indian depredations. As newly installed military commander of the Territory, Carleton found himself in a position, so he thought, to permanently end Indian troubles. Confident, arrogant, and ruthless, the veteran military officer hastily devised a "humanitarian" peace plan to "civilize" the hostile tribes of New Mexico. Simply stated, both the Navajo and Apache would be made to settle down on selected reservation lands and live under military control until they were taught the arts of civilization. As far as the Navajo were concerned, Carleton hoped to divest them of their livestock-based economy and make them into farmers. Because the rugged Navajo homeland made such pursuits impossible, the Diné were assigned to a remote plot of land on the Pecos River in eastern New Mexico. Known as the Bosque Redondo, the reservation at Fort Sumner presented Carleton with an opportunity to conduct what he believed to be a noble experiment in civilizing the savage.[11]

Before any of Carleton's goals could reach fruition, the Navajo had to be forced into compliance. The Kit Carson campaign of 1863–64 accomplished this objective, devastating the Navajo economy and inflicting on them a number of health problems. Mounting a large-scale military effort under the direction of Colonel Carson, the army commenced a "scorched-earth" invasion of the Navajo homeland, intended to lay waste to their economy, cripple their military prowess, and compel surrender through starvation. In June 1863 Carleton ordered Carson's volunteer soldiers to "prosecute a vigorous war upon the men of this tribe until it is considered at this headquarters that they have been effectually punished for their long atrocities."[12] Carson took the field in late summer, invading the heart of the Navajo country, killing those who resisted, destroying crops and livestock, and leaving the Diné with no option but to surrender. The campaign's winter operations proved especially devastating on Navajo food supplies.[13]

Most accounts of the campaign fail to describe in detail the fearful price the Navajo paid for their real or perceived transgressions. The loss of tribal health ranks high on this list. Carson's goal of forcing the tribe into submission through starvation proved effective. Not only did his army obliterate the tribe's ability to grow crops, it destroyed existing stores of food. Captives taken by Carson's men exhibited signs of acute malnutrition. Describing the condition of captives in January 1864, Carson reported that "the generality of the Navajos are completely destitute. They are almost entirely naked, and had it not been for the unusual growth of the Piñon-berry this year, they must have been without any description of food." While the army commander regretted this situation, he viewed it as a necessary tactic, admitting that the starving condition "is owing to the destruction of their grain amounting to about two Million of Pounds by my command on its first arrival in this country."[14]

Carson noted a continuing decline in tribal health following a scout into Canyon de Chelly in January 1864. By then the Navajos were suffering greatly from a lack of food and exposure to freezing temperatures. Many men, women, and children had already perished. Under these conditions, it became evident that the only thing preventing mass surrender was fear that the army intended to slaughter the prisoners. Once Carson assured the Diné that they would not be massacred, and indeed would be fed, the Navajo began to give up in large numbers. Captives were directed to Forts Canby or Wingate to be cared for. Some of the incoming prisoners told the soldiers that they had eaten nothing but nuts and berries for weeks. It appears that the surrendering Navajos received some limited medical attention from army doctors, especially treatment for gunshot wounds.[15]

The arrival of thousands of half-starved Navajos at Forts Canby and Wingate created unanticipated problems. Temporary camps at these locations held the Indians, whose condition ranged from fair to poor, until they could be transported to the Bosque Redondo. General Carleton wrote that "many of the Navajoe women and children which we capture are quite naked; and the children especially suffer from the extreme cold. . . . It is hard to see them perish." The army had promised to feed the captives, but the scale of the surrender, upwards of five thousand, overwhelmed its ability to provide rations. Early arrivals received a pound each of beef and flour per day in addition to blankets, but supplies dwindled so fast that rations ran out. At one point, soldiers relinquished some of their rations to the Indians and Carleton asked the Indian Office for funding to purchase cheap blankets and condemned clothing. As a result of his inability for care for the captives, Carleton quickly ordered the Indians to be sent on to the Pecos where they might be better provisioned. Comfortably situated at Santa Fe, he admitted that Carson's success had been overwhelming to the point of embarrassment.[16]

A shortage of rations comprised only one of the medical problems brought about by the mass surrender. A deadly situation unfolded as the army issued foods not normally part of the Navajo diet. The Diné had no idea how to cook or prepare such items as bacon, flour, and coffee. Navajo memories of the introduction to western foods are remarkably similar. One account relates that "during their stay at that place [Fort Canby] they were issued rations like flour, baking powder, etc. The Diné didn't know what the food was or how to go about using it. They mixed all of the baking powder with some flour and put in hot ashes to cook. It gave them diarrhea and stomach trouble, and some died of it." Not realizing how to prepare bacon, they boiled it, with the half-cooked result producing an outset of dysentery, which also took a number of lives. In general, the Navajos were sickened and further weakened by the food provided them. As one man recalled, "when the people started eating the strange food, they had diarrhea which caused a lot of deaths among babies, children, old people, and even others."[17]

Not until non-Indians showed the Navajo how to prepare the strange foods did the suffering lessen. Although it required a long period of adjustment, many of the western foods first given them as they surrendered eventually became staples of the Navajo diet. In the meantime, some army officers recognized the nature of the problem, noting that the Navajo did not like bacon and wasted large amounts of flour in futile cooking efforts. Eventually some tribesmen received permission to hunt small game, and one officer suggested substituting corn for flour. The human cost of such conditions as existed among the prisoners is unknown, but some 126 people died at Fort Canby within a two-week period at the end of February 1864.[18]

The final phase of Carleton's civilization scheme involved the infamous Long Walk, a trek of some four hundred miles east to the Bosque Redondo reservation. Forced marches began in late winter, with over seven thousand men, women, and children traveling in groups under armed escort. Many perished. The weather remained cold, and although the army brought wagon-loads of food, dysentery and diarrhea continued to take a toll. Despite the well-known fact that the Navajo could not effectively use the government rations, no acceptable substitute could be found. Some goats to provide infants with milk accompanied the emigrants, as did several thousand sheep, but they gave scant relief. Army doctors accompanying the prisoners undoubtedly provided some medical care. Traditional healers could do little, however, as the ailments afflicting the Diné were previously unknown. There were no herbs to cure what they called the "nutrition sickness" and there was no time for ceremonies.[19]

The Navajo world collapsed in less than a year. Approximately three-quarters of the tribe were held captive and on their way into exile. The remainder hid in the hills. From a relatively affluent and well-nourished people, they had lost their means of livelihood, and saw their culture threatened and their health imperiled. The entire Navajo environment changed as suddenly as the seasons. From a medical standpoint Kit Carson's campaign and the Long Walk were a disaster. Stunned, demoralized, and resentful, these people found themselves with no defense. Indeed, things grew even worse at the Bosque Redondo. At least, white doctors were available if the Navajo could be convinced to use their services.

BOSQUE REDONDO

The reservation at Bosque Redondo, created by General Carleton in the fall of 1862, surrounded a squalid army post known as Fort Sumner. Situated along the Pecos River in eastern New Mexico, the reserve encompassed an area some forty miles square, although only four thousand to six thousand acres directly adjacent to the river were deemed arable. Here Carleton planned to house up to ten thousand Navajo, in addition to the four hundred Mescalero Apaches previously placed there by Kit Carson. Carleton regarded the Pecos Valley as a perfect location for the construction of self-sufficient Indian farms. Gathered on the reservation, he wrote, and away from "the haunts and hills and hiding places of their country," and taught the art of peace and the "truths of Christianity, . . . soon they will acquire new habits, new ideas, new modes of life: the old Indians will die off and carry with them all latent longings for murdering and robbing."[20]

Not everyone shared the general's optimism. Michael Steck, New Mexico Superintendent of Indian Affairs, argued that the small amount of good land at the Bosque could not support the large number of Indians forced to live there. Keenly aware that Carleton had taken on more than he could handle, Steck personally favored keeping the Navajo in the Four Corners country. This conclusion, which proved accurate, was based upon the superintendent's knowledge of the area, backed by a report by New Mexico's Surveyor General, which concluded that "it is of course well known to you [Steck] that there is no arable land within the [reservation] above described, except that which can be irrigated by the water of the Pecos river."[21] Unfortunately, with the removal under army jurisdiction, and the Indian Office refusing to assume responsibility, Steck's concerns received scant attention.

Well before the Diné began arriving at "Fair Carletonia," as the Bosque became known, the general made preliminary attempts to improve tribal health. He knew well that the reservation experiment could succeed only if the Indians possessed enough strength to develop and maintain the planned farms. His primary concern, therefore, focused on having a sufficient amount of food on hand to subsist the prisoners until they became self-supporting. With this in mind, Carleton issued orders to the post commander, Major Henry Wallen, that "there must be no mistake made about having enough for them to eat, even if we have to kill horses and mules for them. I have ordered Captain [Amos F.] Garrison to get flour and meat to you as fast as possible." Nonetheless, Carleton admitted being somewhat overwhelmed by the number of Indians coming in. "Our commissariat," he conceded "is hardly able to meet the large demands now made upon it." In February 1864, the general urgently asked the quartermaster at Fort Leavenworth to dispatch a wagon train loaded with 200,000 rations to the reservation.[22] As events soon proved, supplying the Indians with sufficient food would dog the experiment until it failed.

Meanwhile, Carleton made a few half-hearted efforts to provide the suffering tribe with medical care. Among the original New Mexico Volunteers officers assigned to Fort Sumner was Dr. George Gwyther, who for several years acted as chief medical officer at the post. Forty years old when first appointed as a contract surgeon in November 1862, the English-born Gwyther remained at the Bosque almost continually until 1865, being promoted to assistant surgeon in 1863, and becoming surgeon of the First New Mexico Volunteers a year later. Little is known about his medical training other than he listed his profession as an apothecary prior to emigrating to the United States sometime after 1856. A strong partisan of General Carleton, to whom he owed his appointment, Gwyther held racially based views on Indian health, considering natives biologically different than white men. It appears doubtful that he possessed an advanced medical degree or had worked with Indians prior to arriving at the Bosque.[23]

By summer 1864 over eight thousand Navajos resided at the Bosque Redondo. Much to Carleton's distress, the lands along the Pecos failed to produce as he expected. Although the Navajo dutifully planted crops and constructed irrigation ditches, insects and bad weather destroyed their efforts, thereby requiring the army to continue supplying expensive rations. Carelton found it impossible to keep the Indians fed. Lorenzo Labadie, agent for the Mescalero Apaches at Fort Sumner, reported as early as April 1864 that both the Navajo and Apache were suffering from hunger. At that time they received "two and a half pounds of meat and two and a half pounds of flour" every fifth day. "I see their wants myself," wrote Labadie, "and I have no doubt but that they are destitute of the necessities of life. They eat their rations in two days, and during the other three days they suffer, eating hides, and begging wherever they can." Malnutrition manifested itself everywhere, while the brackish waters of the Pecos aggravated already existing problems.[24]

Navajo lore recalls the same deplorable conditions. Howard W. Gorman remembered what survivors had told him: "The Navajos had hardly anything at that time; and they ate the rations but couldn't get used to them. Most of them got sick and had stomach trouble. The children also had stomach ache, and some of them died of it. Others died of starvation. . . . Also, the water was bad and salty, which gave them dysentery." Other stories confirm the constant state of hunger. Although the army provided beef whenever possible, shortages continued. As a result, the Navajo were reduced to eating anything available. One informant reported that if a rat could be found, the rodent, "with bones and intestines, would be chopped to pieces, and twelve persons would share the meat, bones, and intestines of one rat." Several stories also tell of people reduced to searching through horse manure for undigested corn to cook.[25]

Army officers at Fort Sumner recognized the deteriorating status of Navajo health. Major Wallen reported in mid-April 1864 that epidemics of catarrh and dysentery had been noted among recent arrivals. At that time over two hundred Navajos were reportedly being treated by Dr. Gwyther. By this point, the medical situation called for the construction of an Indian hospital to supplement the small adobe hospital used by the soldiers. A few seriously ill Navajos apparently visited this latter facility for treatment, but it hardly sufficed. In December 1863 Carleton became concerned enough to order some fifty beds for an "Indian hospital."[26] Yet no actual building existed until the commander ordered the construction of a hospital specifically for Indian patients some eight months later. Perhaps a reason for the delay rested with Gwyther's optimistic reports, which tended to list only those Indians who applied to him for treatment, thus understating the extent of the problem. Despite daily visits to "the Indian camp," the post surgeon listed only thirty adults and seventeen children as being ill during May 1864.[27]

Hospital construction was well under way by September. Two months later doctors admitted the first patients, although the building did not become fully operational until March 1865. The structure consisted of nine rooms, with the two largest being twenty by thirty feet. One observer described the facility as "built of adobe, one story high, and walls thirty inches in thickness. It is a very cool building." Another called it a "pattern of neatness and regularity." Two of the small rooms were used for surgery and several others for non-medical purposes. In most respects, however, it failed to meet basic needs. Dr. Gwyther, along with several other officers, including George C. Cartwright and Charles L. Warner, presided over this facility prior to mid-1865. Although some concerned individuals regarded the place as unfit, the army doctors seemed satisfied. Because of the limited amount of space, only the most seriously ill patients gained admission.[28]

The hospital might have been even more useful had ill Navajos been willing to be treated there. Aside from a general suspicion of western medicine (discussed below), Navajo fears against entering buildings associated with death prejudiced them against the hospital. Gwyther learned this the hard way following several deaths in the new hospital. Thereafter most Indians stayed away. This turn of events prompted Gwyther to assure that no more fatalities occurred in the building, even going to the extreme of ordering that "all persons who are near dissolution should be carried into an out-house." Even gravely ill patients arriving for treatment departed as fast as possible, much to the staff's distress. Gwyther remarked that his greatest success came in treating pneumonia cases because they could not walk away. He also admitted that if any more deaths occurred in the hospital, he might never see another patient. In actuality, the hospital served only about twenty patients per month.[29]

In addition to staffing the hospital, army doctors regularly visited the Navajo camps where for the first time the Diné were forced to live in extraordinary proximity to each other, thus hastening the spread of disease. Medical reports from these camps document a startling picture of health conditions among the captives, which, although lacking in detail, reveal a substantial death rate. In March 1865, for example, the report listed "14 men, 16 women, 12 children and 1 infant died during the month—disease not known." Another report, several months later, simply noted that "no doubt many have died, but it is impossible to ascertain the number." It is evident, however, that many deadly diseases existed in the Indian camps, often hidden from white doctors. Various accounts indicate that pneumonia, typhoid, dysentery, pleurisy, miscellaneous fevers, various skin problems such as erysipelas, and rheumatism permeated the tribe. In addition, deadly epidemics of smallpox, measles, and cholera struck from time to time. Between February 1864 and June 1865 the army officially recorded 216 Navajo deaths; many more probably went unrecorded. After 1865, however, the death rate appears to have declined.[30]

Reservation water supplies also caused problems. The army defended its use of river water, with Dr. Gwyther exclaiming at one point that it "has never proved detrimental at this post." He quickly added, however, that "it is quite a common occurrence for newcomers to find a temporary relaxation of the bowels." Gwyther attempted to make things look good despite his awareness of problems associated with alkaline content and the fact that it was "saturated with animal and vegetable matter." The Navajo always blamed the water for many of their health problems. Ganado Mucho, a noted tribal leader, told government investigators that his people did not like the water: "The water does not suit us here. . . . We think the water is unhealthy. So much sulphur and salt."[31]

Despite sincere concern for the Navajo, the army doctors generally believed that the native lifestyle caused the high incidence of disease, dismissing suggestions that the location itself was responsible. Gwyther, in particular, believed that a lack of sanitation and cleanliness in the camps caused most of the problem. He remarked on "their exceedingly dirty and imprudent habits of eating and allowing filth of every character to remain near their huts and lodges. They defecate promiscuously near their huts; they leave offal of every character, dead animals and dead skins, close in the vicinity of their huts, and even their own dead they will leave unburied." Thus, he concluded, their medical problems were "wholly owing to their own habits." Although accurate about the relationship between disease and sanitation, Gwyther apparently never considered that the Navajo had little choice and were living under crowded conditions that never existed in their own country. A fair amount of insensitivity also prevailed among the medical personnel with regard to malnutrition. Dr. Warner blamed most of the sickness on "irregularity and constipation of the bowels, owing in part, perhaps, to the fact that, drawing their rations once in two days, they eat too much the first day, and in part to their irregularity of habits."[32] An even more callous view came from Special Commissioner Julius K. Graves, who visited the reservation in December 1866. Graves, a non-medical man, concluded that the "fearful mortality" afflicting the Navajo in various epidemics was the result of "the Divine visitations of God for his own purposes."[33]

One additional and controversial ailment affected the Navajo at the Bosque Redondo. Various forms of venereal disease, especially syphilis, spread rapidly through the camps. Although syphilis had been rare among the tribal population prior to the Long Walk, it suddenly erupted into a significant medical problem, quickly surpassing malnutrition as the most prevalent disorder. With soldiers stationed at Fort Sumner and many Navajo women forced to engage in prostitution in order to feed themselves and their families, the ingredients for an outbreak of venereal disease rapidly materialized. Army doctors acknowledged the threat, assuming that the Indians brought the disease with them.

Infectious syphilis assumed significant proportions during the summer of 1864. That August, Captain Henry Bristol, post commander at Sumner, wrote that "syphilitic disease is spreading among the Indians to an alarming extent; it is not an infrequent thing to see children of both sexes of not more than 14 years of age with diseases of this character." Dr. Gwyther considered syphilis to be a major medical problem. He testified in 1865 that he found the disease to be widespread among both sexes. Admitting that both soldiers and Navajo women had been responsible for communicating the disease, he nevertheless placed the blame squarely on "Navajo women [who] are very loose, and do not look upon fornication as a crime." The actions of soldiers, on the other hand, seem to have been dismissed. Doctors Gwyther and Warner, as well as other post officers, also believed that syphilis had existed among the Diné long enough to become hereditary among the poorer classes. This conclusion may well have been misleading. Some scholars suggest that army medical personnel mistook a glandular form of tuberculosis (scrofula) for the hereditary form of syphilis.[34]

Whatever the source, syphilis became a great embarrassment to the army. Although not necessarily fatal, the disease produced severe discomfort, including skin lesions, fevers, rashes, headaches, sore throats, and hair loss. Severe cases led to crippling, blindness, mental instability, and death. In addition, a number of infected Navajo women, finding themselves in the embarrassing position of becoming pregnant, performed crude abortions, thereby reducing the tribal birthrate. Frustrated post doctors failed to control the disease. In September 1864 Gwyther wrote that "I cannot honestly say that I am certain of having cured a single patient; nor is it possible to do so when your patient asserts the right to run away after two or three days of treatment." Indeed, keeping syphilitic patients in the hospital proved nearly impossible, particularly following rumors that the patients of one doctor had all died. Nevertheless, army doctors continued to treat a high percentage of syphilis cases, most likely using mercury or iodide of potassium. One 1866 report noted that of some 300-plus visits to the Indian hospital, 260 patients "were syphilitic in character, while not one half of the cases are reported from the fact that the Indians have such a horror for the hospital that they will not apply for relief until they are compelled."[35]

Though sympathetic, the army doctors took a fatalistic attitude toward syphilis and other diseases. Several observers remarked that the Navajo healers successfully treated venereal disease with herbs. Rather than picking up on native remedies, however, the army persisted in providing western medications, which even Carleton admitted did not work well. The army also attempted to stop prostitution. Post commanders placed guards between the fort and Indian camps. While this vigilance seems to have temporarily reduced contact, it failed to solve the problem. Because of the desperate condition of many prisoners, soldiers continued to connect with Navajo women, who usually received payment in coins or, more likely, grain. This situation, which the army seemed unable to control, drew harsh criticism from outside sources. In December 1866, the acting governor of New Mexico, William F. M. Arny, summed up the shameful condition that had descended on Navajo society. "The family circle is invaded," he noted, "their wives and daughters are prostituted and diseased by the embraces of a licentious and brutalized soldiery."[36] Arny, who later became the Navajo's agent, held the army accountable for the epidemic of venereal disease.

There is no doubt that the Navajo held captive at the Bosque Redondo suffered from severe medical problems, many of which plagued them for years afterward. They were underfed, confined to crowded and unsanitary camps, mentally distressed, and treated by doctors using alien procedures. The experience proved to be overwhelming. The official record indicates a high mortality rate, although many doctors believed it to be acceptable. Army doctors, to be sure, acted to save lives. However, they generally supported Carleton's reservation philosophy and believed that the ends justified the means. They handed out pills, forced reluctant patients into the hospital, provided vaccinations, and even cured some individuals, but they could not overcome tribal suspicion, resentment, and preference for their own healers. As a consequence, the medical care provided at the Bosque Redondo did little more than add another element to the horror story known as the Long Walk. It did, however, set off a contest between traditional and western medicine that has lasted to the present.

NAVAJO MEDICINE AT THE BOSQUE

Although demoralized by their confinement, the Diné did not abandon tradition. They continually sought to return home, and as one scholar has contended, they used passive resistance to frustrate the reservation experiment.[37] The degree to which such resistance represents conscious plotting may be debated, but it is clear that they hesitated to accept the army's medical program and continued to rely on their own healers. In this sense, their actions represented a form of resistance, precipitating a struggle between Navajo medicine men and army doctors, which the Navajo eventually won. As might be expected, ethnocentric white physicians expressed contempt for traditional healing practices and made little attempt to understand them. With few exceptions they failed to grasp the nature of traditional medical practices and saw them as a threat to the civilizing process.

Post officers noted the reluctance to seek medical assistance almost as soon as the first prisoners arrived. Although suffering terribly, the Diné clearly preferred to rely on their own healers. In November 1864, for example, General Crocker complained that most of the sick Indians sought out their own doctors or "charmers." Captain Bristol, military superintendent of the Navajo during 1864–65, took a fairly enlightened approach to this situation, recognizing some value in native techniques. Providing a fairly good picture of Navajo medicine, Bristol testified that "Indian doctors" effectively used herbs to cure syphilis and other venereal diseases. "For all common disease," he continued, "they use feathers, stones, charms, roots, leaves, antelope toes, cranes' bills, etc., etc. Sometimes they paint themselves with charred wood. They also use sweathouses built of poles covered with grass and dirt, or small excavations in the earth, having been previously filled with red-hot stones."[38]

Curing ceremonies continued under difficult circumstances. Captain Bristol observed that the prisoners actively engaged in ceremonials, which "were done in secret and by a selected few." Navajo oral tradition also indicates that ritual healing practices survived at the Bosque. The Evilway, Enemyway, and Squaw

Dance, conducted to purify individuals contaminated by contact with disease-carrying outsiders or to treat conditions attributable to native causes such as witchcraft, occurred with some regularity on the reservation. Yet, despite a clear preference for their own medical practices, the Navajo accepted some aspects of western medicine. If a positive benefit clearly existed, such as smallpox vaccinations, individuals willingly came in. Pills and pain relievers provided by army doctors also met with acceptance. Native healers, moreover, acknowledged their inability to deal with certain ailments and referred their patients to white doctors. Nevertheless, the Navajo remained cautious and suspicious. Much of what the army doctors prescribed, such as extended hospital stays, made little sense to them. Indeed, some tribesmen retained fears that submitting to a white doctor meant death. One individual remarked that "there is a hospital here for us; but all who go in never come out."[39]

Doctors at the Bosque generally opposed traditional medical activities. Dr. Gwyther attributed the poor state of Navajo health directly to "the influence of their medicine-men," who encouraged the Diné to keep away from white doctors. Dr. Warner expressed much the same sentiment, noting that "from the influence of their medicine men and from their great superstition in regard to medical treatment, many of the sick will not come to the hospital or be treated by us." General Crocker was even more pointed in his opposition. He saw no value in native healing practices. He particularly objected to the custom of compensating healers for medical services, which he viewed as fraud. The post commander wrote that "these Indian doctors are the worse class of humbugs[,] frequently leaving a whole family destitute of clothing for a few days attendance on a sick member of it."[40]

The Navajo also regarded witchcraft as a health threat. There is little doubt that the tribe conducted ceremonies to counter the danger represented by witches. Whites recognized the widespread prevalence of this condition, which Captain Bristol regarded as existing "to an alarming extent." Although he believed all this activity to be superstition, Bristol acknowledged its effect on the Navajo. In one case, a man explained that "the witches at one time put the evil spirit on his wife; she was about to die, when some other witches administered a little bear's gall, dried in the sun, when she immediately recovered." In another instance, General Crocker suggested that the Navajo were desecrating Apache graves in order to procure the toe and finger nails of a deceased enemy. Although horrified by this activity, Crocker concluded that such charms were being used for "the curing of sick in the hands of the [Navajo] doctors."[41]

From the limited evidence available, it appears that the Navajo actively continued to pursue traditional medical practices. Tribal healers remained active in the preservation of Navajo culture, believing that in most cases western medicine offered few advantages. Some medicine men discouraged their people from seeking outside medical assistance. Others may have been more cooperative. In either case, healers did what they could, but their efforts were hampered by a lack of resources (including plants and herbs), the opposition of army officials, and the sheer magnitude of the problem. Under such conditions the concern for witchcraft assumed additional importance, and the Navajo dealt with the situation by seeking ritual protection for their health. It is clear that traditional healers remained a strong and powerful influence within tribal society, and that the efforts of the army to discredit them failed to produce significant results.

THE EXPERIMENT FALTERS

By 1865 problems with the reservation had become obvious. Continued crop failures, escapes, Comanche raids, discontent, and poor health added up to disaster. General Carleton, however, refused to give up on his experiment, maintaining that conditions would improve with time. Nevertheless, the reservation generated a lot of unfavorable comment, much of it centering around health conditions.

In June 1865, a congressional investigating committee, led by Senator James R. Doolittle of Wisconsin, arrived at the reservation to procure an accurate picture of conditions. The committee heard conflicting testimony regarding the medical status of the captives. Most army personnel backed their commander. Acknowledging that some health problems existed, they nonetheless maintained that overall health remained good. Dr. Gwyther told the committee that "I consider it the healthiest place I have ever lived."[42] The nature of the water supply generated heated discussion. Major Herbert Enos, for instance, reported that "the water there is rather alkaline; our officers and men use it; I have never heard them complain of the water; . . . I have not heard of the water affecting the health of the Indians unfavorably." The Indians believed otherwise. Cadette, an Apache, reported that the water contained "too much alkali, and is the cause of the sickness in the tribe and losing our animals." Hererro, a Navajo chieftain, seconded that opinion, stating that his people were afraid to use the water because so many became sick and died.[43]

The Doolittle investigation produced no immediate results, but the muddied nature of the testimony hardly proved reassuring. Doolittle eventually recommended that the Indian Office conduct its own investigation. For reasons that are unclear, the Interior Department selected Julius Graves, a Bible-quoting bigot from Iowa, to review the conditions at the Bosque. After touring the area and meeting with selected Navajo headmen in December 1865, Graves gave the reservation his blessing, backing General Carleton's plans and dismissing most health concerns. He found the water supply more than acceptable, stating that "no complaint was made . . . to the water supply by the Navajos whom I questioned upon this point." Graves also determined that the diseases spreading among the captives, in contrast to the "ignorant and superstitious" Indian belief that they were caused by the unhealthy environment, must be attributed solely to "the divine act of the Great Spirit."[44]

The nagging question of what should ultimately happen to the Navajo assumed increasing importance with the close of the Civil War. Still treated as prisoners of war and under military jurisdiction, the army expected the Indian Office to assume responsibility for the reservation. An increasing amount of sentiment also began to focus on returning the Diné to their homeland. As long as Carleton remained in command, the Indian Office kept hands off, although Theodore Dodd, the agent assigned to the Navajo, regularly reported on tribal welfare. Meanwhile, new medical personnel arrived at Fort Sumner to replace wartime volunteers. Brevet Captain Michael Hillary, a physician trained in Ireland, relieved Gwyther as post medical officer in November 1865. He was joined in April 1866 by Captain John Brooke, who assumed direct control of the Indian hospital a few months later.[45] Both physicians displayed a sincere concern for the Navajo and made no apologies for their condition. As long as the army retained jurisdiction for the Bosque, they worked to improve tribal health.

Medical conditions did change for the better following Hillary's appointment. Just before he arrived, a measles epidemic swept across the reservation, killing a number of people and creating much fear. At one point, some four hundred Navajos reportedly crowded into the hospital seeking help. This incident pointed out the need for changes. Although patients might swamp the hospital in an emergency, they usually stayed away. Indeed, when Hillary took charge of the facility, he found it virtually deserted. By carefully working with the Navajo, the army surgeon eventually generated a more positive response. But as more patients accepted treatment, the building proved totally unfit. The tumbled-down structure appeared to Hillary as "only fit to keep pigs in." Captain Brooke expressed even more concern. He called the hospital "in every respect unsuited for the purpose." Placed in an inconvenient location, it could hold no more than twenty patients. The greatest defect, according to Brooke, rested in a design that made it impossible to keep patients confined to bed until they were fit to return home. Always a problem for western doctors, Brooke wrote that "if they are not cured in as short a time as they think they should be, or if they become dissatisfied for any cause, they leave the hospital, originate any number of new cases of their disease, and probably return in the course of time in a tenfold worse condition." Regarding this as a great waste of money, Brooke proposed that the post military hospital be converted into an Indian facility. Here, he believed, proper hygiene could be maintained and patients kept under close supervision. This suggestion eventually received approval, although the conversion came too late to make much difference.[46]

A beleaguered General Carleton finally stepped down in April 1867, and the army quickly arranged to turn the Navajo over to civilian control. It required six months to complete the transfer, however. During the interim the Interior Department considered how best to provide for these people. In contrast to the conclusions of Commissioner Graves, the Indian Office took a more pessimistic view of the situation. When New Mexico Superintendent of Indian Affairs A. Baldwin Norton met with tribal leaders in July 1866, they asked to return home. Arguing that the reservation remained unhealthy, one headman estimated that the Diné would not last two years if they remained at the Bosque. This same individual related that sickness had killed all but one of his family. The following summer Navajo leaders told Norton that almost half the captives had died since 1864. Questioned about the validity of these numbers, the Indians retorted that an average of five to eight people died per day. Asked if it would not be better for them to see the doctors, he was informed that "the medicine kills them there, they are afraid of it. We prefer our own medicine men [who] don't kill if he cannot cure." By this time the Navajo were pushing hard to return home and undoubtedly exaggerated the situation. On the other hand, Dodd reported that of 7,400 people on the reservation in March 1867, some 228 reported sick but none died.[47] Since the Navajos performed their own burials and had no incentive to report deaths, the truth lay somewhere in the middle.

The Indian Office finally took charge of the reservation on October 31, 1867. Debate had vacillated for some months over how to best provide health care. As early as May 1866 Indian Office personnel recognized that they must at least provide a physician and a clinic. In February 1867, Carleton, still hoping that the reservation might survive, stressed the absolute necessity of maintaining a hospital, medical supplies, "and a competent physician with attendants for the sick of 7500 souls. . . . We can transfer the sick Indians [to civilian control], but to transfer the sick with no one on the ground *at once* to take care of them will be a matter which will doubtless be considered as one of moment." The Indian Office well understood its obligation. Medical care must be provided if the Navajo remained at the Bosque Redondo. Dodd estimated, in November 1867, that the government would have to spend 4,000 dollars to erect a hospital at the reservation, 1,000 dollars for medical supplies, plus 150 dollars per month for a physician and 75 dollars per month for a hospital steward.[48]

At this point, the Indian Office, motivated in part by the expense of maintaining the Pecos reservation, determined to return the Navajo to their homeland. Overwhelming evidence indicated that the Bosque Redondo had failed and would be costly to continue. Agent Dodd wrote in December 1867 that "I am satisfied that the Navajos will never be content, or be induced to remain on this or any other reservation, except one located in their old country." He recommended that no more funds be expended on improving the reservation. Superintendent Norton was even more forceful. Reporting to Indian Commissioner Nathaniel Taylor, Norton described the reservation as a place of perpetual crop failure, scarcity of fuel, and desolation. "The water," he wrote, "is black and brackish, scarcely bearable to the taste, and said by the Indians to be unhealthy because one-fourth of their population have been swept off by disease." Norton asked for their return: "I care not what any man may say to the contrary, these Indians are all dissatisfied, and that dissatisfaction is universal. . . . They will never work there with any heart, and never have done so. . . . O! let them go back."[49]

On June 1, 1868, the reservation experiment ended with the signing of a treaty that permitted the Navajo to reside on a reservation of some 3.5 million acres situated in their old country along the northern Arizona–New Mexico border. In return for a promise to remain at peace, the document provided for the immediate release of the remaining captives. Additionally, the government pledged to help reestablish the tribal economy by providing them with fifteen thousand sheep and five hundred head of cattle. For their part, the Navajo agreed to continue the civilization program by sending their children to government-provided schools. The only comment in the treaty pertaining to medical care came in the vague promise to provide the tribe with a physician.[50]

The Navajo captives started for home almost immediately. The five-year exodus had permanently changed the Diné. Their anguish ended, they now wanted to be left alone. Although the experience provided them with some knowledge of the white men and their medicine, they remained unconvinced of the superiority of either. Indeed, western medicine had been of little help at the Bosque Redondo reservation. Tribal health, on the other hand, was dramatically changed by the experience. Nevertheless, they kept faith in their own healers and hoped that the return home would restore their health.

CHAPTER THREE

MISSIONARIES AND POLITICIANS

The confidence of the Navajos in our remedies has been steadily gaining ground: so that now, there is not-only a willingness on the part of many to try our medicines, but a decided desire by nearly all to use them, at least, in connection with their own.

JOHN MENAUL, AGENCY PHYSICIAN

The Indian Peace Policy, initiated by President Grant in 1869, dominated Indian affairs during the 1870s. Intended as a benevolent effort to provide humane treatment of the native population, the policy focused on developing reservations, creating an atmosphere conducive to acculturation, placing Christian men and women in charge of agency affairs, and eliminating fraud and politics from the Indian Service. Extremely popular at first, the program emphasized a desire to have the Indians adopt major elements of American society. In essence, they were to be "civilized" through heavy doses of Christianity and education.

To improve the quality of reservation life and make the Indians more receptive, advocates of the Peace Policy recognized the need to provide the Indians with federally funded medical care. As a result, religiously oriented agency physicians became a common, if not always dependable, part of reservation life during the 1870s. Like other aspects of the Peace Policy, the efforts of early government doctors were underfunded, unfocused, and largely ineffective. Physicians at most agencies found themselves totally overwhelmed by the magnitude of the job, and even under the best of conditions they accomplished little. Additionally, like the agent's job, the position of reservation doctor gradually slipped back into the spoils system as enthusiasm for the Christian-dominated Peace Policy evaporated near the end of the decade. Meanwhile, Indian health problems accelerated as tribes like the Navajo encountered difficulty in becoming self-sufficient. Indeed, the medical care received under the Peace Policy proved little better than what the Navajo had received at Fort Sumner.

RETURN TO FORT DEFIANCE

As the Diné returned home during the hot, dusty summer of 1868 they wished to leave the Bosque Redondo experience behind them. They quickly discovered, however, that their old life could not be duplicated. The new reservation, consisting of some 3.5 million acres along the New Mexico–Arizona border, contained only a small portion of the original Navajo homeland. Long neglected fields and damaged orchards lay barren. The sheep were gone, too. So destitute were the survivors of Carleton's reservation that the returning group of seven thousand camped at Fort Wingate, just off the reservation, until January 1869, subsisting on government rations. Under such circumstances, it proved extremely difficult to restore prosperity. In a medical sense, problems associated with malnutrition were abundant. In addition, most of the diseases contracted at the Bosque Redondo continued to plague the tribe. Nonetheless, the Navajo occupied their new reservation at the beginning of 1869 with a sense of hope.[1]

Although the Navajo desired to slip back into their old ways, the government had different ideas. In the words of Indian Commissioner Nathaniel G. Taylor, the Indians were to be "elevated and enlightened to the proud stature of civilized manhood." Like all tribes assigned to reservations as part of the Peace Policy, the Navajo were to be provided with tools, farm implements, domestic animals, schools, and Christian missions in hopes that they would begin to acculturate. They were also promised medical care in the form of an agency physician.[2] Recognizing that tribal health conditions directly impacted Indian acceptance of the civilization program, the federal government in the immediate post–Civil War period had begun to add medical assistance to its agenda. A few tribes had been provided with physicians prior to the war, but the series of major treaties negotiated by the Peace Commission in 1867–68 (which included the Navajo treaty) promised to supply each reservation with a doctor at government expense.[3]

In the Navajo case, this commitment was endorsed by the report of John Ward, a special Indian agent sent by the Peace Commission to survey tribal needs in July 1868. Like agent Theodore H. Dodd, Ward believed that the Navajo would be able to raise good crops in their old country, become self-supporting, and advance rapidly toward "civilization." He also insisted that medical care should be provided as quickly as possible. Writing to Samuel F. Tappan in early August, Ward remarked that "a physician should also, by all means, be employed at the agency, and a good supply of medicines and surgical instruments kept always on hand for the benefit of the tribe, and the employés about the agency. A hospital building should also be erected in connection with the agency."[4] Nevertheless, because of the priority given to restoring the Navajo economy in the face of possible starvation, it took four years for a doctor to be appointed. It required another three decades before a hospital came into being.

The government's initial concern focused on returning the tribe to self-sufficiency, administering the reservation, and dealing with missionaries. Once on the reservation, the government divided the tribe into twelve bands, each headed by a noted chieftain. This structure, intended to provide some form of tribal responsibility, seldom worked as planned.[5] In general, these artificial divisions opened the way for intra-tribal conflict, focusing on the distribution of annuities, and creating power struggles among Navajo leaders. In the meantime, a threat of starvation loomed over the tribe.

The first agents in the post-removal era encountered so many problems that the issue of health care seldom surfaced. Operating out of the long-abandoned and run-down buildings at Fort Defiance, they struggled to make the agency buildings livable while meeting basic tribal needs. Theodore Dodd, the agent responsible for overseeing the return from the Bosque Redondo, died in January 1869, being replaced by James C. French, former agent to the Ute Indians. Although competent, French was removed five months later when President Grant ousted most civilian agents in favor of army officers. Captain Frank T. Bennett, then stationed at Fort Wingate and well liked by the Navajo, took control of the agency during the summer of 1869, remaining in office for well over a year.[6]

Despite a high turnover rate, all the early Navajo agents made an effort to keep the tribe healthy, primarily by promoting agricultural self-sufficiency. Progress in this direction, however, was thwarted by persistent crop failures. In a typical report, Bennett wrote that "the majority of the tribe have raised good crops of wheat and corn, but owing to the early frost, the corn crops have been to a great extent damaged." Such emergencies required the government to subsist the tribe with regular food distributions. Federal authorities, of course, expected the tribe to become self-supporting, and thus hesitated to approve additional funding. This placed tribal health in serious jeopardy. As Bennett noted, "I am extremely sorry that the Government have an idea of stopping the rations of the Navajoes. It is my opinion that unless they are fed until such time as they are able to get in another crop, that at least one-third must either starve or steal their means of subsistence." Bennett also observed that some Diné were so hungry that they engaged such unhealthy practices as consuming their corn while green. Despite such concerns, the agent did not believe that a doctor would be of much use until the tribe became self-sufficient. As a consequence, his requests for additional agency staff did not include a physician.[7]

The initial impetus for hiring a full-time physician came instead from the first missionary assigned to the reservation. As part of the Peace Policy program for spreading Christianity among the Indians, the Board of Foreign Missions, Old School, of the Presbyterian church selected Reverend James M. Roberts to work among the Navajo. Roberts, fresh out of theological seminary and full of zeal, arrived at Fort Wingate in January 1869, committed to establishing both a school and mission. After meeting with tribal leaders Manuelito and Barbon-cito, who were not keen on missionary activity, Roberts chose to concentrate his initial efforts on education. He also expressed the opinion that a doctor would facilitate his efforts to win the tribe over. Writing from Fort Defiance to Reverend John C. Lowrie, secretary of the Board of Foreign Missions, Roberts requested the services of a female physician, whom he thought might provide some companionship for the woman schoolteacher soon expected to arrive.[8] Unfortunately, nothing came of his suggestion.

Roberts seldom commented on the hunger being experienced by the tribe, but when Vincent Colyer, secretary of the Board of Indian Commissioners, visited the agency during the summer of 1869, he noted that Navajos were stealing the missionary's chickens, milking his cows, and breaking into his kitchen. Although Colyer treated the situation with some humor, these incidents, which did not amuse Roberts, illustrate the desperation of tribal members. Despite his desire to hire a physician, Roberts became so entangled with opening his school, securing more support for his religious work "among these heathen," and meddling with the morals of white agency employees, that he frequently overlooked obvious health concerns. An example of this occurred in March 1870, when he married a Navajo woman known to have syphilis to a young white man to prevent them from living in sin. Captain Bennett violently opposed the marriage as being a danger to public health and unsuc-cessfully tried to have Roberts removed from the reservation.[9] Although the incident did little more than create bitter personal animosities, it confirmed that venereal disease had begun to spread at the agency. Roberts, however, was more concerned with eliminating immoral behavior.

The Navajo people suffered another crop failure during the summer of 1870, and once again the government found it necessary to feed them. Despite the fact that famine continued to endanger tribal health, Bennett downplayed conditions when reporting to the Indian Office. His 1870 report, filed in August, noted "that there has been but very little sickness among them." This statement contradicts his many remarks that the Navajo were on the verge of starvation, suggesting that he did not view hunger as a health problem. Meanwhile, the possibility of a smallpox epidemic alarmed federal officials, prompting the government to undertake a large-scale vaccination program in the fall of 1870. Although some Navajo had received inoculations during the 1850s and the Indian Office had vaccinated tribes as early as 1832, this effort stands out as the first significant preventive measure aimed at the tribes of the Southwest.[10]

The vaccination program provides information on the degree of Navajo acceptance of western medicine in the early 1870s. The Indian Office appointed Dr. Jules Le Carpentier, an army surgeon, to inoculate the Indians. Using a vaccine virus ordered from an eastern manufacturer, the doctor received twenty-five cents for every person vaccinated. In late August he visited the Hopi, only to encounter opposition from traditional leaders who denounced the vaccinations as an attempt at extermination. Accordingly, Le Carpentier inoculated only a few Hopi, and even this became useless when the vaccine proved defective.[11]

Navajo reaction to the vaccinations contrasted sharply with the Hopi experience and shows much more receptiveness. Dr. Le Carpentier began his work at Fort Defiance on September 15. This time he met with success. The physician found that the Navajo had been well prepared ahead of his visit: "all the Navajoes seemed to understand very well that vaccination was a good thing, and should feel confidence in my efforts." The army doctor vaccinated Navajos at the agency for a month, before visiting major outlying population centers. In all, some 5,915 Navajo were vaccinated without objection. As estimated, 3,000 more could not be reached before the vaccine supply ran out. Le Carpentier calculated that about 3,500 of the vaccinations took, with the rest failing either because people had been previously vaccinated or the vaccine virus had failed. Nevertheless, the surgeon was pleased with the results, reporting in December that "I feel satisfied that I have accomplished my duty as far as it was possible, and I think that the number of cases actually unprotected against Small pox in the Navajo Tribe must be very small."[12]

From this incident it appears that when the benefits were obvious and did not threaten traditional practices, the Navajo people had little hesitation in accepting western medicine. In an interesting aside, Le Carpentier reported that his Navajo patients daily asked him for medicines and treatment. He described them as suffering from syphilis, scrofula, chronic rheumatism, and ophthalmia. Le Carpentier believed that the Navajo would be receptive to western medicine should a permanent physician be provided: "They have full confidence in our treatment of disease, and, I should think that they ought to be furnished with Medical attendance, and medical supplies."[13] The surgeon's report clearly supported the need for an agency doctor.

THE MISSIONARY DOCTOR

Although the Navajo agency did not hire its first physician until early 1872, the man destined to hold that post came to Fort Defiance a year earlier. Concerned that the Indian Office might not face up to tribal health problems and agreeing with Reverend Robert's request for additional missionary support, Mission Board Secretary John Lowrie assigned John Menaul to New Mexico in October 1870. Thirty-six years old when he arrived in the Southwest, the Irish-born Menaul had graduated from Lafayette College in Pennsylvania before entering Princeton Seminary. Despite frequent references to "Doctor" Menaul, he did not possess a medical degree. In preparation for a missionary assignment, however, he had studied medicine for about a year at Princeton, then read informally under the direction of a Philadelphia area doctor while attending medical school lectures. His first church assignment took him to Corisco in West Africa where he labored as a medical missionary, but within two years "the torrid heat, living much on quinine and struggling against the pestential fevers of that unhealthy coast" robbed him of his health and cost his wife her life. Returning to the United States to recover, Menaul requested an assignment among the Indians. Deeply religious, dedicated, and idealistic, the handsome young missionary arrived in New Mexico with considerable enthusiasm, and he was judged by his superiors as competent to handle "ordinary [medical] cases."[14]

Menaul did not at first know where he would be posted. It seemed that he might be diverted to Zuni, a circumstance that displeased Roberts. Yet Menaul finally decided to settle at the Navajo agency, a decision no doubt prompted by his marriage in early February 1871 to Charity Ann Gaston, the schoolteacher at Fort Defiance. Circumstances prevented him from practicing much medicine, however. Because the church provided such little financial support he accepted a job supervising grain issues, offered to him by newly appointed agent James Miller. This familiarized Menaul with tribal health problems, but did not permit him to provide treatment. He nevertheless saw firsthand the "starving condition" that New Mexico Superintendent of Indian Affairs Nathaniel Pope reported in 1871. Later in the year, he witnessed a large gathering of families at Fort Defiance desperately hoping to be fed by the government.[15]

Although Menaul kept busy distributing grain and performing church-related activities, he found occasional use for his medical skills. In addition to caring for agency employees, he aided Reverend Roberts's persistent crusade against "immoral" conduct by agency employees. Roberts, who continued to denounce several government men for living with Navajo women, reported that "loathsome disease" had become common among Navajos of both sexes "who are necessarily induced to hang round Fort Defiance." Roberts believed that immoral cohabitation accounted for the influx of venereal disease being experienced at agency headquarters. The veracity of his accusations seemed confirmed when a Navajo child living with his own family was stricken. Menaul confirmed that the youngster suffered from syphilis; the missionary responded by expelling all Indian children under his care. This incident persuaded Roberts that Navajos living away from the agency were generally free of the disease, but that conditions were "unsafe" for those near Fort Defiance.[16] Just how he expected forced marriages to end the problem went unexplained.

In 1871 the Indian Office finally agreed to hire a physician for the Navajo. Although the agent continued to report that tribal health remained generally good, problems obviously existed. Many deaths went unreported, and as Agent Miller remarked, "there are still numbers of Indians suffering from diseases said to be contracted while at the Bosque Redondo." As a consequence, Superintendent Pope began to demand improved Indian medical services in New Mexico. His concern coincided with federal efforts to employ physicians. Indeed, by mid-1873, forty-one of the seventy-seven existing agencies had appointed a doctor.[17] This commitment to improved Indian health care developed primarily in response to humanitarian efforts to civilize the Indians. Nevertheless, it remained a minor part of the acculturation program. At this time there existed no overall medical strategy, no specific qualifications for agency doctors, and no requirement of competency. As a consequence, the early agency doctors tended to be a highly miscellaneous group.

Agent Miller received authority to hire a physician during the summer of 1871. His first choice was James Aiken, a prominent Presbyterian churchman from Reeseville, Pennsylvania. Aiken apparently accepted the post, but subsequently withdrew because of a family illness. Considering the lack of another qualified candidate and his own personal need for a job, John Menaul applied for the position in February 1872. The missionary doctor explained to Miller that he did not hold a medical degree, but had studied medicine over a period of years. To his credit, Menaul did not pretend to be fully qualified, admitting that his skills were rusty. He offered, should Miller think it necessary, to "spend a few months with Dr. Vickery at Fort Wingate reviewing Medicine, both Theoretically and Practically." Menaul's reputation as a Presbyterian missionary won Miller's endorsement, the appointment was approved, and Menaul entered government service on March 8, 1872, at a salary of twelve hundred dollars per year.[18] At the time he was the only full-time agency physician working in New Mexico.

John Menaul began his practice with very specific ideas. He saw himself as a medical missionary, one who could use medicine as a tool in the lofty goal of converting the Navajo to Christianity. If his care produced confidence in the white man's way, it would encourage the Navajo people to accept his religion and moral concepts. As Menaul wrote, "Medicine and kind treatment [prepare] the Indian for the Glorious Gospel (of our Blessed God)." His goal, therefore, focused on replacing traditional Indian customs with the standards of white society. Menaul thus continued to devote some of his time to missionary activities, a responsibility that increased when James Roberts was fired by the Presbyterian Board, in March 1872, because he could not get along with agency personnel. As the only other church representative on hand, Menaul found himself with the added duty of operating the floundering mission.[19] Despite his dedication to evangelism, Menaul nevertheless launched into the murky waters of tribal health care with enthusiasm. The magnitude of the task before him is testified to by the fact that he was assigned to care for a growing tribal population of ten thousand.

Menaul soon opened a makeshift doctor's office in one of the rundown buildings at Fort Defiance. Having few supplies on hand, he asked the Indian Office to send out enough medicine to last a year. Correctly assuming that no standardized government list existed, he estimated what might be needed. Meanwhile, the physician began to provide treatment to those Navajos willing to visit his office. From the beginning Menaul seemed destined to succeed. Some of his progress may be attributed to the fact that he spoke enough Navajo to impart instructions. Within a month he was "gaining the confidence of the Indians." By May 1872 the missionary doctor could write Reverend Lowrie that "I am succeeding beyond my expectations in my practice of Medicine; have many patients, who are generally well satisfied." A handful of Navajos, some traveling for a considerable distance, thus began calling on the doctor to help with their ailments. By June 1872 the physician's office reported handling an average of eleven patients per day, a remarkable figure given Navajo reluctance to trust whites.[20]

Menaul's success created a problem, however. By May 1872 the doctor admitted that he had seriously underestimated his needs and exhausted his supply of medicine. Embarrassed by this development, Menaul quickly requested more supplies, noting that he was treating cases of syphilis, rheumatism, and sore eyes. Promising to hand out medicines as long as possible, his progress nevertheless appeared to be jeopardized. "I have gained much confidence with the people so far," he wrote in July, "but now, my medicines (after exhausting every resource within my limits) are almost done, and I will soon have to shut the Office till you can forward my supplies." Menaul's two-page request included an assortment of liniments; purgatives; gastric and intestinal stimulants; natural narcotic plant products, such as belladonna and cinchona (quinine); and various ointments. He also requested pill boxes, bottles and corks, crucibles, dental forceps, sponges, and soap. This list indicates that the doctor's primary activity involved preparing remedies in his office for distribution as pain relievers or purges.[21]

Menaul failed to understand the government's hopelessly inefficient procurement system. In attempting to eliminate corruption, the Board of Indian Commissioners had created a special purchasing committee to regulate the bidding procedure and inspect purchases. By the early 1870s the purchase of all goods, including medical supplies, was subject to this yearly process. Although it assured a measure of quality control, supplies could not be purchased as needed. And if Congress failed to make a timely appropriation, as frequently happened, federal purchases might be delayed for months, meaning that neither the supplies nor the funds to ship them were available. As a consequence, requests for supplies often languished in Washington or went unfilled without explanation, a problem that both mystified and discouraged Menaul.[22]

While Menaul anxiously waited for his supplies, events at the agency took an ominous turn. In June 1872 Agent Miller was killed by Ute Indians, leaving Thomas V. Keam in temporary charge of the reservation. While Charity Ann Menaul escorted Miller's wife home to Pennsylvania, her husband penned an angry letter to Lowrie, expressing outrage over "an imbecile" federal policy that coddled the Indians. Although he expressed no fear of the Navajo, Miller's death unnerved Menaul, prompting him to question his ability to accomplish God's work in such a dangerous atmosphere. Menaul may also have been wary of Keam, one of the agency employees accused by Roberts of immoral conduct. The physician was thus somewhat relieved when the Presbyterian Board nominated William F. Hall of Washington, D.C., to assume control of the agency in July 1872. Nevertheless, Menaul's circumstances remained far from pleasant. The condition of the agency buildings, including the physician's quarters, were intolerable, with collapsed roofs, deteriorating walls, rotten beams, and unworkable doors and windows making life miserable. Moreover, hardly a piece of office or household furniture could be found.[23]

Despite his repeated requests for supplies and repairs, the federal government failed to respond, causing Menaul more despair. It seemed to the goodhearted missionary that all his gains might be for naught. With few medical supplies available, the physician's office had all but closed by early 1873. Menaul continually argued his case, diplomatically suggesting that his requests had been misplaced. "I have been without many important Medicines for several months," he wrote in January, "and on that account have had to send about half the Indians applying for medicines away without them." In desperation he asked for a shipment of alcohol and iodine (major ingredients in the most common treatment for syphilis), in order to make liniment so that he might have something to give his patients lest they be disappointed. Still nothing arrived, and four months later he again remarked that it "is useless for me to keep the office open."[24]

The Indian Office, meanwhile, began to take more interest in native health conditions. In 1873 Indian Commissioner Edward P. Smith created a Medical and Educational Division, placing it under the direction of Dr. Josiah Curtis. Although much of the division's effort related to education, it also supervised reservation health, sanitation, and liquor control. At the time of its creation the division possessed practically no knowledge of tribal health conditions, nor an awareness of what its own field doctors were doing. Because most physicians were church-sponsored appointments, in some cases the Indian Office did not even have basic biographical information. One of the first orders of business, therefore, involved collecting basic statistical and qualitative information. As a consequence, in June 1873, the commissioner sent a circular letter to all agents asking, for the first time, questions ranging from the qualifications of field doctors to the yearly amount of medicine required.[25]

Hall's response to the medical circular sheds some light on the conditions at Fort Defiance. The agent noted that they had been almost entirely without medicine for nine months, the physician's office possessed just one small case of surgical instruments, and no records were kept. Leading diseases consisted of pneumonia, syphilis, rheumatism, consumption, sore eyes, and swellings. With regard to how many Indians preferred their own healers, Hall vaguely responded that most Navajo were willing to combine the services of traditional and western medicine. Menaul's comments indicate that he clearly understood the importance of meeting Indian needs: "they do not know one Medicine from another. If they see a bottle they think that ought to do. [But] if you give them medicine which is not what they want, or worthless, you cause mistrust."[26] The physician was obviously treading a fine line in his effort to win Navajo trust and he increasingly resented the lack of government support.

The nature of Menaul's daily medical activities became more evident in September 1873, when he presented his annual report to new agent William F. M. Arny. The physician remained somewhat optimistic, stating that "the confidence of the Navajos in our remedies has been steadily gaining ground: so that now, there is not-only a willingness on the part of many to try our medicines, but a decided desire by nearly all to use them, at least, in connection with their own." Menaul estimated that fifteen hundred patients had applied for treatment during the past year, although many were turned away for want of medicines. In addition to office visits, the physician visited one or two hogans per week, extracted teeth, and treated white agency employees. The

same diseases prevailed, although additional problems had arisen from neglected colds. Of particular note, however, was the fact that eye problems associated with what would be later diagnosed as trachoma were becoming more
common. In sum, he said, "the diseases are much the same as those presented
in any of our Eastern Dispensaries; but require a little different treatment from
the exposed habits of the people." Again Menaul stressed the need for medical
supplies, hoping that some contingency fund might be tapped.[27]

On the subject of native healers, the physician's report expressed some tolerance, admitting their short-term value and seeing some good in their remedies.
Remarking that some of the pro-government chiefs had recently attempted to
destroy the influence of tribal medicine men, Menaul acknowledged that "had
they succeeded, which they did not, they would have placed us in a very awk-
ward position; as we had little or no medicine to meet such a change or maintain our reputation in such a crisis." Menaul's reaction suggests that he realized
how difficult it would be to rapidly replace the entire tribal healing system.

The physician's frustration grew considerably following William Arny's arrival. He had gotten along reasonably well with William Hall, but the agent's
performance disappointed both the Presbyterians and federal officials. As a
consequence, Arny, a former Indian agent then serving a second stint as New
Mexico territorial secretary, was appointed Navajo agent on June 18, 1873, with
the consent of Reverend Lowrie. Although described as a good Presbyterian
and friend of the Indian, the sixty-year-old Arny had become a professional
politician during his many years of federal service. He actively solicited the
appointment and was not adverse to dispensing patronage during his troubled
two years at Fort Defiance. The Indians quickly grew to dislike his pompous
attitude and heavy hand. White employees also fell out with the agent, especially after he fired several men for living with Navajo women. Even those who
regard Arny as well intentioned acknowledge his "uncanny ability to make
enemies." Less charitable evaluations have called him a "hypocritical rascal, a
Bible-pounding moralist who plotted larceny."[28]

Menaul initially supported Arny's appointment, believing him to be a good
and honest Christian capable of doing good work among the Indians. The
physician, however, expressed some concern about the agent's ability to be
truthful. Arny, in turn, supported Menaul's work. Soon after arriving at Fort
Defiance, the elderly agent heard rumors that the Missionary Board might
send the physician to a church in Santa Fe. Arny vigorously opposed this move,
believing that Menaul "could be of more service in the position he now oc-
cupies than anywhere else." He frankly admitted that Menaul's success gave
"him access to the Indians that no other person could have."[29] With Arny

making enemies at the agency and the school barely surviving, John Menaul seemed to be the only success story among the Navajos. Arny needed Menaul's work to offset the unfavorable barbs by his enemies.

Menaul's opinion of Arny soon changed. On December 2, 1873, he wrote Lowrie that the Navajo had turned against the agent and now demanded his removal. More important, the man had embarrassed the church by accepting the job under what Menaul considered false pretenses: "he is not a Presbyterian or anything that would approximate that Faith." Menaul denounced Arny as a "Politico" who had lied to obtain his appointment, played favorites, boasted about his political influence, and even went duck hunting on the Sabbath. He single-handedly seemed determined to tarnish the good record of church appointments. Yet, because he served at the agent's pleasure, the physician hesitated to air his criticism directly, preferring the let others do most of the complaining. He did, however, let Reverend Lowrie know that if things did not improve, he might have to leave the agency.[30]

Medical activity at the reservation reached a peak during the first half of 1874. Menaul was now receiving between 450 and 1,200 Indian patients a month, handing out prescriptions to more than half of them. At the end of each month, as now required by the Indian Office, he filed a report. Although his records contain some statistical information, they fail to discuss methods of treatment. Nevertheless, one gets an occasional glimpse of tribal medical conditions. In March Menaul wrote that "the month has been one of much sickness, and many deaths; owing, in great measure, to the severity of the Winter, and unavoidable exposure of the sick and infirm to the inclemency of the weather." In addition, the shortage of medical supplies persisted, finally prompting Menaul to make the arduous buggy trip to Santa Fe to secure some badly needed medicines. Despite shortages the Navajo continued to accept the doctor's services. He was especially pleased in May when a record 1,229 people asked for treatment. The large turnout was due to a general issue of annuity goods, which "brought all the Indians to the Agency." Yet the fact that so many Navajos brought their ailments to the government doctor indicated that Menaul's limited activities were winning some approval.[31]

Despite a desire to stick to his own business, Menaul continued to be dissatisfied with affairs at the agency. When federal inspector J. W. Daniels visited Fort Defiance in August 1874, the physician commented that the Navajo seemed to be "well disposed toward the whites," except for Arny, whom they disliked. Although Menaul's concerns were now well known, Arny continued to support the apparently successful medical program. In his annual report for 1874, Menaul reported treating 2,204 Indians and handing out over three thousand prescriptions. In response to the Indian Office's increasing focus on record keeping, the physician listed all the ailments he had treated, which ranged from major diseases such as syphilis, gonorrhea, and consumption to minor bruises, sprains, constipation, burns, and headaches. Regrettably, no numbers were provided, making it difficult to determine the extent of major medical problems. It seems certain, however, that he dealt primarily with minor aches and pains, with his treatments consisting of the distribution primarily of pills and liniment. Menaul wrote that "as we have no hospital, the work is more that of [a] Dispensary than of carrying patients through a course of treatment." This fact also seemed to justify his lax record keeping. Because no hospital existed, "we have not kept a Record of treatments by Diseases." He promised to be more specific in the future.[32]

Like Menaul, Arny recognized the need for improved medical services on the reservation. In September he broached the subject of building a hospital: "A hospital is much required, the sick cannot properly be cared for, medicines will not be properly and regularly taken by the sick, and proper nourishment furnished to them unless they are in a hospital." Although his argument made sense, the agent viewed such improvements, should they be funded, as a testament to his leadership. He also believed that a hospital, stocked with "proper medicines and food for the sick," would undermine the influential Navajo healers, who were unhappy with his rule. A visible symbol of "the White Man's Medicine" might destroy the "superstitious 'Medicine' practices, and the 'pow wows' of the medicine-men." He also suggested raising the physician's salary to fourteen hundred dollars per year.[33] As usual, nothing came of these proposals.

Indeed, much to Menaul's disappointment, instead of seeing a raise, on October 1, 1874, he found his salary reduced by two hundred dollars per year. This was prompted by an act of Congress cutting agency funds. But the problem was exacerbated by the fact that Arny had spent all his money, causing him to issue pay vouchers instead of cash, hoping that the Indian Office would honor his overdrafts. Menaul's reaction to this unwelcome development has not survived, but by this time he was thoroughly frustrated. In late October he reported "no change in affairs at the Post." By early December Menaul had had enough. As a last straw, he found himself facing unfounded charges that he had undermined the earlier missionary work of Reverend Roberts. A furious Menaul wrote to Lowrie that he had no desire to remain at Fort Defiance, sarcastically adding that "at an (at least this one) I[ndian] Agency a man's life must be a zero." Defeated and dejected, Menaul and his wife packed their belongings and headed east. The downcast Presbyterian sought to continue working with Indians, however, and in April 1875, he accepted an appointment to the troubled Southern Apache agency, only to resign a few months later because he could not picture himself "packing a six shooter." A year later Menaul became the physician at Laguna Pueblo, New Mexico, remaining there for sixteen successful years.[34]

John Menaul served as the Navajo physician for nearly three years. He was the first white doctor any of them had gotten to know, and by all accounts he was a decent, honest man, sincerely concerned with their welfare. Although he viewed traditional healing practices as uncivilized, Menaul made little effort to oppose the medicine men, realizing that they served a purpose that could not be done away with until the government program became more effective. He considered his medical work successful, primarily because of the sizable number of Diné who voluntarily came in for treatment. Yet that measure of success was based primarily on dispensing pills and liniments. Moreover, his influence did not extend into the large population living away from Fort Defiance. The Navajo could accept his medical services because they did not threaten traditional cures and were obtained on Navajo terms. In essence, Menaul created little fear, helped with aches and pains, and was well liked. Unfortunately, this was insufficient reward for Menaul and his wife. He detested agency politics, especially the antics of Arny. Nor could he understand the lack of government support for his work. Finally, he preferred to preach the Gospel, something he was unable to effectively accomplish from the physician's office at Fort Defiance. Perhaps the 1873 report of the Board of Foreign Missions best summed up his predicament: "The missionary work of [John Menaul] is chiefly that of example, sympathy, and influence, but not of direct evangelizing labor."[35] Given those circumstances, he sought fulfillment elsewhere.

POLITICS AND MEDICINE

For all practical purposes, the Peace Policy at the Navajo agency began to crumble with the administration of William Arny. To be sure, the Presbyterians were still consulted on appointments, but church influence had peaked.[36] After 1875 the commitment of agency employees to Christian work slowly fell by the wayside. Once again, self-interest became an important concern for men accepting appointments to the Indian Service. This trend included the agency physician. In essence, the job of government doctor changed from one focusing on medicine as a way to civilize the Indians to one of seeking government employment, and perhaps even advancement to higher office. In the process the commitment to Indian welfare suffered a setback.

Arny's choice for a doctor to replace Menaul illustrates this trend. Dr. Walter Whitney, a well-connected Republican, had know Arny for several years. At the time of his appointment, the thirty-one-year-old bachelor (who apparently had some medical training) was working in Washington, D.C. His older brother, Joseph N. Whitney, Chief Clerk of the Bureau of Statistics, had provided Walter with several jobs, the last being a clerical position at the Indian Office. The ambitious young man, described as "capable & energetic," actively sought advancement. In 1873 his friend Arny had unsuccessfully attempted to name Whitney to the position of Navajo agency clerk. A year and a half later, in December 1874, the agent renewed acquaintances with Whitney and quickly offered him the recently vacated position of agency physician. After personally confirming the appointment with the commissioner of Indian affairs, the agent belatedly informed Lowrie. Admitting that Whitney was not a member of the Presbyterian church, he nevertheless hoped that "ere long his influence with the Indians will tend to much good, both with respect to their health and religious training." Arny justified the appointment because "Dr. Menaul was not competent to make the reports required by the Department, hence his place had to be supplied by some person fully competent, and as Dr. Whitney was recommended to me not only as fully competent but also in every respect moral, I employed him." Not once did the question of Whitney's medical qualifications come up.[37]

Whitney began work on February 15, 1875. Arny hastily reported that "by his energy and skill he has gained the confidence of the Indians and has been asked by them to give advice in several cases that had been refused to the former physician." In fact, Whitney did very little. During his first seven months at Fort Defiance, he failed to gain the Indian's confidence, treating considerably fewer patients than Menaul. At least, he kept better records. His "Monthly Sanitary Report" for May 1875 shows that he treated seventy-nine people for venereal disease, eighty-three for rheumatism, ninety-three for respiratory ills, and eighty-one for digestive problems (mostly constipation). Whitney also inventoried the agency's medical supplies. His request for additional medicines suggests that he too planned to continue dispensing pills and tonics.[38]

Of all the medical conditions then afflicting the Navajo, none proved more difficult or controversial than syphilis. Whitney's observations confirmed that it remained a major health problem for the Navajo, at least in the vicinity of Fort Defiance. Because of its sexually transmitted nature, it became linked with immoral behavior in the minds of many whites.[39] Western medical efforts, moreover, had been unable to curb the disease. As a result, preventing sexual contact between whites and Indians appeared to many as the most effective course of action. Believing this to be the case, Arny decided to stamp out the disease. No doubt sincerely concerned with Navajo welfare, the agent managed to create more trouble for himself without helping the Indians.

In December 1874 Arny complained to Indian Commissioner Edward P.

Smith about the troops at Fort Wingate. The agent noted that the Navajo had originally contracted the disease at Fort Sumner and that syphilis continued to be a problem because Indian women were permitted to associate with the nearby troops. The extent of the infection was such, he told the commissioner, that "in my judgement the demoralization of the Indians by association with the Soldiers is such that if not prevented will result in the extermination of the navajo nation." To end such "promiscuous cohabiting," Arny demanded that the army keep all Navajos away from Fort Wingate. As might be expected, military leaders failed to appreciate the advice. General John Pope, head of the Department of the Missouri, retorted that while venereal disease often plagued frontier posts, he considered the Indians at fault. Pope defended the "Chastity" of his soldiers, daring Arny to prove otherwise. In Pope's mind, venereal disease was such a common Indian affliction that his troops could not be blamed for its prevalence. He also defended the army practice of letting Navajos remain at Fort Wingate, where about forty were employed at various tasks. Even General Sherman entered the debate, commenting that no one could resolve this dispute. However, if Arny did not want troops at Wingate, "we can employ them to good advantage elsewhere."[40]

The matter might have ended here had not Arny decided to prove Pope wrong. The agent wrote Commissioner Smith that more than one early American explorer in the Southwest, including Kit Carson, had personally affirmed that the Navajo were free of the disease prior to 1846. "My own experience since I have known the Navajos, is that the women, in many cases, go to Fort Wingate from this Reservation, in apparent good health and after remaining a short time there, return here so afflicted with venereal diseases that they have to be cared for and doctored, and two women, within the last year, shortly after their return, died from these diseases." Arny admitted that once the disease had spread, it became difficult to determine guilt, yet he took issue with Pope's attitude: "is it chaste for soldiers to cohabit with Indian women to such an extent that they are too often made unfit for duty thereby?" In this instance, Arny's observations ring true, and preventing contact with the soldiers might have done some good. But his well-publicized tirade, which the Indian commissioner used to chastise the army's "record of burning shame to the American people," alienated frontier army officers, further eroding the agent's base of support. As Reverend Lowrie concluded, "I think the agent very zealous to prevent illicit connections between soldiers and Indian women. [But] I fear he may have given offense by want of good judgement."[41]

With Arny blustering and Whitney doing little, the only noteworthy medical activity at Fort Defiance in the summer of 1875 involved plans for another series of smallpox vaccinations. In April Arny estimated that 9,789 Navajos should be protected as part of a general preventive program ordered by the Indian Office. Problems getting the necessary vaccine crusts soon emerged, once again highlighting the continuing problem with medical supplies. In this instance, crusts for all the southwestern agencies were ordered from Dr. E. L. Griffin of Fond du Lac, Wisconsin. Unfortunately, Griffin could not handle the demand, and the crusts failed to arrive on schedule. In the end, only a portion of the order reached Fort Defiance. But even this may not have been used, as political turmoil soon shook the agency, bringing all medical activities to a halt.[42]

Opposition to Arny's administration peaked during the summer of 1873. After another round of Navajo complaints, Reverend Lowrie withdrew Presbyterian support for the agent, an action supported by Commissioner Smith. Under intense pressure, Arny submitted a letter of resignation, effective at the end of December. But the crusty old politician quickly reconsidered, setting off for Washington to plead his case in person. Trusting no one but Whitney, he left the agency in charge of his protégé. This action hardly endeared the doctor to Navajo leaders, particularly Manuelito, who regarded him as little more than a lackey. Afraid that Whitney and members of Arny's family would loot the agency if the removal was confirmed, the Navajo chiefs forcibly took over the agency on August 19, 1875, running off most employees and making Whitney a virtual prisoner. The physician quickly smuggled a letter to Fort Wingate asking for help, but the army dragged its feet, not wanting to help Arny's predicament. Meanwhile, the agent, unsuccessful in Washington, attempted to return to Fort Defiance, only to be warned by Whitney that "if you come without soldiers I think your life and that of your family will be in danger." Fortunately, tensions eased once the Navajos learned that Arny had indeed resigned. They even agreed to let him return long enough to gather his belongings. Until a new agent could be appointed, however, Major Redwood Price and a company of soldiers took possession of the agency. Government employees, including Dr. Whitney, were permitted to return to their duties.[43]

Whitney quickly antagonized Major Price. Still loyal to Arny, he refused to surrender the keys to agency buildings or help conduct an inventory. In response, on September 12, Price informed Whitney "that I shall have no further need of your services while I am in charge of this agency," ordering him to avail himself of the next wagon to Bacon Springs. A few days later the exiled physician met Arny and the two men returned to Fort Defiance to put the agency records in order. They left again on September 30, after Price seized a store of goods that Arny claimed were his personal property.[44] To the relief of the Navajos, Arny was gone for good. Whitney, however, would be back.

The Navajo had been without regular medical care for months and now they were without an agent or physician. The Indian Office immediately asked Reverend Lowrie to nominate a "Christian" replacement for Arny. That man proved to be Alexander Irvine, then serving at Cimarron, New Mexico. Reporting to Fort Defiance in early December, Irvine returned the reservation to civilian control. Although the doctor's post remained vacant, limited medical services were provided by Dr. John V. Lauderdale, an army surgeon assigned to Fort Wingate. He had come to Fort Defiance with Major Price, giving medical assistance when needed. Without any alternative, Irvine proposed to continue Lauderdale's service by offering him six hundred dollars per year to work part-time with the Navajo. Lauderdale apparently handled a few cases in early 1876, but wisely refused compensation. When the Indian Office discovered Irvine's plan to supplement the surgeon's salary, the agent was curtly informed that such action was "contrary to law." By June Irvine was again searching for a physician.[45]

Appointing a new doctor did not top Irvine's agenda. While Dr. Lauderdale remained at Fort Defiance the agent admitted that only a few Indians came for treatment, a circumstance that alarmed the commissioner of Indian affairs. The trust built by Menaul had deteriorated to the point that only fifteen patients showed up in March 1878. These individuals Irvine described as gravely ill people who were regarded as incurable by native healers. Under these circumstances, Irvine saw no need for the hospital suggested by Arny: "If hospital accommodations were provided they would soon be filled, but principally by the old and infirm, and instead of a Hospital it would be an asylum." Although the agent did nominate one man for the physician's job, it was not approved and the position remained vacant.[46]

Meanwhile, Walter Whitney waited in the wings. After being banished from Fort Defiance, the ambitious young man took a physician's post at the Southern Apache agency, where he became acting agent in April 1877. Whitney hoped to be named permanent agent, but the government abolished the agency instead. Facing a dead end unless something turned up, he agreed to supervise the disposition of agency property while surveying his options. Keenly aware that the physician's job at Navajo remained open, Whitney once again rallied his political friends. Although the Indian Office failed to name him to a permanent job, a smallpox scare in New Mexico prompted the government to temporarily assign Whitney to Fort Defiance for the purpose of administering vaccinations.[47]

By this time another agent, John Pyle, had been handed the task of keeping the Navajo happy and healthy. He and Whitney quickly planned a vaccination program, only to abandon it when the vaccine failed to work. After a round of complaints, the vaccine manufacturer explained that problems existed because the Indian Office's procurement system persisted in using unreliable bovine crusts, which were "apt to lose their vitality and virtue in a short time," instead of the more popular and dependable ivory "points" tipped with dried virus.[48]

Still lingering at Fort Defiance in September 1878, Whitney witnessed a council between General Sherman and Navajo leaders aimed at improving relations. The Navajo quickly let Sherman know that they had no confidence in Pyle and wanted him replaced, a development that surely pleased the opportunistic doctor. Meanwhile, Sherman brought up a growing controversy related to tribal medicine men. Although details are scarce, it is evident that the more traditional healers opposed the activities of pro-government chiefs such as Manuelito and Ganado Mucho. During the summer of 1878, a wave of panic had spread across the reservation as rumors surfaced that disgruntled medicine men were bewitching their opponents. In response, Manuelito, Ganado Mucho, or their followers hunted down and killed more than twenty people associated with witchcraft, prompting Sherman to conclude that the Navajos "are full of prejudice and superstitions, believe in good and bad medicine, sorcery, witchcraft, and very recently have killed (murdered) some of their Bad Doctors, for practicing 'sorcery.' "[49] Although not directly associated with government health care, this event apparently turned some of the more conservative elements in the tribe away from western medicine, which they now began to associate with attempts to undermine tribal culture.

Sherman's visit destroyed Pyle's confidence to such an extent that he took leave of Fort Defiance in January 1879, leaving Whitney as acting agent. Whitney expected to be named Pyle's successor, although the Navajo, remembering the doctor's association with Arny, preferred their trader friend Thomas Keam. The Indian Office instead gave the job to Galen Eastman, who arrived on the scene in late April 1879. Eastman immediately requested authority to hire a new doctor. In the meantime, Whitney continued as acting physician. His career with the Indian Service, however, had come to a close. In May 1879, Eastman held a council with the Navajo chiefs. Manuelito and others demanded Whitney's removal, alleging that he had aided Arny in looting tribal property. Manuelito specifically told the new agent that he "thinks he do some tricks and [we] dont want him here." Two days later Whitney resigned. Eastman admitted that the physician may not have been as bad as the Indians charged, "but suffers from having been like poor dog tray in bad company!"[50] Thus Walter Whitney's adventurous attempt to advance in the Indian Service ended unhappily. He had done little to improve Navajo health or to win their confidence.

TRANSITION

By the time Walter Whitney departed the Navajo agency in 1879, the Peace Policy was in full retreat. The influence of the Presbyterian church had diminished to the point of nonexistence. Among the Navajo, as elsewhere, the humanitarian plan to improve the lives of reservation Indians had run into reality. This opened the door for politicians to regain control of Indian affairs. Although the government remained committed to civilizing the Indians, it no longer felt the need to employ churchmen in that task.[51] By 1880 most observers acknowledged that the use of men and women selected for their moral character had not worked.

At the Navajo agency, the efforts of Peace Policy appointments had done virtually nothing to improve tribal health, although John Menaul made some heroic efforts. Part of the difficulty stemmed from the fact that the government refused to back its commitment with adequate financial or moral support. Even armed with sufficient medical resources, however, it is unlikely that the first agency physicians could have made much headway in replacing traditional healing practices. Indeed, whatever success Menaul attained can be attributed to the fact that his activities posed little or no threat to traditional culture. Nevertheless, in one respect the status of Navajo health did improve as the tribal economy stabilized during the 1870s. Agriculture continued to fluctuate and be unreliable, but stock raising took hold and flourished in the 1870s. By 1880 the Navajo may have owned a million sheep and goats, enabling them to provide for their own subsistence. As a result, the danger of malnutrition and famine eased considerably, and by the last two decades of the nineteenth century the tribe had returned to the level of prosperity it enjoyed before the Bosque Redondo.[52] In this sense, tribal health was better. Yet in other ways they were perched on the doorstep of a dark era, as conditions were developing for an explosion of such communicable diseases as tuberculosis and trachoma.

The Navajo nation consisted of perhaps thirteen thousand people in 1878 and it was growing rapidly. Navajo leaders asked the government to enlarge their reservation to include and protect the many Diné who had settled outside the formal tribal boundaries. As a result, executive orders on October 29, 1878, and January 6, 1880, expanded the reservation by over 60 percent along the east, south, and west sides of the 1868 reserve.[53] These enlargements added thousands of acres of rugged land and many Navajo families to the responsibilities of the agency staff at Fort Defiance. For agency physicians over the next two decades this meant an even more formidable task, one they would find impossible to surmount.

CHAPTER FOUR

A LIKE BARBARISM

> *In a population of 16,000 there is more or less of sickness at all times, and so there are the usual quota of cripples, permanently disabled, and persons decrepit and helpless from old age. It is one of the highest attainments of civilization for a people to tax themselves, and provide humanely for these classes. For some years to come the Navajos could not be expected to do this. The U.S. Government would be chargeable with a like barbarism if it too should neglect them.*

C. H. HOWARD, INSPECTOR

The Navajo people barely noticed the government's assimilation program prior to 1880. The schools and missions of the Peace Policy era failed to produce any significant effect. Nor did the feeble medical efforts of the Indian Office result in much benefit. During the decade of the 1880s, the federal program to civilize the Indians encountered new obstacles, many of them internal. With the demise of the Peace Policy, the Indian Office lapsed back into a patronage system, thereby producing a considerable turnover in field personnel. Once again politicians handed out agency jobs to friends, supporters, and relatives. In spite of some effort to employ suitable personnel the Indian Office was plagued by the appointment of unqualified or incompetent personnel. As one government inspector observed in 1889, "the Indian Bureau has been made the dumping ground for the sweepings of the political party that is in power."[1]

This circumstance directly impacted agency physicians. Indeed, all of the inherent disadvantages of the spoils system showed up at the Navajo agency prior to the creation of Civil Service requirements in 1891. In addition, Congress consistently refused to provide the funding necessary to develop a successful medical program. Medical supplies were seldom adequate, physician's offices and quarters continued to be run down and obsolete, a hospital could not be constructed, and salaries remained low. Despite considerable rhetoric to the contrary, the government simply failed to live up to its responsibilities. Under such circumstances, the program for Indian health care limped along with minimal improvement.

Ironically, the Navajo fared relatively well during the decade. Agents usually reported them to be healthy and free from major epidemics. The yearly statistical summaries published by the Indian Office presents a picture of consistency. Recognizing, of course, that many health problems remained hidden from white observation, it seems evident that venereal disease grew little from previous levels, consumption and other tubercular diseases were minimal, and respiratory problems rose and fell with yearly weather conditions. By far the most persistent of the reported major health problems were diseases of the eye, most specifically conjunctivitis, which could lead to blindness (an oft-reported circumstance). Aside from a plethora of common aches and pains, the Navajo remained remarkably free from other serious problems, including heart disease and cancer.[2] In this environment, traditional healers continued to dominate. A government doctor might persuade individuals to try his drugs and liniments and maybe submit to treatment if all else failed, but the tribe as a whole remained fully committed to the old ways. Submission to western medical practices also posed a threat to traditional lifeways and the transmission of Navajo culture. Knowledge of this threat kept tradition strong and the reluctance to try the white man's way alive. If government doctors were to win the Diné over, they needed a convincing demonstration of the superiority of their medicine.

THE MEDICAL MERRY-GO-ROUND

Medical affairs at Fort Defiance lapsed into total confusion between 1879 and 1889. During this period nine different men served as agency physician, none of whom lasted long enough to develop an effective medical program. The high turnover rate resulted from a combination of things: political changes on the national scene, agency politics, Navajo hostility, incompetence, and the depressing living conditions at Fort Defiance. As became evident, few men possessed the will to work among the Navajo under such circumstances.

The decade started badly. Almost from the moment of his arrival in April 1879, the Navajo disliked their new agent, Galen Eastman. Ganado Mucho and Manuelito, two of the most influential leaders, expressed great distrust of Eastman, being irritated with the agent's inability to procure sufficient annuity goods, his refusal to distribute customary gifts, and his failure to control the liquor trade. Many whites, including the reservation traders, also disliked Eastman. In 1881 Army Lieutenant John G. Bourke summed up the general feeling by describing the agent as "a psalm-singing hypocrite whom the Navajoes despised and detested and whom they tried to kill." According to Bourke, Eastman wrote "glorious accounts" of his imaginary successes among the Navajo, while in fact doing nothing.[3]

Despite such negative opinions, Eastman may have been more inept than anything. Securing the services of a physician to replace the recently departed Dr. Whitney became one of his first priorities. He accordingly asked Commissioner Hayt, in May 1879, if the Indian Office could suggest a suitable person to fill the position. If not, Eastman suggested his friend Dr. J. B. McNett, a small-time politician from his hometown of Grand Haven, Michigan. Desiring to reenforce the nomination, the agent referred Hayt to his own father-in-law, United States Senator Thomas W. Ferry (Michigan), "who knows Dr. McNett very well." The commissioner readily accepted Eastman's candidate, and on November 26, 1879, McNett received the appointment. He quickly headed for Fort Defiance with his daughter Crepe, who was to teach school along with two other women. By the time McNett reached the reservation in December, the Navajo had been without a physician for six months.[4]

McNett's brief stay among the Navajo proved worthless. His monthly reports for December through March show that he treated relatively few patients, mostly for such minor problems as headache, catarrh, and rheumatism. The Navajo were unfriendly to anyone associated with Eastman, and when the agent left for an eastern trip on April 15, 1880, the threats of violence became too much. On the very day of Eastman's departure, McNett and the female teachers fled to Fort Wingate. Their flight left only the ambitious agency clerk, Dr. James R. Sutherland, a man with some medical background, and one other white employee at the agency. Sutherland immediately assumed the office of acting physician, believing that McNett's desertion reflected cowardice. The clerk apparently provided little actual service to the Navajo, who detested him as much as Eastman. Navajo unrest, however, prompted the Indian Office to suspend the agent until his conduct of agency affairs could be investigated. Meanwhile, Captain Frank T. Bennett, the well-liked army officer who had been the Navajo agent in 1869–70, became acting agent. Bennett quickly escorted Dr. McNett back to Fort Defiance to resume his duties. Nevertheless, the physician had seen enough of the Indians. After treating just seven Navajo patients, NcNett headed home, leaving the Navajo once again without a doctor. Bennett acknowledged the need for a replacement, but reported that "no suitable person in this part of the country would accept the appointment." Sutherland, who desired the job, was ordered off the reservation because of Navajo opposition.[5]

Although Captain Bennett knew of no acceptable candidate, the commissioner's office found a replacement with little difficulty. Indeed, by 1880 the nation was awash with medical doctors, many of them Civil War veterans. Many of these men, especially in rural areas, could not maintain a profitable practice. A guaranteed government salary of 1,200 dollars per annum looked especially attractive to men earning on the average between 400 dollars and 750 dollars per year. Using their wartime experience and loyalty to the Union as qualifications, hundreds of doctors thus sought positions with the Indian Service.[6] Accordingly, in late August 1880 the Indian Office offered the Navajo job to Dr. John Little of Bloomington, Illinois. Little immediately accepted the offer, writing Captain Bennett "to inform me where the agency is and how to get to it."[7]

Without doubt, Little was the best qualified physician yet assigned to the reservation. A graduate of Belleville Medical College in New York and Jefferson Medical College in Philadelphia, he had served as a surgeon with the Union army for three and a half years. Since then he had maintained a private practice. Nevertheless, Little was appointed for the wrong reasons. Describing himself as a "good Republican," the elderly doctor wanted to go west for his health, hoping to recover from dyspepsia and catarrh. Little frankly admitted that "I desired to be appointed to an agency to which I could take my family, one near white settlements, one where some of the enjoyments of civilized society could be had."[8]

Dr. Little presumed that his wishes had been honored until he received a return letter from Captain Bennett. The agent delivered a sobering dose of reality, telling him that under no circumstances should he bring his family, "as it is not a proper place for a lady and children." Housing was so dilapidated that he would need to bring his own bedroll and find his own furniture. Even more disheartening, no white settlement lay within a hundred miles, no railroad connection for 125 miles, and it cost more than forty dollars to make the last leg of the trip to Fort Defiance by buckboard. If that were not enough, living expenses at the agency amounted to sixty dollars per month. Thus, although he had sold his practice and rented his home, the mortified physician resigned his appointment on September 16. As he explained, "a younger and less experienced physician might desire such an appointment, but a man of my age and experience as a physician and surgeon, and family to care for, would not care to go so far away at so much expense, exposure, and deprivation."[9]

The Indian Office soon turned to another job-seeking war veteran. Dr. Charles H. Bowen, a resident of Washington, D.C., had served as a physician and surgeon with the Union army before entering private practice. Apparently well known in capital medical circles, Bowen received the support of many prominent Washingtonians, with one describing him as a "courteous, kind and highly educated gentleman." Bowen himself confidently stated that he was fully competent to undertake the duties of agency physician. Although he wanted the Indian Office to send him to the Los Pinos Agency in Colorado, Secretary of the Interior Carl Schurz sent him to Fort Defiance instead.[10]

Bowen, at least, arrived in New Mexico, reporting to Captain Bennett on

October 23, 1880. He soon realized his mistake. Agency facilities remained primitive and uncomfortable at best. In Bennett's words, "this place is so old . . . that the buildings, canals, and all surroundings, are in a most miserable condition. They are certainly not tenantable—very old—tumbling down and filled with vermin. All of the buildings except one stone house have dirt floors, and leak very badly—a heavy rain almost completely inundates . . . the whole place." Although Bowen bravely gave it a try, he resigned within a month, stating that the high altitude at Fort Defiance caused him to suffer from vertigo, fainting, and prostration. By early December Dr. Bowen had returned to Washington, presumably wiser for the experience. Meanwhile, the vanquished James Sutherland, then in Albuquerque, petitioned the Indian commissioner for Bowen's job, a request that was not honored.[11]

Once again the Navajo agency lacked a physician. A December 1880 inspection report commented on the need for a doctor, suggesting that he also be equipped with a horse in order to visit distant patients. In January 1881 Dr. Edward Ebert became the newest Navajo physician. Unfortunately, Ebert got caught up in the political turmoil swirling around the efforts of Galen Eastman to regain control of the agency. The Navajo vocally opposed the return of Eastman, threatening violence against any white employee believed to be sympathetic to the former agent. Traders such as Thomas Keam, as well as local military officers, also opposed his return. Ebert, however, displayed a sense of loyalty to Eastman, thus drawing down on himself threats of violence. On one occasion the danger became so obvious that the physician fled to Fort Wingate. An even more disturbing event occurred in July, when Ebert returned to his room after treating a patient to find two arrows shot into his bed.[12]

Despite Navajo opposition, Captain Bennett was ordered to return control of the agency to Eastman at the end of June. All of the white staff, except Dr. Ebert, promptly resigned, fearing an outbreak of violence. Despite an uneasy feeling, Ebert agreed to remain on duty until the end of the year, a deadline later extended to March 31, 1882. The nature of his medical activities among the Navajo during this period are largely unknown, although he appears to have spent most of his time in the routine of dispensing of pills. A statistical summary for the reservation for 1880–81 identified the most prevalent ailments as eye and respiratory diseases, nervous disorders, and venereal disease. In December 1881 smallpox broke out among construction crews building the Atlantic and Pacific Railroad across northern Arizona just south of the reservation, and Ebert kept himself occupied by giving vaccinations. The coming of the railroad also raised the issue of whiskey. By February 1882 Eastman had become concerned about a significant increase in alcohol consumption near the agency. Although realizing that whites were responsible, Eastman treated the issue as a criminal rather than a medical matter. As he reported, "I have ordered irons to be made and shall improvise a Lock-up, and with [the commissioner's] sanction shall endeavor to hold in confinement any Indian daring to appear at the Agency in liquor." Dr. Ebert appears to have been little concerned with this matter. Indeed, he resigned sometime in March, leaving his post to escape continued threats of violence.[13]

THE MEDICAL CORPS

The high turnover rate and ineffective medical care provided to the Navajo in the early 1880s reflected conditions elsewhere in the Indian Service. In response to such problems, the commissioner's office sought to develop criteria for a more professional medical corps. Although agency physicians had been required to have a medical degree since 1878, no real standards existed. Under Indian Commissioner Hiram Price (1881–1885), the qualifications became more specific, requiring that a physician prove graduation from a recognized medical school, be actively engaged in the practice of medicine, and possess a high moral character. When Price reviewed Indian Service medical activities in 1882, he boasted that government physicians had treated over seventy-five thousand Indian patients during the preceding fiscal year. Despite such impressive totals, the quality of health care remained highly suspect. Even Price admitted to inaccuracy in his information on births and death because many Indians refused to discuss such matters.[14]

Price acknowledged the government's moral obligation to provide reservation residents with permanent and stable medical care. He also understood that it required three to four years for a doctor to get to know his native patients. "It is obvious," he added, "that it is specially desirable to procure efficient and, if possible, permanent medical officers of pronounced moral and temperate habits. . . . It is detrimental to the service to be continually changing medical officers." To supervise the activities of government physicians and assure proper treatment, Price asked Congress to fund an Indian Service medical inspector, a doctor empowered to visit agencies once a year to determine the competency of the resident physician, review sanitary conditions, and investigate complaints. Despite some legislative support, the idea foundered on the rocks of congressional parsimony, leaving the Indian Office with no real means of assuring quality.[15]

The goal of making the medical corps more efficient also formed an integral part of Price's civilization program. One justification for authorizing a medical inspector revolved around the hope that such an individual could be used "to induce the Indians to abandon their 'medicine men,' and adopt a civilized mode of caring for and treatment of the sick." To Price, it seemed essential "that the influence of the 'medicine men' be rendered nugatory." In his 1882 annual report, the commissioner naively proclaimed that physicians were gradually defeating native healers: "The marked contrast between the civilized method of caring for the sick, compared with the barbarous method of the native 'medicine man,' has accomplished much to induct the Indians into the methods and customs of Christian and civilized manhood."[16]

Although sounding good, Commissioner Price's reforms failed to improve medical care. Among the Navajo, with an estimated population of sixteen thousand in 1882, Agent Eastman calculated that a quarter of the tribe were "invalid, aged, blind, or paupers." In July he wrote Price that the lack of a government physician caused him great concern. The absence of medical care also attracted the attention of Indian Service inspector C. H. Howard, who visited the agency that same month. Howard noted a considerable amount of sickness among the Navajo, a condition he considered dishonorable because the government had failed in its obligations. He expressed special concern about the recent appearance of smallpox in New Mexico, remarking that "there were hundreds, not to say thousands, of families of the Navajos who had never been vaccinated." For the safety of both whites and Indians, Howard urged the immediate appointment of two agency physicians, suggesting that they be supplied with horses in order to reach remote areas.[17]

In line with government concerns, Inspector Howard further recommended the construction of a hospital, "not only as an act of humanity but as an essential part of the civilizing process." By this time, the commissioner and most agency physicians were convinced that reservation patients could not be successfully treated outside the "immediate care and control of the physician" because of the tendency to become discouraged when a single dose of medicine produced no improvement. Price also argued that keeping patients confined to hospital rooms would keep them away from the influence of traditional healers. But again, like other suggestions in this era, a lack of government funding prevented any significant response.[18]

Nevertheless, Eastman was able to use the fear of smallpox to press for the appointment of an agency physician. Because of the unavailability of budgeted funds, he linked his request to the opening of the agency's new boarding school. With an anticipated enrollment of over a hundred children, a physician's presence seemed critical to the school's success: any serious illness among the children might quickly alienate the tribe. On September 18, 1882, Eastman sent an urgent telegram to Price stating: "Small Pox Spreading among the Navajos. Several deaths occurred—Physician needed—cannot my request . . .

be granted in connection with the School." The obvious threat to the civilization program struck a responsive cord, and Price immediately agreed to let
Eastman hire his friend and associate, Dr. J. R. Sutherland, as agency physician. Sutherland, who had been nearby, quickly occupied his office. Reporting
that "his services were very much needed," Eastman implied that Sutherland
immediately began to provide the Navajo with medical services, although little
evidence exists to support this statement beyond reference to some thirty-five
vaccinations.[19]

Sutherland, in fact, never gained Navajo trust. Indeed, he soon lost his only
ally. C. H. Howard's report on the Navajo agency, which reached Washington
in October, concurred with tribal opinion that Eastman must be replaced.
Acknowledging the inevitable, the agent submitted his resignation, effective
December 31, 1883. Price quickly replaced the disliked agent with Denis M.
Riordan, a former California Republican politician and businessman then
residing in Arizona. Fortunately, Riordan turned out to be a man of principle,
enthusiasm, and concern. After visiting Fort Defiance in mid-December to size
up his task, Riordan promised to be an active agent, to travel to every corner of
the reservation, and to become personally acquainted with tribal leaders and
their concerns. "I am prepared," he wrote, "to sleep on the ground, go on
mutton 'straight' if necessary, in fact to do whatever the occasion demands in
order to make myself efficient in the position, providing I can secure the
sanction and co operation of the Dept. as long as I do right."[20]

Dr. Sutherland desired to remain at Fort Defiance, but neither Riordan nor
the Indians wanted him. Riordan quickly became convinced that Eastman and
Sutherland had stolen tribal supplies, informing Commissioner Price, in January 1883, that "I believe that every Govt. employe who was in the Agency at the
time I came here was an accomplice of Galen Eastman in robbing the Government." The Navajo were even more vocal. Meeting with tribal leaders on
January 19, 1883, Riordan listened to a long list of complaints. Manuelito, their
chief spokesman, blamed the former agent for his own ailments, implying that
he had been driven to drink and perhaps even bewitched by Eastman. As a
tribe, the Diné requested the removal of everyone associated with Eastman, "in
particular that Dr J. R. Sutherland be taken away saying he was 'tarantula no. 2'
and a great deal worse than Eastman." Ganado Mucho confirmed that the Navajo "feared, hated and despised Dr Sutherland." Riordan supported the Navajo stance, but could do little until the Indian Office approved a dismissal.[21]

Meanwhile, the new agent took an interest in Navajo health. With tribal
leaders reporting a rapidly spreading outbreak of measles in the western portions of the reservation, Riordan explained to the Indian Office that the tribal
population would not consult with his present medical staff; "they refuse

utterly to go near the Agency physician or to have anything to do with him." As a consequence, the agent recruited his wife to explain to the Indians how she cared for her own children, including providing warm drinks and taking care to prevent them from catching cold. Riordan also asked the government to provide him with a limited amount of flour, sugar, and coffee to help comfort the aged and sick. Such measures, of course, were only temporary expedients that could be obviated by the appointment of an effective physician. In April, the tribe finally got its wish and Dr. Sutherland was removed.[22]

Riordan played no role in selecting the next physician, Dr. George P. Sampson. Sampson received the appointment primarily because of political and family connections. A resident of Leavenworth, Kansas, he had married the granddaughter of Colonel W. G. Coffin, a prominent local physician. After teaching school for a number of years, Sampson decided to take up medicine. Attending the Miami Medical College in Cincinnati on a part-time basis, he served an apprenticeship in the office of Dr. S. F. Neely, a former Union army surgeon then serving as mayor of Leavenworth. Upon graduation from medical school, Sampson entered into a medical partnership with Dr. W. V. Coffin, the colonel's son. Sometime in 1882 Sampson decided to strike out on his own. He approached a local Republican politician in Leavenworth, who, in turn, recommended him to U.S. Senator John J. Ingalls. With Ingalls's help, Sampson secured an appointment to the Navajo agency in May 1883. Although most letters of support described him as a young man of ability and compassion, Neely paid him the somewhat less than enthusiastic compliment of "I believe that doctor Sampsons professional attainments will average well with the physicians who hold Similar positions."[23]

Sampson and his wife soon arrived at Fort Defiance. Despite the fact he was destined to remain at the agency for three years, the longest tenure of any government doctor to that point, the young physician soon became embroiled in politics and controversy. Special Agent William Parsons regarded him as an arrogant man who sought to make up for his inadequacies by tearing down the reputations of other employees. "It was his habit," wrote Parsons, "of resorting to low schemes & plots against fellow employes and did not hesitate to resort to slander to carry out his designs." In the same vein, without the agent's knowledge, he wrote Senator Ingalls, seeking trading licenses for some of his friends. Nor did the doctor seem to have been successful in working with the Navajo. In 1885 Inspector George Pearsons observed that the physician was not liked by the Navajo, "who do not ask his advice nor seek his services." Pearsons regarded Sampson as a poor doctor who should be removed from office.[24]

To some degree, Sampson's relationship with the Navajo was damaged by events beyond his control. This stemmed from a disastrous turn of events that followed Manuelito's agreement to send his two oldest sons to the Carlisle Indian School in Pennsylvania as a symbolic move in support of the government's civilization program. Unfortunately, during the summer of 1883 one boy died of tuberculosis and the other one was sent home gravely ill. When the second son died, Manuelito became violent and again turned to drink. Whether Sampson treated the ill-fated boy is unknown, but, as Riordan wrote Carlisle's director, Richard Henry Pratt, "the deaths of Jack and Manuelito Chow created a feeling which was hard to combat. . . . One can reason till the cows come home but he cannot remove the feeling of superstitious dread with which these people associate with the cause of education when these Carlisle boys are mentioned." Riordan feared that the situation would scare the Navajo away from the Fort Defiance school, which he dearly wanted to succeed. This same fear may well have extended to trust in Dr. Sampson. The agent observed a definite change in mood after the two deaths, as many tribal leaders became much more reluctant to participate in the civilization program.[25]

During the summer of 1883, Riordan himself became extremely distressed by the government's failure to provide for the Navajo. He regarded the Diné as a deserving people, who "in native shrewdness and intellect . . . are superior to any other tribe in the country." Complaining that heretofore the government had furnished but little aid to the sick and indigent, he castigated Congress and federal bureaucrats for refusing to provide adequate funding while expecting its field officers to produce results. Once he realized the full scope of the problem, the agent specifically chastised the Indian Office for opening the boarding school in an unfinished building ("without even a water shed or a water closet"), not providing needed irrigation works, and failing to feed starving people. As deplorable as anything, noted Riordan, were his working conditions. "In a word," he wrote, "the agent and employés who were to lift up these people to a higher plane, to carry out the civilization policy of the Government, were expected to live in a lot of abandoned adobe huts, condemned by special, regular, and annual reports as unfit to live in fifteen years ago, . . . and repeatedly damned by all who have been compelled to occupy them." Why, he asked, couldn't "the Government give the agent here as good a shelter as it gives to a mule at Fort Wingate?" The disillusioned agent submitted his first resignation in April 1883, but stayed on with the tribe until June 30, 1884.[26]

Riordan did not expect Sampson and his family to last through the first winter. No one questioned the fact that the physician's situation was extremely unpleasant. In October 1883 Inspector Robert Gardner described the doctor's quarters as an unsafe one-story adobe building eighteen by ninety-five feet, with five rooms and six windows. Sampson himself described the building as constantly damp, in danger of collapse, and totally uninhabitable. From this structure, which included his living rooms, he treated 2,224 Navajo between July 1883 and June 1884. From the published statistics it appears that most of his activities involved relatively minor ailments such as fevers, diarrhea, mumps, headache, constipation, and various wounds, broken bones, and sprains. Of note is the fact that only two cases on consumption and sixty-nine cases of venereal disease were recorded. Far more ominous were the 281 reported cases of conjunctivitis or "sore eyes."[27]

As medical affairs at Fort Defiance followed their usual course, Commissioner Price continued to stress improved medical facilities. Increasingly, however, he focused on the necessity of overcoming the influence of native healers. In 1884 he wrote that a recent jump in tribal death rates could be blamed on the Indian tendency to rely upon healers until it was too late for the agency physician to have any benefit. The acceptance of western medical practices seemed even more crucial to the success of the civilization program. "Could the benefit of sorcery and evil spirits be overcome," he observed, "a long stride would be made in the work of civilization. No one has greater opportunities in this direction than the agency physician, who, in addition to being skilled in his profession, should be a man of such qualities of head and heart as to win and retain the confidence of the Indians under his care."[28] Despite such well-intended convictions, it remained sadly evident from the events transpiring at the Navajo agency during Price's administration that medical services had not improved.

THE PERILS OF PATRONAGE

The election of Grover Cleveland in 1884 brought the Democratic party to power for the first time since the Civil War and produced a general turnover in agency personnel. The new Indian commissioner, John D. C. Atkins (1885–1888), expressed sympathy with the increasingly popular reform idea of extending Civil Service to the Indian Office, but could not overcome party realities, and in the end he replaced most Republican staff with Democrats. Nevertheless, he insisted that employees be competent and fully informed of their responsibilities. Anyone found to be incompetent would be removed at once. As far as physicians were concerned, they needed to present evidence of graduation from a "reputable" medical school and provide references as to their "character, ability, and experience." Beyond such demands, however, Atkins did little to change the philosophy of his predecessors or make substantial improvements. In 1886 he announced that agency physicians were making good progress in enlightening young tribal members in the proper care of the sick. Like Price, Atkins regarded "medicine men" as the greatest roadblock to success. As a countermeasure, he proposed opening small agency hospitals, which might be constructed at minimal expense, as a way of yielding a "prompt and profitable return." This simple concept assumed that "an Indian who had been taken into such a hospital and received rational treatment and good nursing would not be slow to communicate his experience to his friends, and thus lead them to trust in the 'white man's medicine,' rather than in the beating of drums, rattling of bones, and singing and dancing of the medicine men." Atkins also suggested that hospitals be attached to reservation schools, thereby preventing outbreaks of disease among students, which tended to "break up the schools."[29] As usual, no funds accompanied such suggestions.

Meanwhile, the government career of Dr. Sampson took a turn for the worse. Even before the new administration could be sworn in, the physician began to lobby to save his job. This worked to the extent that the incoming Democratic administration did not immediately dismiss him. Nonetheless, Sampson kept the agency in turmoil. Since his arrival at Fort Defiance in July, Agent John H. Bowman had quarreled with the doctor and his wife. Tensions reached a boiling point when the physician charged Bowman with hiring "women of loose character" to work at the agency school. In a mood of righteous indignation, Sampson prohibited his wife from socializing with those employees who were not "respectable citizens of the country." The controversy apparently centered around a school cook who had become pregnant and may have sought an abortion. Bowman defended the woman much to Sampson's dismay, who regarded the matter as an immoral scandal and "the talk of the Indians whom they are supposed to civilize."[30]

Bowman responded to Sampson's behavior by calling in Inspector George Pearsons to investigate affairs at the agency. Pearsons sided with the agent during a November 1885 visit to Fort Defiance, finding the physician incompetent. The grounds for this conclusion did not focus on his treatment of the Indians, however. Indeed, the Navajo were as completely ignored as they had been by their doctor. Instead, the charges of malpractice involved his care of white agency employees, specifically Mr. G. Deasy, the assistant farmer. It all began several months previously, when Sampson had treated Deasy for a broken arm. What should have been a simple procedure turned into a disaster because of improperly applied splints. Suffering agonizing pain for several weeks, Deasy finally went to Fort Wingate where his arm was successfully repaired. The attending army surgeon accused Sampson of incompetence, whereupon Deasy demanded that the "quack" doctor be removed. Sampson, in turn, defended his actions by protesting that Pearsons was not qualified to evaluate a medical procedure.[31]

In response, Indian Commissioner Atkins, who insisted that incompetents be weeded out of the Indian Service, sent Special Agent William Parsons to Fort Defiance in April 1886 to sort things out. Parsons apparently possessed enough medical knowledge to evaluate Sampson's work. Taking note of the situation, he met with all the concerned parties before issuing his report. Sampson was again pronounced totally incompetent. Parsons bluntly stated that Sampson "had in some way obtained a diploma as a physician but he was in no way qualified for the practice of the healing art. He had held the position of agency physician for about three years, but he should never have been appointed." In addition to the obvious mistreatment of Deasy, Parsons watched with astonishment as Sampson misdiagnosed an illness affecting trader Thomas V. Keam. Insisting that the malady was bilious fever instead of pneumonia, Sampson nearly killed Keam before the trader too went to Fort Wingate for care. Faced with considerable testimony against him, Sampson resigned on April 10, 1886, after failing to convince incoming agent Samuel S. Patterson that he should be retained. Parsons believed that the episode had ended satisfactorily. Sampson, "the inventor of most of the slander in circulation, has left the agency in disgrace and with the well deserved contempt of all who know him, there is hope that your office will be less troubled and annoyed in the future with affairs at Fort Defiance."[32]

Parsons's predictions failed to come true. Despite Atkins's stated desire to employ competent physicians, political considerations again got in the way. It proved easy enough to get rid of an incompetent Republican, but it was more difficult to replace him with a qualified Democrat. The new agent, Samuel Patterson, a Civil War veteran hired because he was "a Democrat," turned out to be a good choice, but the same could not be said for the new doctor. William A. Olmstead, a crony of General A. B. Upshaw, possessed questionable credentials at best. Commissioned an army officer in 1867, he had been stationed at Fort Dakota, where he quickly showed his colors. Acting in a manner unbecoming an officer, charges of immoral conduct were preferred against him, resulting in his resignation in 1869. After dropping from sight, he reappeared in the mid-1880s as the Shoshoni agency physician. Again, trouble dogged his footsteps as his behavior drew new charges of misconduct. Among those who knew him in Wyoming was Dr. Thomas Hill, who later wrote that Olmstead was "uneducated as a physician," a "scoundrel," and "unfit to hold any position of trust in any Dept. of the Government."[33]

Under pressure to resign his Wyoming job, Olmstead prevailed upon General Upshaw to have him transferred to the vacancy at Fort Defiance. Arriving on September 11, 1886, he found the agency a "pleasant place" with its high altitude and pure air. Just two weeks later, Inspector Robert Gardner optimistically described Olmstead as "a competent, faithful, and efficient employé,

[who] is active and energetic in the proper discharge of his duties and takes an interest in visiting the indians and prescribing for their ills." In fact, the physician lost no time in stirring up trouble. Subsequent accounts revealed that he immediately began to conspire with the local trader to discredit Patterson so that he could be appointed agent. One man overheard Olmstead say that he was "not particular as to his methods of getting it." During his stay at Fort Defiance, he regularly appeared intoxicated, occasionally used opium, stole government property, and encouraged the Indians to rebel against the agent.[34]

These activities totally negated Olmstead's effectiveness as a physician. Without doubt, his incompetence cost the lives of several Navajo school-children. The agency school, which opened in 1882, had struggled to attract pupils until attendance began to rise during Patterson's tenure.[35] At this critical point, during the winter of 1886–87, a number of students became ill. The school's superintendent, P. H. Cragan, naturally called the physician to attend the children. As reported by Mary Clark, the school matron, Olmstead would stop by the school, "say there was nothing much the matter, they will get well in the morning, and leave without doing anything for them."[36]

This pattern of behavior resulted in five deaths that winter, seriously damaging the school's reputation with the Navajo. Surviving records reveal the extent of Olmstead's indifference. In November 1886, for example, he was called upon to visit Clara, "a bright healthy robust little Girl seven years of age," who had taken sick. The physician responded by saying that the girl was not sick and would be up the next day. Despite the superintendent's plea for treatment, Olmstead refused to do anything as conditions worsened. Just as she lapsed into a coma, the doctor left on a three-day pleasure trip without so much as providing the school staff with any medicine. Four days later the girl died. Superintendent Cragan later wrote that "there is no doubt in my mind that Clara would be alive to day" had he stayed at her bedside. In a similar case, a fourteen-year-old girl suddenly fell ill. Olmstead again did nothing until Cragan insisted, at which point he gave her three ounces of whiskey, declaring that she would be up in a day or two. Once more the result proved fatal.[37]

The other school deaths that year also revolved around the physician. A boy died after being told he was okay. His sister passed away soon afterward. In her case, Cragan believed that Olmstead decided the case was hopeless and thus made no effort to save the patient. When another girl became ill, a dose of castor oil seemed sufficient. Although the patient did not get better, the doctor remained away from the school until she too died. These horrible events prompted Cragan to write that "I earnestly believe that Dr. Olmstead is wholly incompetent and totally unqualified to practice medicine." He also noted the negative impact on the school, remarking that the children had lost all confidence in the physician, calling him a "no good white Doctor" and expressing fear that his medicine would kill them. "He seemed to act like a person who is intoxicated or under the influence of liquor or some drug nearly all the time."[38]

Agency employees also distrusted the doctor. On one occasion, he arrived in an intoxicated state to treat a terminally ill agency employee. Instead of treating the man, Olmstead produced a vial of liquid, instructing an attendant to administer the drug, which he said would "put an end to him." When rebuffed, the doctor laughed off the issue, claiming he had put other patients out of their misery. Through all of this, Olmstead continued to believe that his services were "giving the Indians the benefit of a white practice of medicine." At one point in 1887, he permitted a medical student to work under his direction. The young apprentice, who had come west for health reasons, seemed so well read on the subject that Olmstead suggested leaving the agency's medical responsibilities in his hands while he took a vacation.[39]

By May 1887, Patterson had had enough of Dr. Olmstead. He agreed with one Navajo who said, "Doctor Olmstead was a bad man and his medicine is no good." After collecting statements from agency employees documenting Olmstead's incompetence and "conduct unbecoming an employe of the Indian Service," the agent filed charges against the physician, listing thirteen specific violations of the rules and requesting his immediate removal. Commissioner Atkins responded on June 7, 1887, relieving the physician from duty. As Olmstead left the reservation, Patterson observed that if the man had paid as much attention to medicine as he did to stirring up trouble everyone would have been better served.[40] Again, the Indian Office learned a hard lesson. Bad medical care was worse than none.

RATIONAL TREATMENT

During the spring of 1887 Democratic congressman William Preston Taulbee of Kentucky sought to find a government job for his younger brother, Dr. J. B. Taulbee. As soon as it became evident that Olmstead had been released, Taulbee wrote Commissioner Atkins describing his brother, a resident of Hazel Green, Kentucky, as a promising physician, age twenty-eight, well qualified for the vacated post. As a graduate of the College of Physicians and Surgeons at St. Joseph, Missouri, "he had had an extensive & successful practice for one of his age and is generally regarded as one of the best physicians in his section." The Indian Office lost no time in appointing Taulbee, who, in July 1887, headed west with his wife Molly and sister Clara, who had been hired as school seamstress.[41]

In contrast to his predecessor, the young physician launched into his duties with some enthusiasm. During his thirteen months at Fort Defiance he reported treating about nine hundred persons. Taulbee believed that many Navajos were willing to receive "rational treatment," especially for serious ailments, and were anxious for expanded government services. Because of the great distance that many lived from the agency, however, patients who might otherwise be willing could not regularly come. The distances involved, requiring journeys of a hundred miles or more over treacherous and often impassable roads, lay at the heart of this problem. To make matters worse, Taulbee remained confined to the immediate vicinity of Fort Defiance because the government provided neither a horse nor wagon. As an alternative, the physician urged the construction of a small hospital at Defiance that would provide patients with a place to stay and be fed while receiving treatment.[42]

Dr. Taulbee might have been reasonably effective had he not become involved in a discouraging dispute centering around Agent Patterson. During his short stay at the agency, the physician developed a loyalty to Patterson, in part because the agent attempted to make life a bit more bearable for his staff. Conditions at the post remained so primitive that only two producing dairy cows were available, one of which the physician used and maintained out of his own pocket. Because employees were required to pay their own living expenses, Patterson permitted the doctor (and others) to use coal oil in his residence that was charged to the dispensary, and he was given beans, salt, and meat from government stocks. These practices drew the notice of Special Indian Agent Henry A. Welton, who was rumored to want Patterson's job. In April, just after Patterson left on an official trip to Washington, D.C., Welton showed up to conduct what amounted to an impromptu and biased investigation. Taulbee attempted to shield some of the employees, for which Welton labeled him "somewhat under the influence of liquor" and quarrelsome. Patterson eventually protested the special agent's conduct and four months later the Indian Office sent Inspector T. D. Marcum to sort out Welton's charges. Although Taulbee admitted that he had indeed used some government goods, Marcum's final report proved extremely critical of Welton. For Taulbee, however, the emotional stress, turmoil, and sordid nature of agency politics proved to be too much. As soon as Marcum completed taking testimony, the physician took a leave of absence, returned home, and resigned on September 22, 1888.[43]

Patterson immediately requested the appointment of "a competent physician" to replace Dr. Taulbee. But once again, the system failed to work effectively. The national elections of 1888 returned the Republicans to power and held up the appointment of a new physician until November, when B. D. Williams was hired. By January 1889 Patterson had also been removed. The new agent, Charles E. Vandever, formerly an assistant farmer at the agency, proved to be highly competent, but he had his hands full with Williams, who was unfit for the job. In general, the physician had little contact with the Navajo, treating an average of less than two people per day.[44]

Despite an aversion to Indians, Williams nonetheless became involved in a dispute with tribal healers. Over the years it had become evident that a tug of war was developing with regard to elder tribal leaders. As these influential survivors of the Bosque Redondo aged, native healers, as guardians of the culture, attempted to treat their many ailments by traditional means. Government officials, on the other hand, hoped to persuade the chiefs to rely on western medicine as a method of discrediting traditional ways. The nature of this emotional contest became visible in February 1889, when Ganado Mucho, an eighty-year-old chief with progovernment sentiments, became seriously ill. Living some distance to the southwest of the agency, the old man trusted his care to traditional healers. Some of his worried followers, however, contacted Vandever, requesting him to send "the Agency Physician there for a few days to attend and if possible cure their very ill Chief." Seeing this as an opportunity to demonstrate the superiority of western medicine, the agent asked Dr. Williams to visit the old man at once. Because of snow-clogged reservation roads, a government horse was placed at the doctor's disposal. Williams, however, refused to go, stating that he did not feel comfortable on horseback. Instead, he waited until the roads cleared, but by that time the healers were in full control and "his visit was a failure." The episode proved embarrassing to the government, which Vandever assumed would "lessen the confidence of the Indians in their Agent, and will surely prove a serious barrier in the future effort of inducing them to use the Agency Physician instead of their own crude 'Medicine Man.'" In an effort to save some face, Williams visited Ganado Mucho again the following summer, this time being permitted to apply "the proper remedies." Nevertheless, the healers continued to be so persuasive that Vandever eventually suggested bringing the chief to Fort Defiance, "where he will be away from the machinations of the medicine men, who realize that his recovery would throw them into bad repute with their superstitious adherents."[45]

Williams's bungling in face of a sensitive cultural situation rounded out a decade of misadventures in which the agency physician gave the Navajos, even those favorable to the government, every reason to distrust the effectiveness of western medicine. The patronage doctors of the 1880s never proved effective, nor were they, on the whole, able to win the trust of the Diné or provide them with medical care of sufficient effectiveness to demonstrate the supposed superiority of "rational" care. Beyond the obvious cases of incompetence, the delivery of effective medical care also suffered from the government's inability to convince Congress to expend enough money to construct a hospital, provide sufficient supplies, improve the staff's working conditions, or even supply horses to visit outlying patients. According to one wag, "an impression seemed to prevail in Washington that street cars and elevated railroad trains run all over the reservations." Thus even the best trained and highly motivated physician could have little impact. One government doctor summed up the situation by remarking on the impossibility of performing even a simple surgical procedure when he possessed only "one pair of forceps, two knives—both entirely worn out—and three tenaculums, one broken."[46] It is no wonder that the doctors remained in their agency offices, handed out pills, and dabbled in agency politics. If neglect was a sign of barbarism, then the government was indeed chargeable during the 1880s.

CHAPTER FIVE

NATIONAL DISGRACE

Indian reservations have no hospitals and no place to which persons suffering from acute diseases, severe accidents, contagious diseases, or any other physical malady can be taken, and in which they can receive the nursing and care and medical attendance which they sorely need, and which ought to be furnished them in the name of humanity. . . . Congress has withheld appropriations, and I have been powerless to remedy a great evil, which in my view amounts to a national disgrace.

THOMAS J. MORGAN, INDIAN COMMISSIONER

The decade of the 1890s began with the promise of substantial improvement in the national commitment to provide health care for the native population. Between 1889 and 1892 a number of federal actions strongly suggested that the government sincerely desired to employ better physicians, provide the reservations with enhanced medical facilities, and end the unreliable system of appointing political cronies. Taken together, these developments brought a renewed commitment toward improved medical care on the reservations. As the 1890s progressed these trends showed up in the Indian country, although with disappointing results.

During this period, the Indian Office acknowledged for the first time that physicians needed to provide preventive services in addition to caring for the sick. As early as 1889, the commissioner's office began to notify prospective physicians that they would be expected to do more than sit in an office dispensing pills. Government doctors needed to visit patients in their homes and make efforts to educate Indians in the proper methods of health care. In addition, agency physicians should regularly inspect local sanitary conditions and, wherever possible, be active participants in eliminating particularly dangerous situations. Finally, the medical staff needed to devote special attention to the growing numbers of schools by teaching students the elementary principles of hygiene.[1]

In an effort to improve the quality of medical services, a presidential order on April 13, 1891, brought agency physicians under Civil Service regulations, thereby reducing the political nature of appointments. Civil Service criteria for agency physicians codified earlier guidelines, provided that candidates must have an appropriate education, pass a qualifying examination, possess a good knowledge of hygiene, and be willing to "visit Indians in their homes and educate them in proper methods of living and of caring for health." Prospective physicians, moreover, were required to provide evidence of "good moral character." Civil Service rules permitted women to be school physicians, but they could not serve in an agency post. Physician's duties also explicitly included overcoming the "evil influence" of traditional healers.[2] In this way, it was hoped, active, qualified doctors would henceforth work among the tribes to improve and promote civilization.

Another effort to enhance prevention and care materialized in 1891, when the Indian Office began to employ field matrons. This hardy group of women, frequently recruited from missionary organizations, provided remote reservation areas with simple medical and sanitary services such as nutritional advice and prenatal care. Indian Commissioner Thomas J. Morgan (1889–1893), who launched the program at the behest of various humanitarian groups, expected the matrons to work primarily with native women, where they might exert the most influence. In general, they sought to teach modern homemaking skills, including hygienic preparation of food, proper waste disposal, basic nursing, and the treatment of disease. Although matrons seldom possessed formal medical training, they were expected to provide an element of preventive medicine and expand the reputation of western medical practices among the Indians. Financial restraints prevented the program from growing as rapidly as its sponsors desired, but matrons were quickly dispatched to a number of reservations, thereby augmenting the efforts of agents and physicians.[3]

Morgan also advocated opening hospitals and adding more physicians. Like his immediate predecessors, the commissioner acknowledged that most reservations provided inadequate medical services, the result of which produced "a large degree of needless suffering and hundreds of deaths that might in all probability be prevented." To illustrate his point, Morgan pointed to the Navajo reservation, where eighteen thousand people, spread over some twelve thousand square miles, were served by a single physician. He also complained that the government did not operate any reservation hospitals, something he regarded as a "national disgrace." Morgan lobbied for the construction of as many hospitals as possible, suggesting that they might be staffed at small cost if some of the stewards, nurses, cooks, and laundresses were "Intellectual Indians" recruited locally to work under the "constant supervision" of the physician. Such facilities promised to relieve suffering from contagious disease, severe accidents, and other misfortunes. Confined and supervised, Indians patients could be offered medical and nursing care "in the name of humanity."

Despite high hopes and the obvious need for hospitals, the Indian commissioner was repeatedly frustrated by the persistent refusal of Congress to provide sufficient funding. Although powerless to remedy this situation, Morgan nevertheless committed the Indian Service to opening reservation hospitals as quickly as possible.[4]

A substantial increase in missionary activity also coincided with the federal desire to improve health care in the 1890s. With the passage of the Dawes Act in 1887 and the establishment of effective humanitarian reform groups such as the Indian Rights Association, the Women's National Indian Association, and the Lake Mohonk Conference of Friends of the Indian, missionary interest picked up on reservations for the first time since the demise of the Peace Policy. Although much of this activity focused on education and religion, some groups sought to provide limited amounts of medical assistance. These services developed rather slowly because of inadequate funding and the desire to place religion first. By the mid-1890s, however, the idea of offering medical assistance to the Indians began to take root. These activities dovetailed with federal efforts, providing much needed assistance.[5]

Despite promises by government and church officials to improve Indian health, the Navajo people continued to prefer their own ways. Most of the Diné remained isolated from outsiders by living in family clusters while earning a living from their sheep and agricultural plots. Yet Navajo culture could not remain immune from white influences. By the 1890s the proliferation of trading posts brought them into contact with new products such as manufactured tools and clothing, wagons, and western foods. Traders also performed a few basic medical services and sold patent medicines to their customers. While these goods and services produced changes in their material culture and introduced them to numerous aspects of Anglo-American culture, the tribe generally remained suspicious of anything that threatened traditional values or attempted to impose changes on them by force. Nevertheless, the cultural isolation of the Diné was clearly eroding, even relating to medical matters.[6]

In those circumstances, the treatment of sickness became more and more of a dilemma. A great majority of the Navajo remained fully committed to familiar practices, relying on healers, curing ceremonies, and herbal remedies. If confronted with a choice of treatments, they usually opted for the old ways, which incorporated friends and relatives in the process. Those who had experience with western medicine often found it impersonal and mysterious. Not infrequently, Navajos expressed the sentiment that western medicine might be suitable for the whites, but it did not fit the Diné.[7] Nevertheless, when presented with a direct benefit—such as powders to relieve stomach aches or vaccinations against smallpox—they responded favorably. By the end of the century a small group of Navajos, mostly those living in close contact with whites, were becoming more accepting of western medicine, albeit with a great deal of uncertainty. Never fully trusting government doctors, they openly hoped to combine old and new methods. Unfortunately, the Indian Service refused to acknowledge dual treatment, insisting that "rational medicine" be fully accepted.

A DESERVING GENTLEMAN

Thomas L. Craig, a likable Missouri-born physician, commanded considerable respect in his hometown of Benedict, Kansas. From a career perspective, however, the physician had achieved only moderate success as he neared his fiftieth birthday in 1889. Thirteen years of informal rural doctoring followed by a medical degree from the Keokuk College of Physicians and Surgeons in 1880 had failed to pay off. After practicing in the tiny Kansas hamlet of Guilford for a short time, Craig used political connections to secure a physician's appointment at the Osage agency in Indian Territory. Despite two successful years with the Indian Service, the 1884 Democratic victory cost the doctor his job. Returning to Kansas, he moved to the town of Benedict, establishing a medical practice in the local drugstore. But times remained tight for rural doctors. To make ends meet, he sold drugs, patent medicines, paints, window glass, and stationery. When this proved unsuccessful, Craig sought the help of Kansas Congressman B. W. Perkins in obtaining another government appointment. Appropriate letters, portraying Craig as an "upright and deserving gentleman," soon arrived on the Indian commissioner's desk. On July 19, 1889, following the Republican victory of 1888, Craig became the newest physician assigned to the Navajo.[8]

Although Craig obtained his job through political favoritism and his background bears many similarities to earlier agency physicians, he actually belonged to a new era. Dedicated, involved, and competent, he remained at the agency for six years. During this time he witnessed the first signs of change in the medical environment among the Navajo.

Thomas Craig and his wife arrived at Fort Defiance on August 10, 1889, anxious to begin work. Like earlier physicians, he moved into the old adobe building then serving as the physician's quarters. By this time, an additional structure, in the same derelict condition, had been added to the physician's layout for use as a "drugstore." Although the Craigs left no accounts of their experiences, their situation was undoubtedly similar to that of other Indian Service doctors. If the recollections of Dr. L. W. White are typical, their household furnishings "were far from elaborate or even adequate. Never more than a couple of black iron beds with very hard mattresses, knotty pillows, about four red or white blankets with 'U.S.I.S,' . . . a 'Canon ball' stove for heating the entire quarters and an iron range for cooking. Bathing facilities [consisted] of one round galvanized iron wash tub, water to be heated in the kettle on the stove." The doctor's work space looked equally primitive. A single room served as dispensary, storage space for medical and surgical supplies, an examining room, and office. An "old Army type operating table" might be on hand, yet "this kind of establishment was rarely furnished with running water." So poor were the facilities that "a new physician arriving at a station would sometimes find his office in great disorder and confusion, and in many instances took one disappointed look and immediately silently folded his tent and returned to the more glamorous east."[9]

Fortunately, Dr. Craig was not easily discouraged, although he found the work demanding and at times unpleasant. At age fifty he was older than the Indian Service considered ideal, and his stamina was quickly tested. No sooner had he settled in than an epidemic of throat disease resembling diphtheria spread across the northern part of the reservation. Agent Vandever heard rumors that eight hundred people had perished, mostly infants who contracted the disease in combination with measles and whooping cough. These rumors, unconfirmed and undoubtedly exaggerated, nevertheless kept Craig busy. In fact, his visits to the more remote Navajo families caused some concern. Government inspectors regarded Craig as a good doctor, "willing and ready to respond to any and all calls promptly," but they doubted his physical stamina. To them, the job was only for young men. Vandever, however, contested this opinion, writing that Craig had done everything from setting broken limbs to extracting teeth as well as "any one man called upon to treat a whole tribe scattered over more than 10,000 square miles of territory." When the question of Craig's fitness reached Commissioner Morgan's desk, Vandever's report assured the doctor's retention.[10]

Despite Craig's desire to service remote parts of the reservation, his most important activities involved protecting students at the Fort Defiance boarding school. At the time Charles Vandever assumed control of the agency in January 1889, the school could barely muster twenty students. With hard work and persuasion, the enrollment soon grew to over seventy. The school's thirty-five year-old superintendent, B. J. Mooney and his wife Jeannie, the matron, were responsible for the institution, but Craig worried about their lack of interest in student health. Navajo parents regularly complained about the never-ending series of school-related ailments. This situation presented Craig with a dilemma. He worked directly under the agent and possessed no authority to deal with school matters unless invited by the superintendent or agent. In essence, the school operated as a separate administrative entity and Craig faced censure if he interfered. Despite the risk, he nevertheless began an informal investigation that revealed unacceptable conditions. Although the children seemed satisfactorily fed and clothed, they were seriously neglected in other ways. Medicine prescribed for ill students was not administered by the staff, sick children were permitted to lie in bed unattended, and sanitary conditions in the dormitories approached dangerous levels. "Vessels used by the sick children during the night," Craig discovered, "have been allowed to remain in the room during the following day, with no one to look after them and see that they were properly cleaned." Such circumstances fostered the spread of such contagious diseases as whooping cough, which in one instance killed four pupils.[11]

Because Craig enjoyed no direct control over the school, his expressions of concern to Mooney produced nothing. On one occasion, the superintendent lost his temper, telling the physician that it was none of his business. "If the government wanted sick Indians nursed," he retorted, "they must send a nurse to do it, he and his wife would not do it, as it was not their business." As a consequence, the continuation of medical problems at the school prompted a "large number" of parents to demand that their children be returned home, forcing the school to shut down for ten days. At this point, Craig joined Vandever in asking the Indian Office for Mooney's removal. Their letters, strongly critical of the superintendent and his wife, persuaded the commissioner to dismiss the couple during the summer of 1890.[12]

Because of the school's importance to the civilization effort, Craig continued to keep a close eye on its operations. David Shipley, who became the Navajo agent in December 1890, relied heavily on the physician to keep parents reassured, a task which he managed rather well following Mooney's removal. In general, student health remained rather good, the only problem being a quickly contained outbreak of chickenpox and the ever-present "sore eyes," which affected about a third of the pupils during the 1891–92 school year. Meanwhile, Craig continued to provide care to the local Navajo population. Because of the aches and pains associated with his advancing age, the physician remained close to Fort Defiance, providing medicines to the nine hundred or so patients who came in annually to see him. The prevalent diseases remained unchanged, with bronchitis, tonsillitis, pneumonia, conjunctivitis, and rheumatism topping the list. Only a few cases of venereal disease were reported, however. An additional source of concern developed in December 1891, when an Indian infected with smallpox visited the agency, prompting Craig to vaccinate the entire school population.[13]

During the fall of 1892 the question of child abuse and mismanagement reared its head, again drawing Dr. Craig into a school dispute. By this time a second school building had been finished, enabling the government to house over a hundred students. This controversy centered around the actions of school superintendent George W. Wadleigh, a former real estate salesman from Los Angeles. Recently employed by the Presbyterian Indian School at Tucson, Wadleigh had been recommended for the Navajo position by officials of the Episcopal church, who also expected him and his wife, Harriet, to carry on missionary work. Not content to mind his own business, Wadleigh soon waded into agency politics, illegally firing a man he did not like and quarreling with rival clergymen. For these reasons and more, Craig disliked the new superintendent, whom he described as a man of energy, yet "of a nervous lymphatic temperament, inclined to be erratic, . . . arbitrary and contentious." It was Wadleigh's fondness for harsh disciplinary measures, however, that caused problems. Navajo parents reacted bitterly when their children were abused, protesting vehemently to anyone who would listen. Tensions boiled over in October 1892, when Shipley suffered a severe beating by the followers of Black Horse while attempting to recruit students for Wadleigh's unpopular school.[14]

A month later Navajo leaders formally complained about the treatment of their children. Several cases of abuse drew their anger. In one instance, the mother of an eight-year-old boy complained that her son had been held prisoner in the school's belfry without food for two days. He was finally allowed to go into the school yard with his legs shackled. In this condition, the lad attempted to reach his nearby home "by crawling on his hands and knees." Within a short distance of his hogan, "the boy sank to the ground exhausted where his mother found him and carried him home." Even in this condition, Wadleigh refused to remove the shackles until the mother threatened to call in the agent. In another episode, a thirteen-year-old boy was locked in the school's cellar, a place Craig described as "unhealthy, foul, and damp," calculated to injure the health of anyone confined there.[15]

According to Craig, when confronted with such mistreatment, Wadleigh declared that he did not care how the Indians felt and rejected any interference with his administration. Other Indian Service employees, however, realized the negative impact of such abuse. Even pro-government Navajos expressed anger. One man, Gordie, complained that Wadleigh's policy had caused the Black Horse trouble, adding that the Diné called the man a "Billy Goat" because he "is always butting the rest of the sheep." In a parting shot, Gordie noted that "he is as mean as he looks." Complaints of this nature reached such a crescendo that Shipley was forced to hold a council with Navajo chiefs on November 25, where a long list of grievances were aired. One man, Mariano, reported that "when I brought my boy to school he had two eyes, the next time I saw him he only had one." Others told of schoolboys being grabbed by the throat and practically smothered. Although Dr. Craig disliked Wadleigh, he felt compelled to admit that Mariano's son lost his sight because of disease, not violence. Nevertheless, the Navajo remained firm in the conviction that their children were abused, something the physician agreed with. As a consequence, Inspector Gardner recommended that the superintendent be relieved from duty. Wadleigh fought back, claiming that he was being forced out because he was a Democrat. He also sought the support of Herbert Welsh on the Indian Rights Association. Although not personally acquainted with the superintendent, Welsh argued for his retention primarily because he had been backed by various church officials. Still, Wadleigh had obviously lost the government's confidence. By April 1893 he and his wife were gone and the task of repairing relations with the tribe resumed.[16]

Shortly after the Wadleigh incident, Army Lieutenant Edward H. Plummer became the acting Navajo agent. Plummer worked diligently to improve the school's reputation by making the facility more humane. Dr. Craig participated in this effort to the limit of his authority. Health problems, however, continued to plague the school. Although lacking an infirmary or trained medical personnel, the new superintendent, Ella Patterson, often attempted to handle illnesses without calling in the doctor. With 138 pupils enrolled as of January 1894, this proved difficult. Craig did not hesitate to express concern over this situation, and his fears were substantiated when inspection reports confirmed that school health continued to be substandard. Female students were observed to have head lice and vermin-filled clothes. Quite a few students also suffered from sore eyes. This disease caused particular concern for Craig, who did not approve of the school's haphazard treatment, preferring to handle such cases himself. Nonetheless, school authorities wanted to handle matters themselves. They justified the lack of proper treatment on the grounds that they had no place to isolate contagious patients, and argued instead for the construction of a school hospital. In the meantime, students with untreatable contagious diseases were sent home, which did nothing to improve their health. Although no student deaths occurred during 1893–94, the physician's lack of access to the school proved frustrating.[17]

MATRONS AND MISSIONARIES

Government medical services on the Navajo reservation received a boost in December 1891 when Mary E. Raymond accepted the appointment of field matron. One of the first seven women to qualify for this newly created government position, Miss Raymond received a salary of sixty dollars per month, reporting to the Navajo agent. She resided at Jewett (also called Hog Back), New Mexico, located on the San Juan River nearly one hundred miles northeast of Fort Defiance where the Women's Home Missionary Society of the Methodist Episcopal Church operated a mission. She received church support in the form of housing and use of a horse. In addition, the Cambridge, Massachusetts branch of the Women's National Indian Association provided her with small amounts of cash to buy supplies for the Navajo. From this base among a large but scattered concentration of Diné, Raymond labored with native women, instructing them in the "proper" way to manage a household by teaching such skills as sewing, laundry, and maintaining a clean home. She also offered advice on "adorning the home, both inside and out, with pictures, curtains, home-made rugs, flowers, grass plots, and trees," while actively promoting Christianity and religious training. Last but not least, she provided instruction in personal cleanliness, sanitation, and care for the sick.[18]

Raymond's goal of changing native life patterns proved difficult among the suspicious Navajo, who were not much interested in living in a white-style environment. Fortunately for the matron, she teamed up with Mrs. Mary Eldridge, a former matron at Haskell Institute, who had been sent to Jewett by the Women's Home Missionary Society to work with remote Navajo families. The two women spent endless hours teaching Indian women how to cook, sew, and prepare "simple remedies." With no physician available, they frequently visited remote hogans on their own. In a typical report, Raymond wrote that "we went to see a very sick child whose father came for us. He brought a horse for one of us to ride. We spent several hours there to administer the medicines ourselves. Yesterday (Sunday) I went again. To-day the father came to report and get medicine, and to-morrow we will go again to see the child. The distance to its home is 12 miles." As a general rule, however, the women preferred to remain near the mission since they could treat more people "than when we go to them, because they are so scattered and move about so much." Overall, Miss Raymond reported that between December 8, 1891, and August 15, 1892, she cared for 153 sick individuals and administered medicine to 183 people.[19]

Shortly after her arrival at Jewett, Mary Raymond married Tom Whyte, the proprietor of a trading post at Hog Back. Nonetheless, she continued to work with Mary Eldridge. As far as medical matters were concerned, the two women handed out medicines, many of them provided by the Home Missionary Society. It was not uncommon for Navajo families to travel more than fifty miles to secure medical attention. Although positive about her work, Mrs. Whyte seems to have been overwhelmed by the magnitude of the task. In response to a letter from her in June 1893, Agent Plummer advised that "benefitting the Navajo is a rather hopeless task and seems to me almost an impossibility. If I accomplish anything by work and devotion to the task I would not despair[,] but the best efforts and intentions seem to accomplish so very little that it is most discouraging." Mary herself lamented that the constant wanderings of Navajo families prevented her from doing much good. In addition to a lack of positive results, the work proved extremely exhausting. Although encouraged by Navajo expressions of appreciation, the job took its toll. Finally, in May 1894, Mary Whyte suffered a debilitating mental breakdown after separating from her husband and giving birth to a slightly deformed child.[20]

Plummer suggested that Mary Eldridge replace Whyte as field matron. Writing to Commissioner Browning, he remarked that "Mrs. Eldridge understands medicine. She speaks a little Navajo and understands more. She has a very strong and most beneficial influence over the Indians living about her. They know her and trust her implicitly. I know of one case of a Navajo sending fifty miles to her for medicine, in preference to having a singing and treatment of a Navajo 'medicine man.'" Plummer's support, endorsed by the secretary of the Home Missionary Society, won Eldridge the job. Her activities continued to be closely associated with church work as she teamed up with Miss Mary Tipp, the replacement missionary at Jewett. The two women continued the tradition of ministering to the sick, handing out medicine, and feeding the hungry. In early 1895 Eldridge noted an increase in hunger and starvation, the result of a drought that swept the entire Southwest. Most patients appearing for medical aid suffered from stomach and bowel troubles related to the consumption of insufficient or unsuitable food. Without government supplies to deal with this situation, the matron used her own funds to provide aid, running up a substantial debt.[21]

Despite their commitment to humanitarian work, the field matrons were openly opposed by influential Navajo traditionalists in the San Juan region. It appears that the religious overtones of the women's activities did not sit well with some healers. As early as 1893, Mary Whyte wrote that while many Indians expressed confidence in her remedies, they usually yielded to "medicine men." Whyte believed that her success spurred a growing resentment on the part of powerful traditionalists. Occasionally this resulted in a direct confrontation, although as a matter of practicality, the matron dropped medical cases if a healer appeared on the scene, not wanting to spark a fight. Whyte frequently expressed contempt for traditional beliefs. "Experience will teach [the Navajo]," she wrote, "that our simple remedies do more good than songs, rattles, and feathers, and then we do not take the sick person's horses for pay as the medicine men do." The effort to provide medical care thus developed into a contest between two determined forces. Every time a Navajo could be persuaded to opt for western medicine, it was hailed as a victory for civilization. In one instance, a Navajo woman supposedly abandoned by the healers was nursed back to health, prompting the matron to naively proclaim that "the more progressive Indians are fast losing faith in their medicine men."[22]

As the decade progressed, the medical contributions of the field matron declined. Although Mary Eldridge remained fully committed to her job, "willing to give her very life if need be for the elevation and christianization of the Navajos," it became increasingly difficult for her to focus on medical concerns. In 1895 the Women's Home Missionary Society added to Eldridge's responsibilities by sending her a young female missionary to train and suggesting that she consider opening a new mission on the reservation. A year later the matron became so exhausted that she had to ask for an extended leave of absence. Contributing to her distress was the fact that the Indian Office failed to provide sufficient support. In a typical incident, Eldridge was forced to take over the "laborious work" of the government farmer at Jewett when he suddenly deserted his job.

Once Mrs. Eldridge returned from her well-deserved leave, which included a trip to the Indian reform conference at Lake Mohonk, she immediately plunged into a new venture centering around the Two Gray Hills area. Her interest in this region apparently revolved around the desire of the Methodist church and the Women's National Indian Association, expressed at the Mohonk meeting, to establish a mission hospital. Although this came to nothing, Eldridge became so involved that she purchased land for the use of the project. These diversions, worthy in themselves, took so much time away from the pursuit of other activities that the expected boost to medical care on the reservation by the presence of field matrons had largely evaporated by the end of the decade.[23]

THE MISSION HOSPITAL

Despite the obvious need for a hospital on the Navajo reservation, the government had consistently refused to act. Prospects looked so bleak by 1894 that Agent Plummer decided to take a different tack. Fortunately, Plummer's concern coincided with an eager desire by the Protestant Episcopal Church to enter into missionary work among the Navajo. Under the leadership of Right Reverend J. Mills Kendrick, Missionary Bishop of New Mexico and Arizona, and backed by the financial resources of the Westchester, New York, branch of the church's "Women's Auxiliary," a number of options received consideration. The general lack of Navajo interest in missionary endeavors, however, gave

Kendrick serious misgivings. In an address before church officials in October 1893, the bishop admitted that nothing permanent had yet been accomplished by missionaries in Arizona and New Mexico. "It is difficult to make a beginning," he proclaimed, because "they are jealous of the intrusion of the White Man." Kendrick nevertheless desired to do something, perhaps even fund a field matron. In this frame of mind he visited Fort Defiance in May 1894.[24]

During a highly emotional meeting between Kendrick and Plummer, the question of Navajo needs and missionary projects came up. After some debate, the agent suggested that the bishop might want to consider building a hospital. Plummer placed the idea in an attractive package, putting it squarely in the context of missionary work: "the spiritual enlightenment of these people, would be and could be best accomplished through the erection of a suitable building or buildings and the maintenance of a hospital, at or near this Agency." To bolster his argument, Plummer explained that the agency physician, despite all efforts, was severely restricted: "he has a small office and dispensary, but no room to kep [sic] sick persons. He has several times reported to me cases of broken limbs and severe cases of illness which if means were provided might be successfully treated if he had accommodations to keep patients under his care but would result in cripple and death for want of such means." The agent went on to emphasize that, for the same reason, sick schoolchildren had to be sent home to their "barbarous" hogans. On frequent occasions, Navajos coming in for treatment simply could not be served. Plummer related the story of a man suffering from pneumonia who came to Craig for help: "He was a pitiable sight but we had no place to shelter him and he had to return to his hogan to sure death when he might have been cured if we could have taken care of him here." Thus, if Kendrick really wanted to help the Navajo people, he might consider caring for the sick, which Plummer promised would gradually lead to their conversion to Christianity.[25]

Kendrick immediately endorsed the idea of a hospital. That same day the bishop wrote to Miss Fanny Schuyler of the Westchester Auxiliary, suggesting that the most useful thing they could do for the Navajo would be to help fund a hospital at Fort Defiance. Predicting that the government would never establish its own hospital, Kendrick argued that the hospital would ensure a permanent church presence, make a good impression on the Indians, and open the door for religious instruction. By "getting at the soul through attention to the body, . . . the hospital could be made the center of field work over this portion of the reservation. In time we could connect with this hospital a chapel for religious services." To oversee the facility, Kendrick proposed to employ Miss Eliza Thackera, a devout Episcopalian then working as a matron and teacher at the Fort Defiance school. Financing the project would cost the Westchester women twelve hundred dollars for the building, nine hundred dollars a year for Miss Thackera, and enough money to hire a nurse.[26]

The Westchester women wasted little time in funding the building and hiring Miss Thackera. Thackera, an energetic young woman, clearly knew more about missions than medicine. The daughter of a well-known Florida clergyman, she proved to be a talented administrator. Once committed, she became the motivating force behind the construction and operation of the hospital. Entertaining no illusions about the task before her, she wrote "it is almost impossible to understand the nature of this work. You must live among these Indians and see them in their own country. They do not love Americans (White); these Navajos have had so much to make them distrust us. In entering upon this missionary work, this mission hospital, we will find that we have got to overcome the influence of the medicine men, and here lies the great work we may have to do." In this regard, both Thackera and Kendrick were realistic enough to realize that traditional healers would oppose the hospital and that "patients would not automatically use the facility."[27]

As a privately operated facility, the hospital needed both government and tribal approval. Both Plummer and Craig endorsed the plan after Kendrick, having made no provisions for a separate doctor, made it clear that its facilities would be available to the agency physician. Plummer approached the Indian Office by listing such potential advantages as relief from suffering, overcoming the influence of healers, and promoting civilization. Nor did he anticipate any difficulty in obtaining permission from the tribe to use land near the agency. In mid-September the Indian Office approved the hospital. By then Miss Thackera had already recruited a trained nurse to join the project. A site south of the agency seemed ideal.[28]

On October 20, 1894, Plummer met in council with Henry Chee Dodge, Bagota, Many Horses, Gambler, and other Navajo leaders. They readily agreed to provide a site for the hospital, but when Plummer showed them the proposed location, they became highly agitated. They regarded the area as "Shinde" because a Navajo had died there. After a hurried conference, a site in Black Creek Valley, about a mile east of the agency, was approved. Thackera and Plummer acknowledged that had the original site been used, the hospital would have been doomed from the beginning: the Navajo would not come to a haunted site. To facilitate construction, Plummer persuaded the Indian Office to furnish lumber and coal from agency stocks at a reduced price, justifying the subsidy on grounds that the mission hospital would support the government's effort to help the Navajo.[29]

Construction of the small two-story stone hospital began near the end of 1894. Employing Navajo laborers to cut and haul sandstone and do carpentry work, the building slowly went up. Delays plagued the project from the first, prompted in part by long periods of bad weather and a limited budget. Thackera continually appealed to the Westchester Auxiliary for additional funds. Finally, on March 1, 1897, the Hospital of the Good Shepherd opened its doors, with Miss Thackera serving as the supervisor. Calling it the "white house" (because of the color of the stone), the Navajo, having helped build it, expressed hopes for its success. Nonetheless, there were no guarantees it would be accepted. A critical test came immediately. The first patient, a man with a cancerous arm, faced an amputation. Although the building had yet to be properly furnished, the army surgeon at Fort Wingate agreed to perform the operation, assisted by the agency physician. Fortunately, the surgery proved a success. As one participant wrote to Kendrick, "it was a critical case, for had he died the superstitious fears of the Navajos would have rendered the hospital a failure. His recovery was rapid and complete, and the success of the Hospital assured."[30]

Despite a good start, the Good Shepherd hospital struggled to become fully operational. Proper medical furnishings remained scarce and the actual number of patients treated is unknown. Miss Thackera spent most of her time soliciting funds. As intended, the agency physician utilized the facility from time to time, but it does not appear that this became a regular practice. Government inspector John Lane praised the work of the "excellent christian lady named Thackera," even suggesting that the Indian Office provide funding to help equip and maintain the hospital.[31] Yet no government financial help arrived and the hospital remained a small and poorly equipped facility, perpetually short of funds.

OLD PROBLEMS, NEW FACES

Dr. Thomas Craig did not remain at Fort Defiance long enough to witness the opening of the mission hospital. He spent much of his last years on the job involved with several matters, including how to deal with native healers. Like other government observers, he predicted that the time would come when reliance on traditional medicine would be transferred to the "rational medicine of the White Man." Craig, however, did not underestimate the power of healers, whom he recognized as the "key to the inner court of these peoples affection." Unlike most of his colleagues, the physician believed that the Navajo might be willing to accept both ways. On at least one occasion he attended a healing ceremony, respectfully discussing with traditionalists the way that he treated illness. This low-key approach seemed to be appreciated by the Indians, who listened with "manifest interest." Nonetheless, Craig's superiors remained aloof. Agent Plummer acknowledged that "Indian medicine men" were the most influential element in the tribe, but all they did was encourage superstition. He thus favored an aggressive policy of "throwing off the superstitious and baneful influence of the Indian medicine men," despite Craig's experimentation with a policy of some tolerance.[32]

Craig also continued his interest in the agency school, where he became increasingly concerned about problems related to overcrowding. Despite his vigilance, it seemed that medical problems at the school expanded as the facility grew in size. In a letter to the commissioner requesting one thousand dollars to construct a school sewer system, Plummer provided a vivid description of the deteriorating sanitary condition of the boys dormitory, where wastewater from the building ran through ditches likely to become clogged and "soaked with foul matter." This pollution soaked the floors and appeared to be "the cause of an epidemic of pneumonia, fevers and bowel troubles that have prevailed among the children for several weeks."[33]

Other sanitary problems also racked the school. In addition to a new sewer system, the facility needed new toilet facilities at the rear of the boys' building. Because of soil conditions the original outhouses had been placed some distance away. Many of the schoolboys, fresh from the camps, were unaccustomed to using such conveniences. Until they could be instructed in proper usage, the youngsters relieved themselves wherever convenient, even inside the building. Conditions were especially bad in cold weather. As Plummer put it, "in inclement weather boys going out at night will step outside the building instead of going some distance to a closet. With their habits and life out of doors they will go out without clothes or shoes and go back to bed with dirty feet, besides catching cold." Overcrowding also caused problems, with as many as three youngsters sleeping in a single bed. "This crowding," noted Plummer, "after their open life is dangerous with the most healthful buildings and surroundings, but with such conditions as have existed here is a wicked risk of human life." Despite such dangerous conditions, the government made only minimal improvements. In 1898, with almost two hundred students in attendance, conditions in the boys' building remained unsatisfactory. Not until well after the turn of the century were indoor lavatories constructed.[34]

Dr. Craig left the agency sometime early in 1895, to be replaced by Leven P. Logan. In many respects Craig's departure marked the end of an era in which agency physicians were distinguished primarily by their personality. New doctors, selected by the Civil Service System, now possessed with minimum credentials, rotated in and out of the agencies without much notice and without any long vacancies. Their qualifications and motivations remain somewhat obscure, although many struggling physicians undoubtedly regarded the security of a regular government paycheck as a prime motivator. The fact that an Indian Service physician's salary dropped from twelve hundred dollars to eleven hundred dollars between 1874 and 1900 did not discourage doctors from heading for such primitive outposts. In less than a year after arriving at Fort Defiance, Logan gave way to C. J. Finnigan, a thirty-two-year-old physician from Montana, who remained for three years. Finnigan's evaluation simply stated that "character, education, habits & qualification are good."[35]

Meanwhile, the Good Shepherd hospital continued to struggle to survive, its half-dozen beds providing only limited value. Despite the initial flurry of optimism, it quickly became obvious that agency physicians found the small facility insufficient and began to distance themselves from its activities. Once Miss Thackera realized the danger presented by government defection, she decided to recruit her own doctor. Consequently, in 1898 Mary E. Pradt Harper came to work at the little hospital. Dr. Harper brought impressive credentials. Possessing a medical degree and having practiced at a hospital in Madison, Wisconsin, she had lived for eight years among the Indians of New Mexico as a medical missionary. In addition, she believed that a "Lady Physician" could be especially effective. "I know from experience," she once said, "that a woman physician has a great opportunity for improving their [Indians] condition, and am certain that when they know more of the laws of health and hygienic living they will come nearer being good citizens.[36]

Dr. Harper and Miss Thackera single-handedly kept the facility operating. For the most part, the hospital treated routine cases of eye, ear, and lung problems, although Harper did perform a number of surgeries. In addition, the physician often ventured out onto the reservation on horseback to visit outlying patients. Accompanied only by an Indian guide, she sometimes remained in the field for several days, camping out at night. Nonetheless, her medical services were always placed in a religious context, being regarded primarily as a way to convert the Navajos. Indeed, patients coming in for treatment were usually pressured to accept baptism, something that few did. Thackera also used every opportunity to demonstrate the advantages of western medicine. On more than one occasion, the bold young church worker persuaded native healers to let her attend curing ceremonies. On such occasions she quietly waited until they had finished "their wild incantations over the sick"; then she would say, "My Brothers, you have done your part, now I will do mine," offering up her own remedies and a prayer. Whether these methods produced any acceptance cannot be determined, although Bishop Kendrick claimed that she eventually won the confidence of some healers.[37]

Nevertheless, the little Episcopal medical outpost continued to flounder. In

December 1899 Mary Harper resigned in order to open a private practice in Gallup. During the four months before another doctor could be found, the agency physician attended patient needs, which were minimal. Meanwhile, Miss Thackera continued to face a series of financial problems and staff shortages, which prevented any real effectiveness. In fact, between September 1900 and January 1901, only twenty-seven patients were cared for at the hospital. The financial crisis also took its psychological toll, causing Bishop Kendrick to fear for Thackera's health. And still things worsened. The Westchester Women's Auxiliary, which had pumped so much money into the venture, began to waver. In 1901 the group suggested that a "Rich Arizonan" be found to provide future support. Although they did not withdraw from the project, the New York benefactors had clearly lost enthusiasm and plans for future expansion were dropped.[38] By the turn of the century it became obvious that the Good Shepherd hospital could not serve as a substitute for an Indian Service hospital.

Meanwhile, smallpox threatened the Diné. The epidemic, which started in 1898 among the Pueblos, alarmed federal officials, who feared that the disease would spread. Those fears came true when smallpox erupted among the Hopi in December. Because some of the more traditional villages refused government vaccinations, a deadly situation rapidly materialized among the residents of First and Second Mesa. By the time the disease ran its course in the spring of 1899 almost two hundred Hopi had perished. With the Hopi population surrounded by Navajos, Agent George W. Hayzlett found himself confronted with a serious situation. Fearing a similar outbreak among his own wards, he ordered the agency physician, C. J. Finnigan, to remain at home, preferring to rely instead on Mary McKee, the school physician at Keams Canyon, and doctors provided by missionary groups to deal with the Hopi.[39]

In January 1899 several cases of smallpox were reported among the Navajo near Red Rock. Hayzlett acted with dispatch, sending the tribal police to quarantine anyone exposed to the disease. This resulted in a small group of Navajos being forced to live in an isolated hogan until the danger passed (which required three months). As a defensive measure, Hayzlett also quarantined the Fort Defiance school to prevent "Old Indians coming to visit the children" and inoculated all the students. Although these precautions proved effective, they were clearly aided by the fact that many Navajos had previously been vaccinated. Unlike the Hopi traditionalists, Navajos actively sought out vaccinations, keeping both the agency and mission hospital busy. In this instance, Diné receptivity to western medicine prevented the debacle then occurring among their neighbors. In fact, only five Navajos were reported to have perished during the epidemic.[40]

END OF THE CENTURY

In October 1899, Calvin K. Smith, a forty-three-year-old Iowa physician, be-came the last doctor to serve the Navajo during the nineteenth century. In many respects, he found working conditions unchanged from the time when Dr. Craig had arrived a decade earlier. Little had improved, despite attempts by the Indian Service to better the quality of its medical services. Facilities and care remained extremely primitive. An inspection report in 1900 described the doctor's office as "a very poor one story adobe building in bad repair, it has a prop on one side of its building to keep that side from falling out." Smith remained the sole government doctor assigned to a growing Navajo nation. A colleague later recalled that not only was Smith the only physician, but "there were no [government] hospitals and I don't remember any trained nurses. . . . It was almost impossible . . . even to dress a wound for an Indian. The great call was for liniments, cough syrups, and castor oil. The obstetric work was all performed by Indian women. About all the medical doctors had to attend was the sick children at the schools at Fort Defiance and Tohatchi."[41]

Thus the grand promises made at the beginning of the 1890s remained largely unfulfilled. Despite Commissioner Morgan's desire to construct more hospitals, federal funding never materialized. Although the Episcopalians had generously built a hospital, its small capacity and its focus on religious activities proved totally inadequate for government purposes. Six beds for a population of twenty thousand hardly fit the bill. The employment of field matrons on the northern part of the reservation also did little. These dedicated women, over-worked and overwhelmed, could do little more than dispense advice and a few medicines. In reality little more than goodwill ambassadors, Mrs. Whyte and Eldridge worked against overwhelming odds. Under these circumstances, nei-ther the agency physician nor the field matron were able to do much with prevention. Living conditions on the reservation were little changed, if at all, by their efforts, although some Navajo were clearly willing to accept pills, liniments, and vaccinations. Despite this accommodation, the power and in-fluence of native healers remained undiminished. Indian Service efforts to destroy the "medicine men" had been largely unsuccessful. The Navajo were not yet prepared to give up traditional approaches to health care.

CHAPTER SIX

A SCOURGE ON THE LAND

It is known that tubercular infection is the very commonest of all conditions which the Indian Service physician is called upon not only to face but to treat professionally. Pulmonary tuberculosis is widespread. It is common. It is fatal. It is insidious. It is everywhere.

WILLIAM J. MCCONNELL, USIS INSPECTOR

The opening decades of the twentieth century brought with them a crisis in Indian health care. During this period the government began to recognize the full extent of reservation health problems. As a consequence, the nature and quality of Indian medical services increased slightly. Offsetting this trend, however, came a rapid acceleration of deadly and debilitating diseases that dramatically increased Indian morbidity rates and brought about a new level of tribal suffering. Indian Service efforts in improving Indian health thus encountered a number of horrendous obstacles that rendered progress nearly impossible.

Historian Diane T. Putney suggests that the federal government awakened to the extent of Indian illness during the first decade of the twentieth century, and for the subsequent thirty years Indian health remained at the forefront of policy issues. Between 1900 and 1910 tuberculosis and trachoma, both highly contagious diseases, became epidemic among the native population. The spread of these diseases can be attributed, in part, to the expansion of the civilization program, especially the effort to force more Indian children into boarding schools. This phenomenon began with an edict issued by Indian Commissioner William A. Jones (1897–1904) demanding that schools be filled to capacity. Disregarding health and sanitary implications, reservation and off-reservation facilities were quickly crammed with native children. Almost immediately, deadly epidemics spread through the Indian school system. Despite attempts to isolate ill students, the pressure to fill schools became so overpowering that superintendents placed children in cramped rooms, fed them poor food, and overlooked unsanitary conditions. Indeed, some schools became known as death traps.[1]

The medical results of school overcrowding were noted by a number of Indian Service physicians. In 1897 one school doctor wrote that "these Indians are dying off of tuberculosis and nearly all of the children are afflicted with it, and to have them, weak and healthy ones bunched in clusters of eight [beds], coughing and expectorating, and sputum drying and contaminating the air all around in and through this cluster exposing the healthy who are in the cluster is a thing which is not right."[2] Facilitating the spread of disease among the general reservation population were school policies that returned seriously ill children home to die. Although these practices may have saved some schools from taboos associated with death, the return of highly contagious children to their relatives tended to spread these diseases even more rapidly. Once established on the reservations, where sanitary conditions were notoriously poor, these diseases spread.

TUBERCULOSIS

Of the diseases to reach epidemic proportions among the Indian population following the turn of the century, tuberculosis exacted the greatest toll. This malady had been known for centuries, dating back as far as ancient Egypt. It increased significantly during the medieval period, but did not become widespread until the eighteenth and nineteenth centuries, when it reached epidemic levels and began killing men, women, and children at an alarming rate. In the United States tuberculosis spread rapidly during the nineteenth century. America's most deadly disease in the early part of the century, it still affected a quarter of the population in 1884. By the end of the century nearly 120,000 Americans per year (184.8 per 100,000) perished from what became known as the "White Plague." These figures represented 11 percent of all deaths in the United States, somewhat less than heart disease, but three times the rate of cancer.[3]

Known by various names over the centuries—consumption, phthisis, scrofula, inflammation of the lungs—tuberculosis is a virulent bacillus (*Mycobacterium tuberculosis humanis*) that develops in dark, damp places, needs oxygen to survive, and reproduces rather slowly. The disease is spread by means of airborne droplet particles and is highly contagious. It can affect any part of the body, the most common form being pulmonary tuberculosis, "a chronic debilitating disease of the lungs, requiring at least several months, and usually many years to run its course." Severe cases of pulmonary tuberculosis are frequently accompanied by painful lesions in the larynx and intestines. The disease develops in stages, leaving the victim in a weakened condition that, before the development of effective antibiotic methods of treatment in the 1950s, frequently led to death.[4]

Although no cure for tuberculosis existed a century ago, medical experts believed it to be treatable. Recognized as contagious since 1865 and known to be caused by the tubercule bacillus since 1882, treatments generally favored rest and isolation. This resulted in the widespread popularity of sanatoriums between 1880 and 1950. The idea was quite basic. Sanatoriums "were medically supervised refuges from bad air," unsanitary conditions, and poor nutrition, where consumptives could rest, eat a properly prepared diet, and breathe fresh air. Because of the contagious nature of the disease, sanatoriums also served to isolate tubercular patients from the rest of the population. In this healthful environment, many believed, the lungs could naturally heal or defeat the bacillus, provided the disease had not progressed too far. Centered around a regime of rest and fresh air, the number of sanatoriums grew rapidly after 1900, especially in locations believed to have a healthy environment. Mountainous and desert areas of the West thus blossomed with both private and commercial hospitals, as "lungers" flocked to medical meccas.[5] Despite their great popularity, sanatoriums primarily benefited wealthy citizens who could afford the time and expense required for intensive care. Nevertheless, as the Indian Office began to focus on the problem of tuberculosis, it quickly agreed that sanatorium hospitals were the most desirable, albeit expensive, way to attack the problem.

The emergence of tuberculosis as a deadly killer came rather late to the Navajo, primarily because of their isolation. Statistical reports during the 1890s indicated few cases, and as late as 1900 government officials expressed little concern. The disease quickly gained momentum, however. A 1901 investigation criticized the school superintendent at Fort Defiance for permitting several tubercular students to enter his facility, which, in turn, led to six tuberculosis deaths at the school that year. In response, school authorities acknowledged for the first time that tuberculosis (along with rheumatism and diseases of the eye) was one of the principal diseases afflicting the tribe.[6]

Meaningful studies detailing the extent to which tuberculosis spread among the native population began to appear during the first decade of the twentieth century. By far the most active investigator in this area was Dr. Ales Hrdlicka, a well-known medical anthropologist associated with the U.S. National Museum. Between 1989 and 1905 Hrdlicka led six scientific expeditions into the Southwest and northern Mexico. In 1905 he delivered a paper summarizing his findings on the prevalence of disease among American Indians. Based on statistical information provided by Indian Service physicians as well as on his own research, he estimated that the tuberculosis morbidity rate among native groups ranged between 9.7 and 15.0 per thousand. Lacking comparable data for the general U.S. population, Hrdlicka nevertheless believed this to be a much higher rate than among the white population. He noted that pulmonary tuberculosis, once rare among the Indians, had become much more common: "It follows a rapid course in some individuals and moderately rapid in others, and is nearly always fatal." In 1906, Dr. Isaac W. Brewer conducted a more focused survey of tuberculosis among the tribes of Arizona and New Mexico. Again, he found the disease on the increase. At the Colorado River Agency in Arizona, for example, 95 percent of tribal deaths could be attributed to the disease. Brewer's information on the Navajo reservation indicated that tuberculosis, while not yet widespread, was on the increase.[7]

The first significant government attempt to deal with the spread of tuberculosis came during the tenure of Indian Commissioner Francis E. Leupp (1905–1909). Just prior to Leupp's appointment, the Indian Service conducted a survey of agency physicians, confirming that the disease was more widespread among the Indians than whites, and speculating that its prevalence was caused by poor sanitation, poorly prepared food, intermarriage between whites and Indians, "taking peoples predisposed to tuberculosis from camp life and confining them in schools," school overcrowding, and a lack of proper medical attention after detection. Concerned with conditions in the schools, Leupp suggested opening a sanatorium for tubercular school children, which "would insure to the unfortunates the special care and the chance for recuperation which is their due." He also ordered school superintendents to pay greater attention to "hygienic conditions" and avoid admitting unhealthy children. Reminding them that "Indian children should be *educated*, not destroyed in the process," school officials were "positively forbidden to receive pupils without the proper medical certificates as to physical soundness." School physicians were advised to carefully handle cases of tuberculosis and to send afflicted pupils home before the disease could spread.[8]

Despite such orders, Leupp failed to act decisively, and things continued to worsen. So widespread was the disease by 1908 that the Indian Service agreed to join with the Smithsonian Institution in determining the scope of the problem. Dr. Hrdlicka readily agreed to lead the investigating team. His subsequent report, titled "Tuberculosis among Certain Indian Tribes of the United States" was presented to the Sixth International Congress on Tuberculosis in Washington, D.C. It represented the findings of a two-month summer visit to five tribes and one off-reservation school. Although the Navajo were not included because their mortality remained comparatively low (estimated at 1.7 per thousand versus 6.0 per thousand for the Sioux at Fort Totten, North Dakota), the overall conclusions were extremely disturbing. To Hrdlicka, the most important reason for the alarming spread of the disease involved Indian ignorance of the disease's etiology. He found that Indians overheated their homes in cold weather, freely visited with consumptives, expectorated on floors, and allowed homes to become infected with tubercule bacilli. Indian households did not isolate infected individuals: "They eat with the same utensils as the rest of the family, and these utensils are not properly cleaned. They sleep with others until the symptoms of their disease become too annoying. Their soiled clothing is in no case washed separately." Because of these conditions, chances of infection were greatly increased in native communities.[9]

The Hrdlicka survey of 1908 spurred Leupp into action. Acknowledging that "in general the tuberculosis scourge is the greatest single menace to the future of the red race," he committed the Indian Office to "doing more than has ever been done before in the way of protecting the Indians against the ravages of this disease." As a result, Dr. Joseph A. Murphy, a tuberculosis specialist, was installed as director of the Indian Service's medical corps. Murphy first focused on the schools, advocating the opening of "sanatorium camps," where tubercular students could be isolated rather than being returned home. By 1909 tubercular tent camps had been opened at Colville, Washington; Laguna, New Mexico; and Phoenix, Arizona. Murphy also demanded improved sanitary controls in the schools and better training for government physicians. Soon thereafter, he began to emphasize the importance of prevention, noting that Indian Service physicians had done little to that effect in the past. It is imperative, he reported, that physicians "must not only treat the ills which actually present themselves, but make persistent, systematic, rigid examinations and frequent thorough inspections of all the Indians under their charge for the purpose of detecting cases of contagious diseases, submitting them to treatment and checking them in the incipient stages, and in addition, correcting insanitary customs and conditions which are responsible."[10] How all this might be accomplished by overworked and underpaid doctors remained a mystery.

None of these efforts and promises, moreover, did much to check the increase of tuberculosis among the Navajo. A 1912 survey indicated that in Arizona, which recorded the highest native death rate of all states containing a sizable Indian population, the incidence of tuberculosis among the Navajo had grown to 8.3 percent. The report concluded that the appointment of competent doctors was essential, that "hospital facilities should be provided on reservations for the care of advanced cases of tuberculosis," and that children suffering from pulmonary tuberculosis should not be admitted to any day or boarding school. For schoolchildren with active cases of the disease, the report recommended the establishment of school sanatoriums.[11] Thus, by 1912 tuber-

culosis loomed as a growing problem for the Navajo and the medical staff
assigned to help them.

TRACHOMA

The other disease assuming epidemic proportions among the Navajo following
the turn of the century was trachoma, a condition that had been observed
among the tribe for many years. Often called sore eyes or conjunctivitis, trachoma was highly contagious. Simply described, this eye disease caused granu-
lar bumps to grow on the inside of the eyelid. It spread rapidly in hot and dry
climates, and was usually associated with crowded and unsanitary living conditions. Once started, the infection spread through the transmission of materials
(tears, for example) from sick eyes to healthy ones. Shaking hands, sleeping in a
common bed, and other forms of personal contact spread the disease, as did
insects such as fleas. Once contracted, the virus passed through a number of
stages, the first of which were not readily evident. If left unattended, granules
covered the surface of the eyelid, scarring the eye. Victims almost always
suffered from impaired vision, and extreme cases caused blindness. Unfortunately, contemporary medical science possessed practically no information on
treating the disease and there was no known cure.[12]

During the first decades of the twentieth century trachoma spread rapidly
among native groups. Because tuberculosis received most of the government's
attention, however, Indian Service physicians sometimes downplayed the
problem. With prevention virtually impossible, scientific information unavailable, and resources scarce, only superficial treatment could be offered. Under
such circumstances, trachoma soon reached catastrophic proportions and
blindness became common among many tribal groups. Nevertheless, because
the disease did not kill, the federal government was reluctant to admit that a
serious problem existed.[13]

As with tuberculosis, the first significant effort to deal with trachoma came
during the administration of Francis Leupp. Leupp's concern for Indian health
translated into the first primitive attempt to control trachoma. In response to
mounting evidence that diseases of the eye had reached epidemic proportions,
Congress appropriated twelve thousand dollars in 1909 to determine the extent
of the problem, to treat afflicted individuals, and to prevent its spread. This
action was prompted in part by a cursory examination of boarding school
pupils, which uncovered a considerable amount of trachoma. Backed by Surgeon General Walter Wyman, who acknowledged that the disease was wide-

spread in the Southwest and could endanger the white population, the Indian Office began to tackle the problem.[14]

That same year the government singled out trachoma for special attention by opening an experimental eye hospital on the campus of the Phoenix Indian School. Dr. Ancil Martin, the oculist who directed the program, immediately set out to determine the extent of infection in central Arizona. An examination of students indicated that an astonishing 75 percent suffered from some form of the disease. Based on this discovery, Martin estimated that an equivalent percentage of infection would be found on local reservations, where the number of long-term adult cases could have produced more blindness. The physician immediately launched a student treatment program, simultaneously sending a school doctor to visit reservations near Phoenix "for the purpose of examining the reservation Indians and suggesting to them that they avail themselves of the privilege of the eye hospital at the school."[15]

Over a two-year span, Dr. Martin treated hundreds of Phoenix students. The brutal method of treatment left patients with an experience few would forget. With no known method of curing the disease, Martin opted for a surgical procedure known as grattage. Employing a special scraping instrument, the granules were cut off the inside of the eyelid, thus removing the cause of irritation. Although grattage may have provided temporary relief, the operations were painful and terrifying. One Hopi girl later recalled that the "eye operations were done without anaesthetic. . . . During the operation they cut off little rough things from under the eyelid. It was a grisly scene, with blood running all over. The children had to be held down tight." As treatment became more widespread, it became a bit more humane once doctors began to use powdered cocaine as a local anaesthetic. Patients received follow-up care involving the application of copper sulfate to the membrane of the lid. Nevertheless, the granules frequently reappeared and the eyelids of many patients never returned to normal.[16]

Although the eye hospital at Phoenix seemed to improve the sight of some students, it failed to impact the reservation population. Few adults were willing to make the trip to Phoenix, suffer through a painful surgery, and then remain at the hospital for the required thirty-day recovery period. Upon release, reservation residents were instructed to report back to the hospital at specific intervals or to visit the agency physician for continued care. Considering the distances involved and Indian reluctance to seek treatment from white doctors, many of those who had their vision temporarily improved lapsed back into unsatisfactory condition upon returning home. By 1911 it was apparent that reservation residents would not receive much benefit from special hospitals of the type established at Phoenix (which soon closed). The following year, a Public Health Service survey of health conditions among the Indians confirmed the high incidence of trachoma in the Southwest. An examination of 7,331 reservation residents in Arizona and New Mexico revealed an average infection rate of 24.8 percent. Navajos in the vicinity to Fort Defiance registered 30 percent. Survey doctors concluded that trachoma was out of control, a problem exacerbated on the reservations because few agency physicians were trained to deal with the disease, were "hindered with an overwhelming amount of general medical work, and in consequence little progress could be made."[17] All these conditions appeared among the Navajo, as agency physicians attempted to handle a growing crisis.

THE QUESTION OF PROFESSIONALISM

Coincident with the spread of tuberculosis and trachoma among the native population, Indian Service physicians struggled to improve their standing in the profession and to upgrade their services. By the 1890s agency doctors readily admitted that many of their predecessors had been unqualified, a fact that cast an unfavorable shadow over their activities. Toward the end of the century several government physicians urged the formation of an in-house professional organization to enhance their image and lobby for improved working conditions. In 1898, Dr. Joseph G. Bullock and several colleagues formed a group called "United States Indian Medical Service." Their efforts focused on securing more federal recognition of the Indian medical corps, acquiring modern equipment and medicines, and replacing regressive administrative procedures. Among the suggested changes, the creation (within the Indian Office) of a separate medical division, supervised by a chief surgeon, authorized to determine health policies, to approve the construction of hospitals, and to purchase medical supplies, seemed most imperative. They also suggested an independent board of medical examiners to approve the qualifications of appointees, and that doctors be given the authority, without interference from agents or school superintendents, to determine agency and school policy as it related to health matters.[18]

Unfortunately, the Indian Office did not share the concern of its field physicians. Commissioner Jones opposed the organization, primarily because it threatened to disrupt the established bureaucratic structure. Faced with opposition from Washington, the "United States Indian Medical Service" soon disappeared. Nevertheless, the need to professionalize the medical corps remained an issue with some employees. Indian Inspector William J. McConnell cut to the heart of the matter when he suggested that agency physicians be afforded the same benefits as army doctors, who were granted leave to pursue postgraduate education, supplied with up-to-date equipment and medicines, and provided with current medical literature. Despite the validity of McConnell's comparison between army and Indian doctors, the Indian Office failed to do anything.[19]

Following the turn of the century, agency doctors turned their attention to working conditions and the quality of medical supplies. Many were concerned that their surgical instruments were old and inadequate, and that the only way to get state-of-the-art tools was to purchase them on their own. The Board of Indian Commissioners backed the doctors on this issue, reporting in 1900 that "we strongly recommend providing at the expense of the Government, for each agency, such a set of surgical instruments as are required for practice, by the latest demands of well-established medical and surgical science." Once again, however, Commissioner Jones failed to act.[20]

A somewhat related matter involved the question of medicines. Since the 1880s all medical supplies had been ordered from a standardized list provided by the Indian Office. By 1900 this list was hopelessly outdated. Despite pleas for the addition of modern medicines, the Indian Office continued to procrastinate, preferring that doctors mix their own prescriptions from bulk supplies rather than the use of pre-manufactured pills and tablets just coming into general use. Washington officials defended their position on grounds that doctors should precisely mix medicines for each individual patient. Field personnel responded that such activities consumed too much time and they seldom possessed the necessary measuring equipment. This stalemate lasted until 1905, when newly installed commissioner Francis Leupp authorized the adoption of new medicines.[21]

The Indian Office's negative response to modernization and professionalism proved demoralizing and discouraging. Nevertheless, the quality of and dedication of the field medical personnel continued to improve, despite the overwhelming array of obstacles. In general, USIS doctors were not specifically trained to deal with epidemics of tuberculosis and trachoma, nor were they encouraged to acquire additional medical education. Agency physicians found themselves increasingly overworked while their salaries failed to keep up with professional standards. Even worse, working and living conditions at the agencies remained primitive, supplies inadequate, and hospital services almost nonexistent. The attitude of the Indian Office, moreover, continued to be one of parsimony, refusing to invest sufficient funding in Indian health care. Under these circumstances, the outlook for improved medical facilities for the Navajo looked bleak as the twentieth century dawned.

NEW AGENCIES

Given the discouraging conditions within the Indian Service, it did not appear that medical activities on the Navajo reservation were destined to improve. Administrative changes totally unrelated to health, however, served as a catalyst to bring more doctors and eventually government hospitals to Navajoland. This occurred as a result of tribal expansion, which by 1900 reached a size where it could no longer be administered from a central location. In response to population growth—which forced the Congress to provide more territory for the Navajo—reservation boundaries expanded until they reached the junction of the Colorado and Little Colorado rivers, some 150 air miles west of Fort Defiance. Within this remote and isolated expanse resided approximately twenty-one thousand Navajo as well as several thousand Hopis.[22] Faced with vast distances, few roads, and unpredictable weather conditions, a physician and two field matrons could hardly be expected to meet the medical needs of the Diné.

Difficulties in administering this huge area caused the Indian Office to create a number of semi-independent agencies (often called subagencies). In July 1901 the first of these units came into existence when the lands north and west of the Hopi reserve were detached to create the Western Navajo Agency, a division that proved inadequate. In 1903, therefore, the remaining portion of the original Navajo agency was again split, with the northern half becoming the San Juan Agency centered at Shiprock, while the southern half continued to be known as the Navajo Agency. In 1908 another agency was created at Leupp in the southwest corner of the reservation. With the addition of the Pueblo Bonito (Crownpoint) Agency on the eastern border, five separate administrative centers existed by 1908, although the Navajo agency at Fort Defiance still served as reservation headquarters.[23]

The creation of subagencies, each centering around a boarding school, prompted the government to place a physician at each location. The new doctors, however, seldom come into contact with the general Indian population. At the Western Navajo Agency, for example, Dr. Albert L. Tilton was assigned to the boarding school at Algert in August 1901. Paid only nine hundred dollars a year, Tilton eked out a spartan living at this remote facility, which was soon moved twenty miles west to Tuba City. Fortunately, he did not face major medical problems. Navajos living in the western portion of the reservation remained so isolated from the outside world that their health was relatively good. Nevertheless, the threat of a smallpox outbreak at one point forced Tilton to quarantine the school, and on another occasion an influenza epidemic sickened fifty children. Not until 1903, when a small boy perished

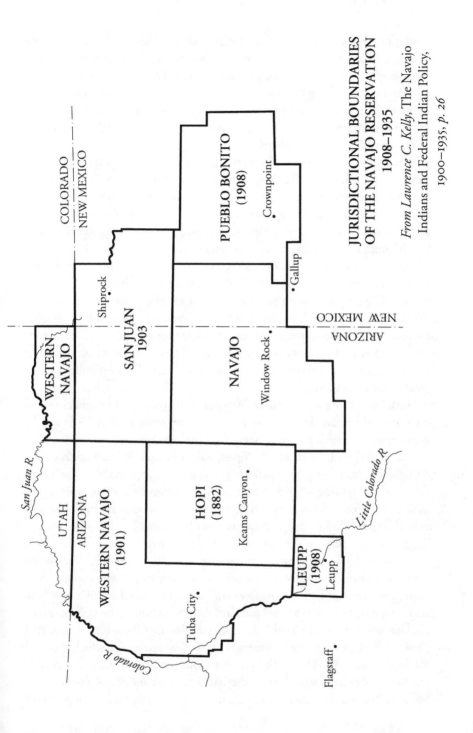

JURISDICTIONAL BOUNDARIES
OF THE NAVAJO RESERVATION
1908–1935

*From Lawrence C. Kelly, The Navajo
Indians and Federal Indian Policy,*
1900–1935, *p. 26*

from pneumonia, did the school suffer a death. Despite a relatively light caseload, living conditions in the community were so primitive that government employees seldom stayed for long. In Dr. Tilton's case, he lasted little more than a year, being replaced by Dr. Charles W. Newton (at a salary of one thousand dollars per year), who soon resigned to be replaced by another doctor.[24] This turnover rate, typical in remote locations, prevented any beneficial exchange with the local residents.

Beyond the arrival of new physicians, however, little changed. A 1905 report authored by Dr. Albert M. Wigglesworth, the physician at Fort Defiance, summed up conditions among the Navajo. Acknowledging that scattered settlement patterns made Navajo families resistant to certain diseases, he nevertheless found much suffering, especially among the elderly. Venereal diseases had become rare, but eye problems seemed to be everywhere. Tuberculosis, while not yet prevalent, was clearly on the increase "and is always fatal when the lungs or meninges are involved." Recognizing the danger posed by tuberculosis, Wigglesworth asked for the construction of a sanatorium so that patients could be isolated. In contrast to the scarcity of government medical facilities, Wigglesworth remarked that "medicine men are plentiful and largely patronized as a matter of religious fanaticism." The physician explained that he could not compete with traditional medicine because of poor supplies and the great distances involved.[25]

Notwithstanding the obstacles, Wigglesworth proved to be an active and interested physician. In addition to his regular work at Fort Defiance, he became involved with the Good Shepherd hospital, donating time and services as well as soliciting funds for the Episcopalian facility. When such activities raised questions among his superiors (at one point it appeared that the Indian Office would bar the physician from using government time to work at the hospital), Commissioner Leupp acknowledged the value of his work and permitted it to continue. Leupp's decision made considerable sense, since most of Wigglesworth's effort at the hospital focused on trachoma. Indeed, the physician molded the facility into something of an eye clinic by sending all trachoma patients appearing at his office directly to the hospital, where, using a technique pioneered in Japan, Wigglesworth surgically treated enough people to acquire the reputation as an eye specialist. Administrators at the Episcopal hospital became so pleased with this development that they began to advertise that facility as a "pioneer in eye treatment." Furthering this image, which was used for fund-raising, Wigglesworth himself announced in 1912: "The Hospital of the Good Shepherd still leads in the Medical work on the Navajo reservation. . . . Apparently these poor savages never dreamed that there was any relief from their misery. They accepted blindness as something inevitable. The idea of restoration of sight [now] is spreading all over the reservation."[26] As events would soon demonstrate, however, this picture proved overly optimistic.

Indeed, well before Wigglesworth issued the above statement trachoma cases had overwhelmed agency capacity. On a few occasions agency personnel agreed to send special cases to outside doctors. In 1906, for example, Navajo Agency Superintendent Reuben Perry made arrangements to send the Navajo employee of a white man (who had already spent one hundred dollars of his own money to treat the man's eye problem) to Albuquerque at government expense because Wigglesworth could not handle the case. To ease costs, Perry arranged for the Albuquerque Indian School to house and feed the man while he was treated by a private physician.[27] This special treatment appears to have been authorized as a favor to the white employer. Clearly, the general Navajo population did not qualify for such expensive procedures and had to depend on availability of government help on the reservation.

HEALERS

Opposition to traditional healing increased along with the number of government physicians. With additional medical personnel coming into contact with the Navajo, government officials reported a growing number of incidents related to native medical practices. Almost every government employee admitted that traditional healing activities remained as common as ever. As a consequence, agency superintendents launched an informal campaign to stamp out "medicine men." This became evident in 1906, when the acting superintendent at the Navajo agency, Samuel B. Daire, attempted to suppress any ceremony that appeared harmful. He took this action after becoming outraged when a Navajo man, who reportedly had been told by a healer that he was under the influence of a witch, committed suicide at Ramah, New Mexico. Daire wrote to a local trader that "I am very anxious to [arrest] this medicine man, because I believe that he is the seat of the trouble in your neighborhood," expressing regret that the healer had not been the one killed.[28]

Three years later Superintendent Peter Paquette made it quite clear that he intended to destroy the influence of healers. Admitting that it was "one of their oldest and deepest established customs" and not wanting to be "harsh," he nevertheless pulled out all stops, even to the extent of encouraging Navajos to inform on those who conducted healing ceremonies. Writing to an employee of the Rehoboth Mission near Gallup, Paquette stated that "I intend to stop the practice of Medicine Men on this reservation and hope to cause the prevalence of 'Sings' to diminish considerably in the future. I hope to bring this about by a slow, persistent yet firm attitude of opposition to it and you may inform your man [a local healer] that if he continues his operations as a medicine man and I hear of a case where he has caused undue suffering to anyone thereby I will have him brought here at the Fort for punishment." Although Paquette hoped to make his quest a "bloodless battle," he expressed no hesitation at jailing offenders. "Victory must be *ours*," he emphasized.[29]

This negative attitude failed to produce the hoped for results. Navajos continued to rely on tradition and to avoid white doctors. Healers offered a comfort and knowledge of native ailments that could not be replicated by white doctors. Indeed, given their cultural traditions, it was impossible to view diseases such as tuberculosis with scientific distance. The Diné had no words for "germ" or "bacteria." Traditional custom held that the disease came from lightning. Thus if a person used firewood from a tree hit by lightning or if something went wrong with a chant, problems with the throat and lungs would result. Treatment therefore consisted of prayers, chants, and inhaling the smoke of special herbs.[30] Despite the efforts of government doctors to discredit these ideas, western treatments seemed impersonal, unnecessary, painful, and ineffective. Nonetheless, government officials refused to accept the value of native healing, and they seldom did anything to inform patients about what they were doing. White medicine thus remained a mystery to most Navajos.

Despite minimal success in discouraging native medical practices, reservation officials kept up the pressure, frequently blaming their own lack of progress on native custom. The superintendent at Leupp wrote in 1910 that "Indian Medicine men" exploited and controlled the tribe; "they squeeze their fees from them and keep them under superstition." It thus remained difficult, he wrote, to get them to accept treatment from white doctors. Even the argument that western medical services were free met with rejection as some Navajos responded that "the white man's medicine is no good, because he doesn't charge for it." At Western Navajo Agency, Superintendent Clarence R. Jefferies described the Navajo as a primitive people. "They are very superstitious," he wrote, "and still adhere to many of their old customs." In 1911 he acknowledged that the Diné continued to conduct a large number of dances and sings, universally believed in witchcraft, and invariably relied upon "medicine men" in cases of serious illness. Another superintendent believed that communal ceremonies tended to spread contagious disease.[31] Such activities frustrated Indian Service employees, who were aware that they could make little headway until the federal government committed more resources to their effort.

HOSPITALS IN NAVAJOLAND

By 1910 medical conditions in Navajo country bordered on chaos, with disease spreading at an quickening rate. Navajo Agency Superintendent Paquette reported that tuberculosis now made up half of all medical problems, and that 30 percent of the tribal population was afflicted by trachoma. To federal observers, Indian disregard for hygiene seemed to be the cause of most problems. Although traditional hogans were well ventilated, conditions inside caused considerable concern: Earthen floors absorbed infection from expectoration, "their blankets and beds while daily aired are never washed and must serve as a source of infection, reeking as they are with body contamination." Joseph Maxwell at Leupp seconded this opinion. Despite the fact that tuberculosis had yet to become epidemic in his area of responsibility, Maxwell nevertheless remarked that Navajo homes were always in an unsanitary condition. The only redeeming feature of this lifestyle, he wrote, "is that they frequently move about . . . leaving nature to purify the ground that has been vacated." Unfortunately, Maxwell concluded, little could be done to improve reservation living conditions.[32]

Effective delivery of medical services appeared stymied at every turn, and superintendents flooded the Indian Office with complaints. Understaffing and lack of resources headed almost every list. At Leupp, where the physician had to cover nine hundred square miles of reservation, the superintendent reported: "It is needless for me to say that one physician, . . . could thoroughly cover this great territory. It is impossible for any one man to do so. Had the Indians confidence in the doctor, they could convey their sick to some central point—as they have no confidence in him, he has to seek them wherever they may be." From Fort Defiance, Paquette remarked that his physician could barely deal with the agency boarding school and the Episcopal hospital: "No pretense is made to answer calls to the Indian homes unless very near or that it is very sure the case is an emergency one. A great loss of confidence and distinct gain for the Medicine Man is thus affected." Jefferies at Tuba City lamented that the reservation was so large that his physician could not cover the ground, thus producing very unsatisfactory results. In many instances the doctor never saw his patients, making a diagnosis from information supplied by relatives. "All instructions as to treatment are verbal," he noted, "and it is exceedingly doubtful whether these are carried out."[33]

Another obvious problem involved government parsimony. Because a physician's salary averaged one thousand dollars per year, agency and school doctors were continually moving from one location to another, looking for greener pastures. As one official noted, the salary "is just about enough for a man with a family to exist on. The Government seems to think more of the care of stock than it does of the care of the Indians, since the least it pays to a veterinary in the Agriculture Department is $1400 per annum." During a two-year span at Leupp, for example, four different physicians came and went, with none of them becoming well-enough acquainted with the Indians to foster any confidence. Just about every field official asked for more doctors. They also stressed the need for hospitals. For a successful campaign against trachoma, wrote one man, "it will be necessary to provide a hospital, where they can be taken in and cared for—where the conditions will be such that the disease may be handled."[34]

Faced with persistent complaints about the lack of medical resources, Congress finally appropriated forty thousand dollars for Indian health services during the 1911 fiscal year. This proved to be the first significant appropriation for general Indian health and it became a permanent feature of Indian policy. When added to other available funds, it gave a needed boost to health-related services. An undetermined amount of this money reached the Navajo agencies, prompting at least one superintendent to request additional staff. In October 1911 Navajo Agency Superintendent Paquette asked for two physicians and an equal number of nurses to relieve the suffering of his wards. By this time, construction on a school hospital at Fort Defiance had also commenced, although Paquette did not have the funds to hire a staff. Nevertheless, the superintendent was so optimistic that he urged the construction of a general hospital at the agency to care for the increasing number of adult cases. He noted that "the Indians are practically demanding a place where they can leave their sick for our treatment."[35]

With funding now available, a small-scale building program began on the reservation. At Leupp and Tuba City the government constructed small school hospitals, each with a capacity of eight beds. Both were in operation by 1912, along with a twelve-bed facility at Shiprock. That same year the school hospital at Fort Defiance opened for business. Built on a much larger scale, the well-constructed frame building could care for forty patients. But the Indian Service still failed to provide sufficient staffing, causing Paquette to request the services of additional nurses and male attendants. Although the opening of the school hospital significantly helped the situation for schoolchildren, it complicated things in other ways. In particular, adult Navajos began to seek admission to the school hospital. With "the present school nurse . . . unable to care for reservation patients," Paquette declined most such requests. He did, however, ask for the construction of four small frame buildings near the hospital, where he could care for "outside Indians" suffering from diseases such as tuberculosis. He also requested more physicians, observing that "at the present time, . . .

physicians have little or no time to visit camps or otherwise gain a practice among reservation Indians."[36]

Funding for additional medical facilities at Fort Defiance soon increased, undoubtedly prompted by the 1912 congressionally funded survey of reservation disease conditions, which discovered significant rates of tuberculosis and trachoma. Responding to this unfavorable report, Congress enhanced the now annual appropriation for Indian health services to 300,000 dollars in 1915.[37]

One of the federal priorities for this new money involved the construction of tuberculosis sanatoriums, and in 1914 the Indian Office approved the construction of a sanatorium at Fort Defiance to care for the general reservation population. Superintendent Paquette confidently predicted that when completed, the twenty-bed facility would enable him to isolate adult tuberculosis cases from the schoolchildren, keeping them out of danger of infection. The Navajo Agency Sanatorium opened in late 1915, becoming the only Indian tuberculosis hospital in the Southwest between Phoenix and Laguna. As usual, insufficient funds kept the sanatorium from being fully staffed. Nonetheless, the facility represented a major advance in medical care on the Navajo reservation. And indeed, it appeared that more Navajos were willing to utilize government medical services at Fort Defiance. Paquette attributed the advance in medical work to the new facilities and to the dedication of Dr. Wigglesworth, whose long stint as agency physician seemed to be winning the confidence of tribal leaders. "Indians now come for treatment voluntarily who heretofore would not have come except by force," he commented. "It is no uncommon feature to have patients brought in voluntarily to the hospitals from distances up to 100 miles." This sentiment was seconded by Navajo Frank Mitchell, who called Wigglesworth "the first good doctor the people ever had."[38]

Even with a school hospital and sanatorium, medical problems at the Navajo agency in the years just prior to World War I remained overwhelming. Epidemics of childhood diseases such as diphtheria continually erupted at the schools, primarily because the pupils came into constant contact with "camp" Indians. As one observer noted, "Too little attention is paid to epidemics among the camp Indians and epidemics sweep unchecked from one side of the reservation to the other, causing great loss of life among children." Authorities continued to blame the widespread existence of these diseases on a lack of hygiene in Navajo dwellings. The Indian Office reflected these concerns when it launched a national campaign to reduce the high infant mortality rates in 1915. Called "Save the Babies" by Indian Commissioner Cato Sells (1913–1921), this crusade developed in response to statistics indicating that nearly three-fifths of Indian infants nationwide perished before age five. Noting that we cannot "solve the Indian problem without Indians," Sells ordered agency personnel to improve reservation sanitary and nutritional standards in all ways possible. He also ordered that every hospital bed not required for disease or injury be made available for mothers in childbirth.[39]

Attempts to put this ambitious program into effect among the Navajo were frustrated by personnel, financial, and logistical problems. Although Superintendent Paquette maintained that "Navajo mothers more and more are realizing the necessity of hospitals," he admitted that his hospitals contained little room for expectant mothers. Another aspect of this program involved field matrons, who were expected to make sure that pregnant women were properly provisioned, well fed, and prepared medically for birth. Field matrons at the Navajo agency, however, seldom accomplished these functions. The position was often left vacant as matrons transferred or resigned because living and working conditions proved intolerable. Since "it takes a field matron sometime to become acquainted with and obtain the confidence of the Navajos in her section," Paquette noted, their effectiveness was quite limited. In addition, the matrons, hampered by the migratory nature of Navajo life, regularly lost track of their clients.[40] As a result, very few Navajo women were helped by this well-meaning government program.

Trachoma also continued to present problems, despite an Indian Office announcement in 1916 that eye disease among schoolchildren would soon be solved. This optimistic prediction coincided with the dispatch of a group of special ophthalmologists to the reservations. Among the Navajo, government physician George O. Keck surgically treated schoolchildren whenever possible, but soon realized that the only thing he could do for adults was to refer them to the Episcopal hospital, which was already overflowing with eye cases. Faced with the situation, and a lack of general hospital space, in early 1916 the school hospital at Fort Defiance began admitting the general Navajo population. Even this proved to be insufficient. Moreover, appropriations for the two medical facilities at Fort Defiance did not keep up with needs, preventing any expansion.[41]

BACIL WARREN COMES TO THE NAVAJO

Although the medical capabilities at Fort Defiance grew rapidly after 1911, facilities at the smaller subagencies failed to keep pace. Nonetheless, by the time war broke out in Europe physicians of higher caliber were beginning to fill positions with the Indian Service. This fact can be observed at the little medical outpost at Leupp, which had been plagued by a high turnover rate since its creation in 1908. Located in the extreme southwestern corner of the reservation, in 1914 the subagency consisted of a cluster of government buildings, including a hospital, school, laundry, mess hall, and employee cottages. Isolated by poor roads, the nearest rail connection lay some fourteen miles distant, while travel to the closest town of any consequence, Winslow, required a day's buggy ride. A solitary government doctor, serving both the school and the eight-bed hospital, provided medical services at Leupp. Largely confined to the agency, he seldom managed to get into the field. The rare occasions when he could get out, however, appeared to be worthwhile. In 1910, for instance, the physician spent three weeks in the camps, where he discovered, among other things, that personal visits did much to overcome Navajo reluctance to seek medical attention. Indeed, "many of his patients in the camps later sought him out at the hospital for further attention."[42] Unfortunately, few doctors stayed at Leupp long enough to take advantage of this situation and medical care languished.

A degree of medical stability arrived at Leupp in April 1914, when Dr. Bacil A. Warren assumed the duties of school and agency physician, beginning a stay that lasted for three years. Warren's experience was not unlike that of many doctors in the Indian Service at the time. Born on May 6, 1873, in Hexton, Wisconsin, Warren grew up with the desire to become a medical doctor. He fulfilled this goal in 1902 by graduating from Chicago's Rush Medical College. Shortly thereafter he married Adell Norman, a trained nurse who had worked for the Indian Service at Albuquerque and in Oneida, Wisconsin. Although the young doctor entered private practice at Merrill, Wisconsin, he and his wife almost immediately sought employment with the Indian Service. As he explained in November 1903, "My wife and I are desirous of getting a position where she can have charge of a Hospital and, preferably where I can have the privilege of doing outside practice besides the school work." Nothing came of the application, however, and for the next decade the Warrens moved around, living in Colorado and Wyoming, practicing medicine and operating a drugstore. Criticized by their family for not settling down, and perhaps not doing well financially, Bacil and Adell applied to the Indian Service again in 1912. This time they were offered jobs. Unfortunately, Adell was detailed to the Yuma, Arizona, Indian Hospital, while Bacil received an appointment to the Kiowa school at Rainy Mountain, Oklahoma. Soon thereafter, Adell transferred to Rainy Mountain; then, in the spring of 1914, the couple was assigned to Leupp.[43]

Bacil found medical conditions at the subagency to be mixed. Tuberculosis remained rare at the remote location, but trachoma presented a major problem. Superintendent Charles Dickson estimated in 1914 that this disease had become extremely serious in his area, with perhaps as many as 50 percent of the Indians being affected. Not long after Warren's arrival, an epidemic of measles, chicken pox, and smallpox swept the school. After successfully quelling this outbreak, the physician described conditions at his small facility. We have, he reported, "a nice little Hospital (two wards of four beds each, Nurses room, kitchen, drug room) which is modern in the way of baths and toilets, hot and cold water, acetylene gas lights, etc. and is pretty well equipped with surgical chair, microscope, instruments, etc." Nevertheless, the hospital seemed totally unsuited for dealing with a major epidemic, and Warren strongly suggested the construction of a hospital addition equal in size to the current building. He also recognized the need to find more time to work among the adult population, which, if successful, would prompt more Navajos to come in for "surgical operations, eye treatment and other treatment," thereby placing additional demands on the hospital. Superintendent Stephen Janus, who endorsed an expansion of the hospital, applauded Warren's "energetic" action.[44]

Although the Indian Office ignored this suggestion, Warren worked hard to enhance his medical skills and improve living conditions. In general the family liked "it very much here at Leupp." They got along well with the Navajo people and adopted a number of their ways. Adell regularly made "Navajo Bread," the family listened to Indian stories, and the birth of their first son, Bacil B., drew considerable local interest, although some Navajo women expressed disappointment that the baby was not placed in a traditional cradle board. Meanwhile, the Warrens attempted to retain as much of their home lifestyle as possible. Older daughter Mary was permitted to keep pet rabbits, goats, and a canary; family outings occurred regularly (including a trip to the Pan Pacific Exposition in San Francisco); and friends and relatives visited often. Bacil enlivened the little cluster of government employees by organizing regular meetings and supporting their literary society as "a splendid addition to the social life of this little community." He also sought permission to open an employee's reading room, where people might pool their magazine and newspaper subscriptions as well as peruse materials obtained from the Arizona State Travelling Library. Despite this homelike environment, the Warrens worried about the isolation. In particular, as Mary reached high school age, Bacil pondered moving to a "good size" town in order to find a proper school. In the end, Mary attended school in Flagstaff, not only because of the school problem but also because, as she later recalled, "my parents thought it important for me to go because there was so much trachoma among the Navajos."[45]

Indeed, the prevalence of trachoma figured prominently in Dr. Warren's effort to improve his professional skills. During his years in private practice he had gained some knowledge of the disease, but quickly found himself overwhelmed by the Navajo situation. Desiring to "make myself as indispensable as possible," in the summer of 1914 Warren traveled to Los Angeles for a postgraduate course on eye diseases. With this knowledge, he felt more comfortable about treating trachoma. During 1915 and 1916 Warren regularly treated eye cases both at the hospital and at the small mission school at Tolchaco. When the Indian Office sought advice from field physicians about substituting cheaper drugs for the one commonly used to treat trachoma, Warren responded with a learned analysis of the benefits of drug therapy.[46]

Warren kept himself informed about the activities of other Indian Service doctors through correspondence. In addition to becoming "pretty well acquainted" with Medical Director Joseph A. Murphy, he frequently wrote to Dr. Wigglesworth at Fort Defiance and other physician friends. Nonetheless, he felt professionally isolated. He wrote to Dr. A. J. Wheeler in Washington, D.C., in September 1916: "You have been around the Indian Service enough to know how isolated many of the physicians are. It is seldom that I have a chance to meet another Indian Service physician or any other physician for that matter so I try to make letters, to some extent, take the place of personal meetings." Hoping to improve this condition, Warren expressed the hope that Wheeler might persuade the Indian Office to authorize general medical meetings once or twice a year: "It seems to me . . . that we doctors in the Indian Service should hang together and help each other all we can."[47]

Warren's relationship with his Indian patients appears to have been good. In 1915 he acknowledged that some "of the medicine men know a few very good remedies and treatments and I never was too old to learn and am not yet and I often let a medicine man assist me in the treatment of a case and give credit where credit is due." Although he liked the Navajos and acknowledged their healers, it is also clear that he made little effort to understand the Indian point of view. He regarded traditional medicine as "about a thousand years behind the modern physician in medicine, surgery, sanitation and hygiene." Recognizing that "results count" with the Indians, he believed that most native ceremonies were futile when compared to the methods of white doctors. This fact, more than anything else, would eventually succeed in winning the Indian over.[48]

In Warren's opinion, the greatest obstacle to reaching the Indians with modern techniques involved a lack of medical resources and satisfactory salaries. For this reason, he continually requested the expansion of his small hospital: "We want to make our facilities equal to the actual demands in view and then go out, reach out, extend and organize the medical department of Leupp School and Agency so that it will be of the greatest service to the Indians." If these services could be provided, he argued, Indians would flock to him for care and would not have to be turned away because of a lack of resources. Salaries also needed improvement. Warren's annual wage of 1,250 dollars, plus the 720 dollars earned by Adell barely sufficed at Leupp, where the remote location kept the cost of living extremely high. He regretted not having enough money to attend professional conferences, and at one point even considered taking a job as traveling physician if it would pay better.[49] Unfortunately, the Indian Office never possessed enough resources to respond favorably to Warren's suggestions.

The desire to improve his capacity to serve the Navajo extended throughout Warren's stay on the reservation. A continuing problem involved his persistent inability to reach remote locations. As Janus wrote in 1916, "The weakness here is a common one in my experience in the Service, and is that the work is more in the nature of an 'office practice' than the extensive work contemplated among the Indian homes. No matter how competent[,] one physician could never cover the ground under this jurisdiction and keep posted as to the danger spots. When cases are reported by the Indians they are usually desperate." Both Warren and Janus realized that until the physician could regularly visit the scattered camps, "they will not entrust themselves or those they love to a stranger." As a result, the physician attempted to increase his mobility by asking the government to buy him an inexpensive means of transportation, either a motorcycle with side car or a small three-wheeled car imported from England. Meanwhile, he asked the Indian Office to hire an Indian boy to serve him as an interpreter. Writing to Commissioner Sells in 1917, he remarked that "you can readily understand that an exact diagnosis can not usually be made by the physician without an interpreter and without such diagnosis the matter of treatment becomes largely haphazard guesswork." He also believed that an Indian assistant would permit him to make more effective trips to the camps. Meanwhile, in an effort to stretch resources as far as possible in the face of government frugality, he created an unauthorized hospital "annex" by converting an employee's cottage into a ward for sick boys.[50]

In sum, Warren enjoyed working on the reservation, despite the frustration and hardship. Described by Janus as "entirely competent in every way" despite some physical limitations, he was the first government physician to serve the district well enough to become acquainted with his patients, even though his effectiveness was restricted to the immediate vicinity of the agency offices. By 1917, however, the physician had tired of his circumstances. Criticized by some officials for not doing more to reach the adult population, disheartened by a lack of support, concerned about his daughter's education, and stricken with an unexplained illness (which Warren at first believed to be tuberculosis), the doctor asked for a transfer in March 1917. More than likely, he would have remained with the Indian Service had not the United States gone to war in April 1917. Like many other physicians, Warren volunteered for military service and within a month he was appointed regimental surgeon with the Tenth

Cavalry, then stationed on the Mexican border.[51] Although he retained an interest in Indian affairs, Dr. Warren never returned to the Indian Service.

INADEQUATE CARE

As the United States entered World War I, Indian Service employees on the Navajo reservation could express some satisfaction with the improvement of medical facilities. Four facilities now provided a total of seventy-six federal hospital beds. During the fiscal year ending June 30, 1917, these facilities served a total of 589 patients. Five or six physicians were stationed around the reservation, supported by nurses and field matrons. This looked impressive on paper. Indeed, in 1916 the Indian Office boasted that the "widespread prevalence of tuberculosis and trachoma" had engendered "vigorous efforts" to meet reservation health needs. As a result, the Indian Service had increased the number of hospital beds nationally from 1,256 in 1912 to 2,045 in 1915. Moreover, "substantial increases have also been made in the number of field matrons and nurses." As a consequence of such advances, outside observers often predicted that "the Indian is turning more and more to the white man's physician and his medicine, and the day of the Indian medicine man is rapidly passing on every reservation."[52]

Close scrutiny of the medical situation among the Navajo presents a different picture. Tuberculosis and trachoma remained unchecked, hospitals were inadequate and underfunded, and employees' living conditions remained primitive. Although government doctors were now able to service school-children and hospital patients, it remained impossible to effectively reach the general population. As one superintendent wrote, "No steps can be taken for reservation Indians or children not eligible for schools under present conditions and with present facilities." Given these circumstances, efforts like the "Save the Babies" campaign could not get on track and healers continued to work their skills in defiance of government wishes. In reality, traditional medical practices remained as common as ever. Superintendent Paquette at Fort Defiance succinctly summarized the situation by noting that "nearly all Navajo dances are for the ill and as a sufficient number of physicians are not yet provided to take care of the over 12,000 Navajos on this jurisdiction they revert to the medicine man and dances for relief."[53] Even if more physicians had been available, a scourge existed on the land, and in the years following World War I disease problems would explode among the Navajo, overwhelming all forms of medical care. As Dr. Warren had predicted, government facilities would prove inadequate in an emergency.

CHAPTER SEVEN

EPIDEMICS, CAMPAIGNS, AND EXPERIMENTATION

At the beginning there were no doctors, so we depended on the singers to cure these sicknesses. The government had first-aid stations out here with emergency medicine. There was no transportation, no x-rays, hospitals, doctors or medicine. We just had one-, two- or five-night ceremonies, one- or two-hour sandpaintings. The singers would go according to the hand-trembler's advice.

FRANK MITCHELL, NAVAJO

There will be organized July 1, 1924, or as soon thereafter as practicable, under the medical direction of Dr. J. S. Perkins, special physician in charge of the district of Arizona and New Mexico, a campaign against trachoma among the Indians of these States, to be known as the "Southwestern Trachoma Campaign."

CHARLES H. BURKE, COMMISSIONER

American participation in World War I caused medical services on the Navajo reservation to break down. Doctors and nurses, responding to the patriotic call of their country, volunteered for national service, seriously depleting medical staffing in the Indian country. In addition, although congressional appropriations remained stable between 1917 and 1919, wartime demands "greatly increased prices of all supplies, particularly medicines, drugs, and surgical instruments." These circumstances set back government medical efforts among the Navajo to such a degree that even the limited program of treating school-children for trachoma collapsed.[1] Many locations went without doctors for months on end and nurses were almost impossible to find. Those people available for service sometimes made poor replacements for the more qualified men and women serving with the armed forces. This was followed by a period of postwar financial retrenchment, which prevented the Indian Service from making a rapid recovery. During these hard times medical disasters overwhelmed the reservation population, increasing death and suffering among the Navajo people.

Some measure of the problem caused by wartime cutbacks could be seen in connection with a 1917 outbreak of smallpox in Navajo country. Because of a lack of physicians, caused partly by "the demand of the War Department," no one detected the infection until it had spread widely. Fortunately, the Navajo had long accepted the value of vaccinations, although as Commissioner Sells put it, "like many white people they are likely to wait until danger is present before protecting themselves." Once the extent of the disease became known, the Indian Office dispatched its chief medical supervisor to deal personally with the problem. Within a short period of time, government employees were busy vaccinating the Diné. In the Marsh Pass District (Kayenta), where "nearly every unvaccinated Indian has had the disease," almost eight hundred vaccinations were given. This rather heroic effort saved the day, but it was aided by some favorable circumstances: Navajo willingness to be vaccinated, the fact that many were immune because of prior inoculations, and the mild form of the disease. As a consequence, relatively few deaths from smallpox were reported.[2] Other disease would not prove to be so easy to contain.

Trachoma and tuberculosis continued to present serious problems. Although the superintendents tended to downplay these diseases in their yearly reports—usually claiming that general health was good—they clearly represented great concern. Not only did officials acknowledge this in their persistent requests for more doctors, nurses, and hospitals; it also showed up in such comments as "tuberculosis and trachoma prevail as heretofore" and "there were several [tuberculosis] deaths from this dread disease." Trachoma control became a casualty of war when the program of sending special doctors into the field to perform grattage procedures or to train agency doctors had to be curtailed for lack of manpower. When special physician George O. Keck visited the Navajo reservation in early 1917, he remarked that "altho they have been fighting trachoma on this reservation a great many years, there is lots of it left and no doubt it will take a long time to stamp it out." A year later the Chinle boarding school reported that half its students were infected with trachoma.[3]

Constant appeals for more staff and improved medical facilities illustrated the deteriorating medical conditions. During the war only one hospital, a forty-bed structure at Shiprock, was authorized. Completed in 1918, it was dogged with problems: first a kitchen fire, then a heating system failure. As a consequence, the facility did not become fully operational until late 1919. Meanwhile, superintendents argued that the only way to improve medical conditions was to open additional hospitals and hire more doctors. For the San Juan Agency, the superintendent asked for small hospitals at Tocito and Aneth and two doctors to supplement the pair currently stationed at Shiprock and Toadlena. From Western Navajo Agency came a similar plea for physicians: "To expect that one physician could anywhere near take care of the medical needs of this jurisdiction, is out of the question. There should be authorized at an early date, at the very least the allowance of one or two additional physicians to be located at points in the northern part of the jurisdiction, where our Indians are so isolated and live so far distant from the agency headquarters." As things then stood, some schoolchildren were over seventy-five miles from a physician, and adults could be even more isolated. Superintendent Paquette at Fort Defiance also remarked on the urgent need to provide medical care, suggesting it would be necessary to build more hospitals and hire "better paid physicians and nurses so it would make it worth while for them to remain in isolated places."[4]

Retaining the services of existing physicians proved equally distressing. For several months during 1918 no permanent doctor resided at Fort Defiance. At Shiprock, with two authorized doctors, things changed rapidly in early 1918, when the local missionary physician, who had been helping out, joined the army, leaving his responsibilities to the government staff. A month later, one of the government doctors was transferred, leaving only Dr. Walter K. Callahan to handle all medical responsibilities. Although he performed "more work than most army surgeons," he could not keep up with demand for his services, despite using a horse or automobile to visit sick reservation residents over a hundred miles distant.[5] Under such circumstances, few hoped for much improvement until the war's end.

In only one area did the superintendent's decline help. To a man, they argued against the use of field matrons. Superintendent Walter Runke summed up the general attitude when he wrote: "So far as providing Field Matrons for work among the Navajos of this Jurisdiction, I consider it as yet impracticable. These Navajo homes are scattered so far and wide that the expense involved in reaching them would be more than excessive." Paquette believed that the position should be abolished, while the superintendent at San Juan regarded them of little use. Instead, he suggested the employment of "two or three mature women who are trained nurses who would be willing to act as field matrons and treat women and children in the out-of-the-way places where the physicians do not reach."[6]

None of the requests to improve health-care capacity in the Navajo country were realized. During the war (and well afterward) government health officers were obliged to make do with what they could beg, borrow, or steal. The most they could offer were vaccinations, the treatment of miscellaneous outbreaks of measles and diphtheria, distribution of common medicines, advice on sanitation, and supervision of the vital but limited work being done at hospitals and schools.

Meanwhile, Navajo healers continued the practice of traditional medicine.

Official reports indicated that healing ceremonies remained as popular as ever. Rituals, attended by all elements of the tribal population including returned school students who were supposedly "civilized," occurred on every part of the reservation. The Squaw Dance (to cure maladies caused by ghosts or enemies) and the Yeibichai Dance (held to cure eye, ear, and other head ailments, as well as rheumatism and arthritis) seemed to be regular events. The Yeibichai, in particular, was quite elaborate, requiring up to nine days. With the prevalence of trachoma, some healers specialized in this ailment. One man, who never took more than three patients at a time, was said to perform the Yeibichai Dance solely for this purpose. All of these rituals required financial support. "Medicine men" were in great demand and they charged for their services, which seemed entirely appropriate to the Diné. Frank Mitchell recalled that his family "went through many expenses having ceremonies for those with tuberculosis. At the beginning there were no doctors, so we depended on the singers to cure these sicknesses. . . . If the sickness lasted a long time, of course, we had to have long ceremonials. These were expensive. But you have to do something with your mother and relatives dying right there in front of you. If you have anything to pay the singer with, you do not consider the value of them; you just do it."[7]

Most white observers described the "sings" as elaborate and intricate affairs that attracted great crowds. Although government officials denigrated traditional medicine as a waste of time and money, which ruined families and kept old superstitions alive, they also realized that the rituals could not be ended without the use of force or a more effective replacement, neither of which seemed to be forthcoming. A few of the more perceptive observers reluctantly acknowledged that Navajo ceremonials were a sincere attempt to "heal the sick."[8]

THE FLU EPIDEMIC

During the fall of 1918, as the conflict in Europe neared a conclusion, a pandemic of Spanish influenza swept over the United States, killing people by the tens of thousands. Imported from Europe, the disease struck every element of the population. Not ordinarily considered a fatal illness, the Spanish strain became particularly virulent as it spread rapidly through human contact. Often called "the Flu" or "the Three-Day Fever" it struck quickly, causing weakness, soreness, and a high fever. The disease usually ran its course in three to four days, with the patient either recovering or suffering complications. Most deaths were actually caused by the onset of pneumonia, which proved to be the real killer.[9]

The epidemic advanced across the country from east to west during September and October. In cities such as Boston, New York, and Chicago so many people perished that burial services could not keep pace. Hospitals and clinics filled to overflowing as the U.S. Public Health Service sought in vain to cope with the disease. Although death rates in rural areas may have been somewhat lower, the hinterland did not escape the plague. Indian reservations proved no exception. Mortality rates, of course, depended on location, but on the whole it was estimated that over 9 percent of the reservation population died.[10] With neither the government nor traditional medicine prepared for the devastation, the Navajo would suffer significantly.

Influenza entered the Navajo country about the first of October, reaching epidemic proportions by mid-month. The exact source is unknown, but railroad communities along the southern edge of the reservation (Gallup, Holbrook, Winslow, and Flagstaff) all suffered major outbreaks around the same time. Winslow, for example, reported some six hundred flu cases on October 9.[11] The disease seems to have hit many reservation communities at once, although specific dates are difficult to ascertain. What is clear, however, is that a number of circumstances combined to produce a significant death toll among the Navajo. In the first place, government facilities could not cope with the demand and were completely overwhelmed. Additionally, medical service personnel were also taken ill, putting many of them out of action at the height of the epidemic. Navajo healers suffered from the same problems, as they too were overrun with illness. Fear of the dead also played a major role, as the Diné fled from outbreak sites, carrying the disease with them as they moved into the backcountry. In some cases so many family members were infected that no one could care for the sick. Many thus perished from pneumonia or starvation. Conditions became so overwhelming that by October 11, Commissioner Sells wired all agents about the importance of preventing the development of pneumonia.[12] Unfortunately, few opportunities existed in the Navajo country to implement these precautions.

Tales of heroism and tragedy came from everywhere, as government employees attempted to combat the epidemic. One of the most complete accounts of events came from Albert B. Reagan, who arrived at Tuba City to take charge of the Marsh Pass boarding school just as the epidemic broke out. Although a number of government employees were ill, no one suspected a serious problem as Reagan departed for Kayenta. On October 18, he was called back to Tuba City because almost all the employees were prostrate: "Indian

Agent Walter Runke was not expected to live [he did survive]; Mrs. Butler, the Missionary's wife, was dying, . . . and 59 Indian boys and 79 Indian girls at the school were down." With no one to provide routine cleaning, sanitary conditions quickly deteriorated. Fortunately, neither Reagan, his wife, nor agency physician N. O. Reynolds became ill. Nevertheless, they could do little, despite working day and night. By October 22, 250 schoolchildren were sick and 2 girls died. Fearing that the pupils would "stampede" if the deaths became known, the corpses were carried out of the dormitory at night and buried "with lights darkened so the other pupils could not see what we were doing." Happily, the school epidemic ended as quickly as it began, with no additional deaths.[13]

Such was not the case in outlying areas. As soon as the disease broke out in their camps, many Navajos took to the hills: they "all fled toward Navajo mountain and Black mesa with their flocks." This spread the highly contagious disease into the backcountry, which had traditionally provided them with some measure of protection. In all, an estimated 4,000 of the 6,360 Indians residing in the Western Navajo jurisdiction contracted the disease, resulting in about 200 deaths. To combat the flu, the Indian Office dispatched Dr. Grady Shytles, a special physician, to visit the camps. He was joined by a number of nurses sent out from Flagstaff. One missionary nurse "went on horseback for days to the hogans, carrying dressings, comfort, medicines, and sympathy."[14]

To get closer to the problem, Reagan returned to Marsh Pass school in early November, accompanied by Doctors Reynolds and Shytles. They quickly converted the school into a hospital, which immediately filled to overflowing. Meanwhile, Navajos perished at an alarming rate. Reagan recounted many terrible events: sick family members left to die of starvation; whole families wiped out; a group of families living together all perishing except for a boy out tending sheep. In one instance, a family was overtaken by the disease while gathering piñon nuts and all were found dead near their wagon. Similar stories abounded. Most of the dead were simply abandoned unburied or covered with a few scoops of dirt. "The Indians were so terribly afraid of the dead, or so weakened by disease themselves, that they fled from the 'death hogan,' begging the whites to bury their dead," the schoolteacher remarked as he listed by name over seventy Navajos who perished within a twenty-five mile radius of Marsh Pass.[15]

Despite the unusual willingness of ill Navajos to come to the temporary hospital at Marsh Pass, they remained wary of western medicine. This presented problems for the medical staff, especially when a patient died. As Reagan told it, pandemonium erupted when the first person died: "With wild eyes they started to leave 'the place of the dead'; even a sick man who could scarcely hold his head up the evening before was out of bed, trembling from head to foot." When a local healer predicted that anyone staying at the hospital would die, all the patients left. It required great persuasion to convince most patients to return. To prevent a repetition, the doctors began the practice of placing terminal patients in a separate building and burying the dead at night. In all, nine people died at the old school building.[16]

The epidemic proved to be even more deadly on the eastern side of the reservation. At Fort Defiance, the disease appeared on October 2, when an infected Navajo laborer returning from Zuni mixed with the schoolchildren. Ten days later 250 pupils and 20 employees were down with influenza. By the eighteenth, hospital and school dormitories were filled with the sick, and 8 pupils, 2 employees, and 4 others had perished. The Indian Office responded by ordering Special Physician Hubert V. Hailman and a number of Public Health Service nurses to Fort Defiance. This was partly offset when the agency physician, Dr. Wigglesworth, contracted the disease, becoming "so severely ill that his life was in the balance a number of days." Even if all the medical personnel had remained healthy, however, the flu could not be contained and it quickly reached the outlying population. Observers recorded that the "epidemic spread very rapidly among the Navajos and in some instances whole families were stricken with the disease and died." Hogans containing dead bodies were discovered, and in one case a stricken man reportedly went crazy, murdering his wife and children before committing suicide. An estimated 780 deaths occurred within the boundaries of the Navajo agency during the epidemic. In addition, some 22 school students perished along with perhaps as many as 45 hospital patients.[17]

Officials at the Pueblo Bonito subagency estimated that half of the local population contracted the disease, with some five hundred perishing (including five school children). From Shiprock came similar stories. Admitting that he did not know how many people died, the superintendent remarked that the disease was brought into his jurisdiction near the first of October by Navajo laborers working on a highway project near Durango, Colorado. As soon as the disease appeared, the Indians fled back to the reservation with disastrous results: "Some died in Durango, some on the road home, and others after they reached home. But they scattered the disease pretty well over the reservation with a resultant heavy death rate." Government services quickly broke down. Dr. Callahan became ill, forcing the superintendent to rely on any physician who could be sent out on temporary duty. In fact, very little could be done, with the temporary doctor limited to handing out aspirin and quinine tablets. Corpses were left where they lay and the unopened Shiprock hospital became a morgue.[18]

The flu also wreaked havoc at Leupp. Despite heroic efforts to quarantine the school, the disease "spread like wildfire," leaving only a couple of government workers on their feet. Quick action by Winslow physician George P. Sampson, however, prevented disaster. Faced with a loss of medical workers, Sampson recruited four local schoolteachers to serve as nurses for the sixty stricken pupils. As a result, only two students died. Nevertheless, conditions on the reservation were terrible. Superintendent Janus lamented that "I could not get medical attendance of any kind for the Indians. With their habits it is doubtful if doctors and medicine would have done much good."[19]

Not all the heroic effort was expended by government personnel. The Navajos themselves also worked to alleviate the epidemic. Much less is known about their activities, but scattered reports indicate that they used both natural and ceremonial remedies. Because they believed that the sick should be fed, patients in some cases were forced to eat large quantities of meat and corn (something whites believed to be detrimental). Horsetail soup was also utilized, as were plant and herbal drinks, and natural fumigants, with some degree of success. From a ceremonial perspective, healers relied heavily on the Yeibichai Dance. Reagan probably missed the point when he observed that "as a faith cure, it is a good remedy, but it failed to cure influenza." Healers did what they could, which was often as much as the whites could offer, and they too worked day and night. Residents at the Black Mountain trading post recalled that the "exhausted medicine men seemed to rest only when they stopped at the store to be warmed and fed." With every one sick, Diné healers were in such demand that needs could not be met. One man seeking help remarked that "I went for a medicine man, and another, and another, many of them, but they were sick themselves or were singing chants for others who had the sickness."[20]

The epidemic ended almost as quickly as it began. By December the disease had passed. Estimates of the death toll were inaccurate at best. Official counts were extremely general and many of those who perished were never recorded. Newspaper accounts that over 2,000 Navajos had died in the vicinity of Fort Defiance, however, caused the Indian Office to send Dr. L. L. Culp to the agency to verify the death toll and determine why it was so high. His report concluded that although the newspaper accounts were exaggerated, the mortality rate was nevertheless extremely high at 1,046, which was caused by the inability to establish an effective quarantine, a lack of medical staff, and inadequate hospital facilities. Overall, the epidemic exacted a heavy price from the Diné. Between 2,100 and 2,500 people perished in the five jurisdictions. Based on a total population of about 28,000, this produced a mortality rate between 7.3 and 8.4 percent, depending on the sources used. By any standard, it proved to be a truly terrible event. As one trader accurately observed, "It was a long time before the Navajo tribe recovered from the disastrous effects of this epidemic."[21]

RETRENCHMENT AND SPECIAL PHYSICIANS

Unfortunately, the devastation created by the influenza epidemic failed to produce any significant improvement in government health care for the Navajo. Postwar appropriations remained flat, and despite the obvious need for more services the Indian Office failed to keep existing positions filled. As a consequence, debilitating disease problems continued unabated. By 1920 the Indian Office fully recognized that tuberculosis and trachoma needed special attention, a fact brought home by statistics compiled that year for all five Navajo jurisdictions. Although the morbidity estimates appear to be very general, they were at least based on the examination of sample groups. The overall results indicated that, with a total reservation population of 28,569, 2,733 (9.5 percent) were estimated to have tuberculosis and 3,480 (12.1 percent) suffered from trachoma. Disease rates, however, varied greatly from area to area. Tuberculosis ranged from a high of 35.2 percent at Leupp to a low of 5.3 percent in the San Juan jurisdiction. Trachoma, on the other hand, varied from 2.3 percent at Western Navajo to 48.1 percent at Pueblo Bonito.[22]

To deal with these problems, the government operated six hospitals for the Navajo: Tuba City (six beds); Leupp (eight beds); Crownpoint (twelve beds, opened May 1920); Shiprock (forty beds, opened November 1919); and Fort Defiance (a forty-bed general hospital and twenty-bed sanatorium). In addition, the government provided some support for the twenty-bed Episcopal hospital at Fort Defiance, which handled all local eye, ear, and throat cases. These facilities ranged in effectiveness from primitive to reasonably modern. Superintendents and doctors regularly asked for more support. At the newly opened Shiprock hospital, Dr. J. C. Graffin reported the lack of an adequate staff, "including a capable and efficient nurse." The Fort Defiance general hospital, clearly the most elaborate reservation facility, contained a surgical arena, laboratory facilities, and even a two-bed maternity ward, all supervised by a hospital matron. A total of nine doctors were assigned to the Navajo country by 1920. In addition to those posted to hospital sites, doctors were quartered at the Toadlena, Chinle, and Tohatchi schools. A number of nurses also served the Navajo. To a degree, working conditions for medical personnel had improved since 1900. Most physicians were supplied with a cottage, complete with running water and indoor plumbing. Only the doctors at Chinle and Tohatchi remained in primitive, one-room quarters. Nurses usually lived at the hospital. Salaries were also slightly improved. The head physician at Fort Defiance received 1,600 dollars per year, while the average doctor's salary remained at 1,200 dollars. Nurses commanded the princely sum of 840 dollars.[23]

Many doctors and nurses broke down under the demanding conditions. Although automobiles were generally available to reach remote locations, the work nevertheless took a heavy toll. With increased pressure to combat disease among the adult population, physicians found themselves responsible for thousands of square miles of rugged territory. Seasonal Navajo movements complicated matters. Dr. George A. McEwan at Toadlena observed that "the Indian here is nomadic [in] nature, due to the fact that he has to change his abode quite frequently on account of water for himself and flock of sheep." As a consequence, unless they resided near the agency, most Navajos did not seek out government medical help unless the situation became serious. Even then, healers frequently advised against calling in the government doctor. Indeed, a common justification for more doctors and hospitals was to "put [the medicine man] out of business."[24]

Government doctors remained frustrated by their lack of influence over the general reservation population. They firmly believed that little could be done to conquer disease until sanitary conditions improved and the Diné understood germ theory. Acknowledging that many Navajo families kept their hogans clean, they nevertheless disapproved of traditional residences. Said one superintendent, "their hogans cannot be improved upon for ventilation, . . . [but] if not properly built there is more or less smoke to contend with which tends to irritate and produce trachoma." Others believed that sanitary conditions were not what they should be, advocating that the Navajo build American-style homes with more doors and windows. Although such activities as medical lectures may have done some good, the general lack of communication and persistent conditions of poverty prevented any radical change.[25]

In 1919 a number of personnel changes occurred that would have a lasting impact on Navajo health care. The first step came in August when Dr. Albert Wigglesworth, the hardworking and well-liked head physician at Fort Defiance, transferred to Albuquerque "in order that he may have school facilities for his children." His fifteen years at the Navajo agency had earned him a solid reputation among the Diné. An evaluation of his work by Dr. L. L. Culp, in February 1919, praised him as "one of the few physicians in the service who cannot be replaced by any other. His personal manner, professional qualifications, ability and inclination to accomplish results are rarely so happily combined in one individual." His ability to speak the Navajo language and the trachoma work at the Episcopal hospital had created a special bond with his patients. As Dr. Culp remarked, "No other white person has a greater hold on the confidence of the whole tribe." His transfer was thus viewed as a great loss.[26]

Fortunately, the Indian Office appointed Dr. Polk Richards to replace Wigglesworth. Richards would become deeply involved with federal efforts to relieve Navajo suffering for the next two decades. Educated at Indiana University, the quiet, dedicated doctor served as a hospital administrator and special physician before wartime military service. Like his predecessor, he was regarded as an eye specialist. In 1919 he returned to Indian work, quickly earning the reputation as "one of the best doctors in the service." Richards readily acknowledged, however, that originally he had not been trained in this specialty. "We are mostly just ordinary pill and liniment doctors," he wrote later, "who have picked up a little here and there from sheer necessity. It was rubbed into us, so to speak, since trachoma, its complications and sequelae everlastingly hound us." Not only did he assume supervision of the two Fort Defiance hospitals; he volunteered at the Episcopal hospital, where "his coming was most timely, for the hospital was filled with trachoma cases, that dread disease which was fast becoming a scourge among the Navajos."[27]

Faced with the inadequacies of a system based on general physicians, the Indian Office began to place more emphasis on special physicians qualified to deal with specific major problems. Assigned to one of six general regions, they were intended to work the hot spots. Although a few special physicians had been utilized prior to the war, the concept received much more emphasis as the 1920s progressed. Of particular importance to the Navajo would be the selection in 1919 of Dr. J. S. Perkins as Special Physician at Large for the Southwest. The rotund, bespectacled doctor had joined the Indian Service in 1894. After a stint at Chilocco Indian School in Oklahoma, he worked in Arizona as both a physician and school superintendent. As a special physician, Perkins made numerous trips to the Navajo country, usually accompanied by a nurse. In December 1920, for example, he responded to an outbreak of typhoid fever at Shiprock, where twenty-three people died, including Dr. John C. Graffin, the agency physician. Joined by Dr. R. E. L. Newburne, Indian Service Chief Medical Supervisor, Perkins remained at agency headquarters until this dangerous situation was cleared up.[28]

Like the other special physicians, Perkins focused primarily on trachoma. As reports continued to indicate a spread of this disease, the physician took to the road. During the early part of 1921 he paid a visit to the school at Tuba City, examining 187 children for eye trouble. Discovering that 25 percent of the students were infected by trachoma, Perkins performed twenty-one operations. He also managed to get over a hundred reservation residents to come in for treatment, twenty-five of whom received surgical treatment. Following his visit, Perkins reported to Indian Commissioner Charles Burke (1921–1929) that "the [Tuba City] hospital is entirely too small. It is a dark, dingy building, no operating room and is entirely unsuited for hospital purposes." A later trip to Shiprock confirmed that eye problems were out of control. During a brief stay, the physician treated over a thousand Navajos for eye problems, performing more than six hundred grattage operations. The situation was so severe that the "Navajo came to the hospital very willingly, gladly I am sure, and in great numbers." Despite his optimism, the special physician encountered problems. In particular, he resented the lack of cooperation from agency personnel. In 1922 he asked that federal employees be instructed to cooperate more fully, "in order that the Indians needing his services may be brought to him, so that he will not have to waste so much time running around hunting up cases." Perkins was particularly insistent that reservation Indians suffering with trachoma be notified as early as possible of the specialist's visit.[29]

Although Perkins did not spend all his time on trachoma or the Navajos, his reports clearly indicate that eye disease had reached unacceptable proportions among the Indians of the Southwest. Obviously, neither the agency physicians nor a few trained specialists could handle the situation. As Perkins concluded, the Navajo "were in great need of eye treatment. . . . There is necessity for a lot of work of this kind among the Indians." By the end of 1923 Commissioner Burke agreed, admitting that "there is need for a general clean-up of the trachoma in this section [Navajo] of the Southwest."[30]

THE SOUTHWESTERN TRACHOMA CAMPAIGN

When the Harding administration took office in 1921, it named Charles Burke to head the Indian Office. Although Burke expressed a desire to improve Indian health, he was reluctant to oppose the conservative financial policies of the Republican party. As a consequence, medical affairs limped along with minimal funding while tuberculosis and trachoma rates continued to increase. Burke hoped to counter this trend through prevention and health education, but without any significant additional funding he could do little to improve sanitary conditions and the reservation standard of living. The commissioner's belief that "the medical service is a social uplift service" intended to "restore to a race its pristine health and virility" quickly floundered on the rocks of reality. The failure to make any headway led to a clash with a rising group of reformers who saw the deterioration of Indian health conditions as a symptom of a bankrupt Indian policy.[31]

Feeling pressure to improve Indian health care, the Indian Office finally launched an effort to secure special funding in 1923. Although tuberculosis remained the most deadly medical problem, Burke placed most of his emphasis on a massive trachoma campaign, which seemed more likely to produce quick results. Working closely with the Board of Indian Commissioners, the Indian Office pressured Congress to appropriate an extra 130,000 dollars, primarily to "conduct an extensive and aggressive campaign against trachoma among the various Indian tribes." Delighted with this success, optimism prevailed in government circles. George Vaux, chairman of the Board of Indian Commissioners, confidently predicted that the extra funding would stamp out trachoma.[32]

Conditions among the Navajo did much to shape the trachoma campaign. A shocked Herbert J. Hagerman, the newly appointed Commissioner to the Navajo Indians (a position created in connection with the establishment of the Tribal Council in 1923), called the attention of government officials to the extent of the disease among the Diné. In response, during the spring of 1924 Commissioner Burke and Secretary of the Interior Hubert Work toured the Navajo reservation to plan a campaign. Meeting at Gallup with reservation superintendents and physicians, the two officials proposed an elaborate assault, to begin in just two months. Because of the high incidence of trachoma at the Navajo (Fort Defiance) Agency, this area was "selected as the first battle ground." The fact that Superintendent Paquette's popularity might be used to persuade the Diné to submit for treatment also figured in the decision to target this jurisdiction. The Indian Office wanted results as soon as possible. As Burke told Paquette, "This campaign is important and the Office is very anxious to materially improve the present conditions with special reference to trachoma."[33]

The 1924–25 trachoma campaign was a nationwide affair, although most of it focused on the Southwest. Dr. Newburne, chief of the recently organized Medical Division of the Indian Office, provided overall supervision, advised by Dr. John Mullen, a U.S. Public Health Service surgeon nationally known as an expert on trachoma. Initially, seven special physicians and thirteen nurses were assigned to specific regions of the country. Four of these physicians formed the core of the "Southwestern Trachoma Campaign," which formally began on July 1, 1924, with a budget of sixty-five thousand dollars. Overall supervision of the Southwestern Campaign fell to Dr. J. S. Perkins, "chief ophthalmologist." Under him were three operating field units, directed by "consulting ophthalmologist" Polk Richards at Fort Defiance, Dr. Ralph H. Ross at Tohatchi, and Dr. Wigglesworth at Chinle. The necessity for a special campaign became evident when a preliminary survey discovered that the schools at Fort Defiance, Tohatchi, Chinle, and Lukachukai registered infection rates between 51 and 56 percent. The program provided each field unit with a nurse, a Ford automobile, and several tents. Once residents of the Navajo agency had been treated, the teams were to proceed to other Navajo jurisdictions before the onset of cold weather, when they would move on to reservations in southern Arizona and New Mexico. Commissioner Burke expected this aggressive approach to produce dramatic results. "When a few are cured," he wrote, "the news will be broadcasted in their own way throughout all the Navajo country," resulting in a flood of new patients.[34]

The most controversial feature of the trachoma campaign involved the recommended use of a radical surgical procedure advocated by Dr. L. Webster Fox, an eye specialist at the University of Pennsylvania. With no actual cure for the disease, Fox convinced the Indian Office that drastic measures were required because the disease was spreading so rapidly. Believing that the Indians would not submit to any form of prolonged treatment, the famed ophthalmologist recommended unrestricted use of tarsectomy and radical grattage because they "remove the disease more quickly and with less deformity than the way Nature goes about it." Tarsectomy was especially precarious because it removed the entire tarsal plate supporting the eyelid. Nevertheless, such treatment was adopted by the special physicians and taught to regular Indian Service doctors for use in the field.[35]

The Southwestern Trachoma Campaign began with a flurry. Superintendent Paquette immediately proclaimed it a complete success, remarking that many Indians had come in for treatment. Indeed, working with both schoolchildren and reservation adults, the doctors found themselves overwhelmed. School buildings were turned into temporary hospitals and everywhere physicians "had more patients than they could handle." After three months, Dr. Perkins reported that the physicians had examined 7,445 people, of whom 1,585 were found to be trachomatous. An astounding 1,280 trachoma operations were performed, along with 273 other eye surgeries.[36]

The human suffering caused by trachoma overwhelmed the doctors. It seemed as if the Navajo were rapidly drifting into a state of universal blindness. Many cases were so far advanced that little could be done; nevertheless they came to see the doctors in hopes of restoring their sight. Terrible stories of personal tragedy surfaced again and again. One case history noted: "This woman is almost totally blind. She can only distinguish between light and shadow. Both eyes are perforated as a result of trachoma. Her case is the same as hundreds of others—incurable. She is only thirty-five years old." In another case, a sixty-five-year-old man and his sixty-year-old wife showed up at Tohatchi: "The old man is totally blind from trachoma. His wife is almost blind but can see enough to enable her to get around and care for him. In going from place to place he holds to her shawl and follows behind her with the assistance of his stick. In this way they came in from their home to be treated by Dr. Ross at Tohatchi. They refused to leave until their sight was restored but the doctor informed them that all he could do for them would be to make them more comfortable, which he did by operation and treatment." Other cases proved more successful: a middle-aged woman "was led in totally blind from trachoma and Trichiasis but after being operated on for both she went away able to see her way and distinguish persons."[37]

In spite of the large number of initial patients, the trachoma campaign encountered problems from the start. It quickly became apparent that a budgeted hospital stay of six days per patient was totally inadequate. Field doctors recognized that radical surgeries required considerably more follow-up care. A member of the Board of Indian Commissioners raised similar concerns, noting that a real question existed as to whether an effective follow-up could be expected given the scattered Navajo lifestyle. "This being the case," she wrote, "it would seem that in the majority of cases the advantages of the operations that are to be performed will be minimalized by the inability to give the necessary after-treatment." Given this circumstance, little permanent relief could be anticipated until more hospitals were erected. Perhaps more important, many Navajos fled after their initial surgical treatment, refusing to have anything more to do with government doctors. In one typical case, a nearly blind grandmother and her totally blind seven-year-old granddaughter came in for help, only to run away from the hospital after the first treatment, disappearing into the reservation. Despite such failures, Burke did not respond to requests for additional resources.[38]

Surgical techniques also created problems. Dr. Perkins heartily approved of the radical tarsectomy advocated by Dr. Fox, and used it with some regularity. Nevertheless, the procedure remained experimental and the results could be unfortunate. This became evident in early November, when Perkins held a clinic at Fort Defiance to demonstrate the Fox method of "the intensive grattage operation and the removal of the tarsal plate" to agency and school physicians. Almost immediately some of the clinic's demonstration patients experienced unfavorable reactions, especially an inability to close the eyelids. In addition, many of the agency physicians proved unable to perform the radical procedure or they felt uncomfortable with such a drastic operation. Polk Richards, in particular, advised caution, recognizing that "patients disfigured [by badly performed operations] are walking advertisements that will react on us in a way that will cause a loss of confidence in our methods and thus failure of cooperation on the part of the Indian." Richards frankly admitted that the operations had failed in a few cases, thus doing "more harm than good." Unfortunately, Burke ignored these warnings and ordered the radical campaign to proceed, bolstered by assurances from Dr. Fox that the operations were easy to perform.[39]

Richards's predication that the Navajos might become reluctant to cooperate proved accurate. Although it soon became evident to the Indian Office that radical surgeries "should be very carefully selected," the campaign on the Navajo reservation continued in full force during the next two summers. Bouncing across rugged roads in their rapidly deteriorating automobiles, the special physicians crisscrossed the reservation. Despite Perkins's record number of radical surgeries, other doctors proved much more cautious. During the first year, Polk Richards performed only 266 trachoma operations, just 10 percent of the people he found to be infected (he preferred to treat with ointments). The physician at Tohatchi operated on a comparable percentage of cases. Nevertheless, as word of the painful procedures spread, reservation residents became more hesitant to seek treatment. Special Physician Hubert V. Hailman, working out of Tuba City during the summer of 1926, reported that the Navajo refused to seek help voluntarily. At Kayenta, for example, he could only persuade three people to be treated at his mobile clinic during a two-day visit. Under these conditions, the physician preferred to visit nearby hogans and examine anyone he could catch. Although residents were more cooperative at Dennehotso (which recorded an unusually high rate of disease), enthusiasm had obviously diminished.[40]

The campaign additionally ran afoul of ceremonial activities. In more than one instance, government doctors blithely scheduled their clinics to coincide with an important dance or ceremony. Perkins, in particular, resented such rituals, arguing that the Indian Service should forcibly stop ceremonies during his visit. In one case, he set up shop during a week-long Squaw Dance, then complained when only a handful of people showed up for care. In a remark more accurate than he realized, the doctor sarcastically concluded that "apparently the dance was considered more important than the campaign."[41]

After two years of fieldwork it became obvious that the trachoma campaign was not proving successful, particularly among the adult reservation population. Dr. Perkins stubbornly clung to the vigorous approach, stating again in August 1926 that "I consider Tarsectomy the surest cure for trachoma." Other physicians were much less optimistic. After his experience, Dr. Hailman concluded that the current program would not succeed. Writing to Commissioner Burke, Hailman observed that ignorance of disease and "superstitions" stood in the way of progress. In addition, the Navajo could not be forced into accepting hospitalization because of the economic consequences. To effectively complete the job, Hailman reported, entire families required simultaneous treatment. With no one to tend their sheep, the animals would be lost or destroyed. Given such conditions, radical surgery for large numbers of adults appeared to be impossible.[42]

Faced with a potentially embarrassing failure, the Indian Office shifted emphasis at the end of 1926. Admitting that adult Indians could not be readily cured and fieldwork was often "a waste of time," it decided to concentrate on schoolchildren. Working primarily through the schools seemed to possess obvious advantages. Children might be treated in a controlled environment, with dietary and sanitary conditions regulated. Accordingly, in December 1926, Commissioner Burke set aside the Fort Defiance boarding school as a special trachoma school. Adopting the old idea of segregating infected pupils from healthy ones, the Indian Office justified its actions thus: "Transferring all children with well eyes to other schools where there is no trachoma and filling their places with children afflicted with trachoma is much to be commended. Afflicted children will be kept in schools until cured and no longer capable of infecting others. At the same time they will receive as much education and vocational training as the condition of their eyes allow."[43]

Growing criticism of the trachoma campaign among medical specialists undoubtedly hastened the decision to concentrate on schoolchildren. During the summer of 1926 Dr. William C. Posey led a special team of ophthalmologists appointed by the American Medical Association (AMA) on a tour of Arizona, New Mexico, and California, spending most of their time among the Navajo. They found trachoma everywhere. Living conditions seemed especially conducive to the spread of disease among the Navajo where shepherds "caring for their flocks are exposed to the extremes of cold and heat in winter and summer, and to the irritating dust of the desert, and have scant facilities for bathing or cleanliness." The doctors, at least, took some satisfaction in the fact that most government doctors seemed to favor a conservative plan for treatment. Nevertheless, tarsectomy was still common enough to disturb the AMA team. "We saw some evil results of tarsectomy," wrote Posey, "such as retracted lids and undue scarring of the conjunctiva, and we heard of one case in which loss of both eyes followed the operation." The advisory committee issued a report in March 1927 that confirmed the opinion of Indian Service doctors that little could be done for reservation adults as long as living conditions remained the same. It, too, backed special trachoma schools as the most promising approach.[44]

The adverse publicity surrounding radical surgery and the obvious fact that the trachoma campaign had failed caused Burke to back down in 1927. During the summer of that year he ordered government physicians to follow more conservative procedures. Finally, in September 1927, he prohibited the use of tarsectomy and radical grattage without prior permission from his office. These orders effectively ended the much-heralded trachoma campaign. Three years of costly effort and experimentation had yielded little more than a confirmation of the extent of the problem. Indeed, many individual Navajos suffered more from the treatment than from the disease. As historian Lawrence C. Kelly has concluded, the trachoma campaign was "worse than unsuccessful—it was irresponsible and unjust to the thousands of Indians who were subjected to the treatment."[45]

THE MERIAM REPORT

Criticism of the Indian Office mounted during the mid-1920s, as reformers, led by John Collier, demanded an investigation of national Indian policy. These vocal protests convinced the Interior Department to fund a survey of Indian administration in 1926. Prepared under the direction of Lewis Meriam and a staff of experts, the so-called Meriam Report was released by the Brookings Institution on February 21, 1928. This lengthy document, the product of two years of work, provided the country with a detailed review of nearly every facet of current Indian policy, analyzing administrative and financial conditions, tribal economies, legal problems, and education. As might be expected, health conditions received a significant amount of space. Prepared under the supervision of Dr. Herbert R. Edwards, the health section scrutinized the status of Indian health, the organization of the medical service, public health issues, and hospital facilities.[46]

Overall, the survey proved extremely critical of government health care, stating that "taken as a whole practically every activity undertaken for the promotion of the health of the Indians is below a reasonable standard of efficiency." A consistent lack of adequate appropriations accounted for much of the failure by preventing the employment of sufficient medical staff. Salaries were so low, moreover, that properly qualified personnel avoided the Indian Service, thus forcing the Indian Office to lower its standards in order to fill vacancies. Although the Indian Service could boast of a number of highly qualified and dedicated health professionals, "the average falls below a reasonable minimum standard." Lack of funding also accounted for the inadequacy of facilities to care for sick Indians, or to carry out programs for prevention.[47]

Most of the survey's criticism reflected conditions on the Navajo reservation. Acknowledging that statistics related to Indian health conditions were inadequate, the survey nevertheless documented a major health crisis. It noted, for example, that the tuberculosis death rate in Arizona was seventeen times higher than that of the general population. This was accounted for by the fact that early detection was nearly impossible; diagnostic facilities, including X-ray and tuberculin tests, were unavailable to Indian Service doctors; and many reservation hospitals were not equipped to prevent contamination. None of the tuberculosis sanatoriums met the minimum requirements of the American Sanatorium Association. In fact, only four sanatoriums exclusively served adult patients, the smallest of which was Fort Defiance. Unfortunately, these institutions kept such poor records that no one could determine how cases were classified or treated. Moreover, "there is no method of follow-up for cases, nothing is known as to what becomes of them once they leave the hospital." The buildings themselves were old, inadequate, and ill equipped. Despite the fact that up-to-date laboratory equipment was "absolutely essential for a modern sanatorium," it seldom existed. More sanatoriums, if properly constructed, were badly needed.[48]

With respect to agency hospitals, the survey noted that many Indians avoided them because they had little confidence in white medicine. Disinterested and poorly qualified personnel contributed to this feeling. Many hospitals were badly located and poorly constructed. The survey thus endorsed proposals that promised more efficiency, such as one to create a hospital "center" at Fort Defiance because it could administer the needs of the entire Navajo country. Still, the construction of modern and well-equipped facilities necessitated a "much larger appropriation" than planned. Administratively, agency hospitals were also defective since physicians had to defer to the agency superintendent on operational matters. Additionally, hospital doctors were expected to perform "reservation work," which often caused them to neglect hospital responsibilities.[49]

As far as trachoma was concerned, the report endorsed the concept of segregating trachomatous schoolchildren from healthy ones in special schools, but only as a temporary measure until all schools developed proper facilities for treating the disease. The much ballyhooed Southwestern Trachoma Campaign was labeled a failure. Not only was the disease as prevalent as ever, but the radical surgical methods of Dr. Fox had failed to prevent recurrence. A lack of case follow-up also received criticism. Rather than experimenting with unproved methods, the study suggested that more attention be devoted to prevention, including a study of the role diet played in causing the disease.[50]

The survey took a deep look at Indian Service doctors and their working conditions. In general, it found that physicians were deficient in medical training, with very few having done postgraduate work or belonging to professional associations, primarily because such activities had to take place on their own time with their own money. The government, moreover, provided the doctors with no medical literature. As a consequence, many physicians failed to meet the standards of other federal medical services. And discontent was everywhere: "The general causes for dissatisfaction among Indian Service physicians have been thru subordination to lay authority in professional matters, the low salaries paid, and the poor housing facilities available." Seldom could they do more than dispense drugs while waiting for the Indians to come to them.[51]

Given all the problems, the report's conclusion were obvious: "The medical and health service of the Indian Service in its operation has as a rule been curative and not, . . . educational and preventive." Trained public health personnel seldom worked for the Indian Service, clinics for follow-up care did not exist, statistical analysis was inadequate, sanitation and hygiene were overlooked, and water supplies were insufficient. In addition, cooperation with other agencies, such as the Red Cross and Public Health Service, was limited at best. The survey thus recommended that the Indian Service seek to employ a well-trained force of public health physicians and nurses, to open reservation clinics, and to place more emphasis on prevention.[52]

Publication of the Meriam Report stirred great controversy. Many Indian Service employees resented the criticism, although they often recognized the truth of its conclusions. Reformers, of course, used the report to support their attack on the old assimilation approach to Indian policy. More important for this study, the report brought home the sad medical situation existing among the Navajo and other tribes. Although not every issue could or would be addressed, the Meriam study prompted the government to consider a number of changes.

FORT DEFIANCE IN THE LATE 1880S

The desolate and windswept headquarters of the Navajo Agency offered few comforts. This picture shows the agency buildings, including the three-story school. The physician's office and residence was located in the row of buildings to the right of the schoolhouse. (Courtesy Gertrude Hill Muir Collection (CP GM 359), Arizona Collection, Arizona State University Libraries. Original photo by Ben Wittick, Courtesy Museum of New Mexico, Santa Fe, Neg. #16023).

JOHN MENAUL

Presbyterian physician and missionary John Menaul in 1902 (two years before his retirement). He served as the agency doctor at Fort Defiance in the early 1870s. (Courtesy The Menaul Historical Society, Neg. File D-23).

NAVAJO MEDICINE MAN

Traditional healers like this unidentified man guarded tribal culture. They wielded significant influence and often opposed government medicine. Indian service personnel regarded them as impediments to the assimilation program and frequently attempted to discredit them. (Courtesy Arizona Historical Society, Tucson, AHS #41,939).

RESERVATION ROAD, 1920

Trying to bring medical care to remote parts of the reservation proved frustrating for government physicians because of the great distances involved and the rugged terrain. (Courtesy Leo Crane Collection, NAU.PH 658.198, Cline Library, Northern Arizona University, Flagstaff).

DR. J. S. PERKINS

The Special Physician in Charge of the Southwestern Trachoma Campaign (seen here en route to Chinlee, Arizona), Perkins attempted to eliminate trachoma by establishing treatment units and training physicians in radical methods of eye surgery. (National Archives Photo).

TRACHOMA PATIENTS

This Navajo couple suffered from trachoma. The man was totally blind, but the wife could see well enough to get around and care for her husband. In moving about the man held onto the woman's shawl and used a walking stick. (National Archives Photo).

ELDERLY TRACHOMA PATIENTS, FORT DEFIANCE

These two Navajo men were brought to the Fort Defiance clinic in 1924. Both were nearly blind, but were treated successfully and returned to their homes with improved vision. Being friends, the two men remained together during treatment. (National Archives Photo).

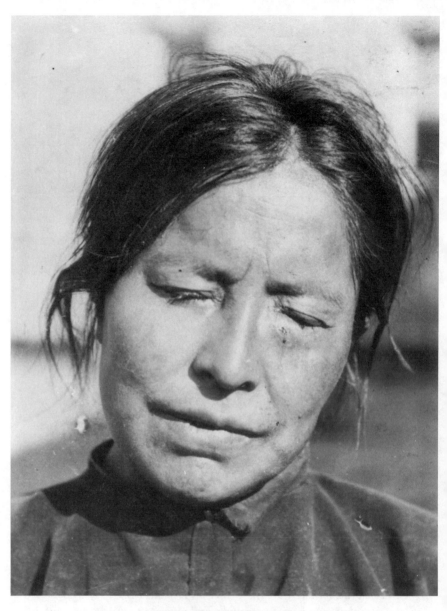

FEMALE TRACHOMA PATIENT

Generally positive results were obtained in the case of this thirty-five year old woman who came to the Fort Defiance clinic totally blind. After an operation, her vision improved to the extent that she could move about on her own. (National Archives Photo).

KAYENTA SANATORIUM, 1933

The tuberculosis sanatorium at Kayenta was one of the most isolated government hospitals during the 1920s. This view looking north shows the entire facility, including the main hospital (once a school), boiler house, pump, and employees cottage. (National Archives Photo).

EMPLOYEES QUARTERS, KAYENTA

By the mid-1930s reservation housing for the medical staff had improved somewhat. This building, which once had been school recital rooms, was converted into living quarters for the sanatorium staff, two of whom pose on the porch. Despite the availability of electricity for lighting, conditions remained quite primitive. (National Archives Photo).

SPECIAL NURSE AND TYPHOID PATIENTS, 1933

Although the Kayenta Sanatorium focused primarily on tuberculosis, it was nevertheless the only medical facility for miles. As a consequence, the medical personnel stationed at the facility dealt with just about everything. Here a special nurse is seen with three recovering typhoid patients. (National Archive Photo).

NURSE AND DRIVER/INTERPRETER

In the late 1930s a field nurse displays an X-ray image in an effort to explain the need for getting a patient to the hospital. In addition to providing direct medical care, field nurses sought to educate Navajos on the merits of modern medicine. (Courtesy Helen Post Collection, P1985.50.939, Amon Carter Museum, Fort Worth).

DEDICATION, NAVAJO MEDICAL CENTER

On June 20, 1938, the Indian Service formally opened its new hospital at Fort Defiance. In keeping with John Collier's interest in accommodating Navajo tradition, prominent tribal leaders and healers attended the ceremonies to bless the building and pledge cooperation. As dignitaries delivered speeches, the traditional Navajos listen in silence. (Courtesy Dodge Collection, SPC 125:4, Arizona Collection, Arizona State University Libraries).

PUBLIC HEALTH NURSE, SANOSTEE TRAILER SCHOOL

By the time the Public Health Service assumed control of reservation medical services in 1955, the Indian bureau had significantly modernized its activities. Here a nurse gives shots to school children at one of the remote schools. (Courtesy Milton Snow Collection, ACC #4094, Museum of Northern Arizona Photo Archives, Flagstaff).

TRAINED NAVAJO NURSE, FORT DEFIANCE

In 1954 Laura Gilpin photographed a Navajo nurse at work. The professionalism captured here indicates the advancements made by the Indian Service in training and employing Navajo women as nurses and nurse-aids. (Courtesy, Laura Gilpin Collection, 4317.1, Amon Carter Museum, Fort Forth).

CHAPTER EIGHT

TRANSITION

The problems related to health and prevention of disease among Indians are enormous. To meet them will require not only improvement and expansion in the personnel and facilities of the Indian Bureau, but also the advice, cooperation, and constructive criticism on the part of individuals and organizations qualified and interested in helping this work.

M. C. GUTHRIE, CHIEF MEDICAL DIRECTOR

Publication of the Meriam Report encouraged Congress to allocate enough money for the Indian Office to embark on a limited effort to expand and modernize its facilities. These enhancements, however, failed to make a substantial dent in the overwhelming array of reservation health problems. Indeed, during the transitional period between the Meriam Report and the New Deal Navajo health conditions continued to deteriorate. In 1929 the superintendent at Tuba City succinctly summed up the problems facing government medical efforts. Doctors, he noted, were insufficient in number to have adequate contact with the adult population; they seldom learned about illnesses in a timely fashion and thus were called out primarily for chronic or terminal cases, could not persuade Indians in the early stages of tuberculosis to enter a hospital, and possessed no ability to carry out sanitary medical and surgical procedures in reservation camps. At the same time, a growing number of Indians were accepting government services, overwhelming the limited facilities available for their care.[1] Despite efforts to correct this condition in the years following 1928, results proved unsatisfactory.

Although the Meriam survey deserves credit for stimulating many of the improvements attempted between 1928 and 1932, the Indian medical corps had actively been working in the same direction for some time. In fact, some of the criticism had been tackled years before the Meriam documents became public. This was particularly the case after Dr. Marshall C. Guthrie, a Public Health Service surgeon, became Chief Medical Director in 1925. Assisted by Dr. L. L. White, an Indian Service field physician well acquainted with reservation conditions, Guthrie acted rapidly to enhance the salaries of his doctors by tapping into the first significant increase in congressional appropriations in a decade. No one questioned the need for better wages, which had averaged between 1,000 dollars and 1,200 dollars per year since the 1870s, but it took Guthrie's determination to more than double existing salaries over a two-year period. By 1926 the senior physician at Fort Defiance earned 2,400 dollars, while Dr. Polk Richards, then a special physician, commanded 3,000 dollars plus expenses. Nurses also received better pay, with graduate nurses able to command as much as 1,680 dollars per year. Though still below prevailing professional salaries, these increases greatly improved morale. They also helped to recruit a better class of physician.[2]

Guthrie understood the crisis facing his office. Writing in 1927, he described medical conditions in Indian country as enormous. Tuberculosis, which continued to stymie the medical community, headed the list of problems. Recent figures showed that the disease had advanced from 21.4 percent of all reservation deaths in 1923 to 25.9 percent two years later. Both tuberculosis and trachoma remained prevalent and in some locations were "unusually high." To deal with these and other serious health problems, the Indian Service operated some ninety-one medical stations, most of which were very small. That such services needed to be expanded was "beyond question."[3]

During the first years of his administration, Guthrie actively sought funding for the construction of new hospitals and the enhancement of preventive activities. Faced with a deplorable medical situation, he frankly admitted that the government had not done enough to combat "the grave health conditions" on many reservations. Aside from more funding, Guthrie hoped to adopt innovative new approaches. One particularly promising and economical approach seemed to be available by replacing field matrons with public health (or field) nurses, who were specifically qualified to provide medical care. Working with physicians or on their own, they seemed better suited to handle emergencies, to provide medical education, and to overcome the "natural reluctance of these people to take on new ideas." Encouraged by Elinor Gregg, his Supervisor of Public Health Nursing, Guthrie thus argued that a corps of field nurses might have a beneficial impact, and he sought any opportunities to implement this and other new ideas.[4]

HOSPITALS

Dr. Guthrie took advantage of the Meriam criticisms to press for better hospital facilities and additional medical staff. As medical knowledge became more sophisticated, the myriad of Navajo medical problems required increasingly advanced health-care facilities. For many years, of course, tribal members had accepted the medications dispensed by doctors and nurses on an out-patient basis, but by the mid-1920s they increasingly, if reluctantly, sought hospital treatment. Unfortunately, hospital conditions on the reservation were totally inadequate. The Fort Defiance general hospital was so short of modern equipment that Superintendent Duclos suggested starting all over again with a new building. Even when the small mission hospitals at Fort Defiance, Ganado, Red Rock, Indian Wells, and Rehoboth were added to government facilities, hospital bed space was stretched to the limit. The only sanatorium on the reservation, the thirty-bed Navajo Sanatorium at Fort Defiance, frequently housed forty-five to fifty patients under unfavorable conditions.[5]

The shortage of sanatorium space was particularly significant. Many tubercular Navajos, especially from remote areas, could not secure treatment. In one typical case, Leupp Superintendent Harmon P. Marble attempted to admit an eighteen-year-old Navajo girl to the Fort Defiance sanatorium because "this girl cannot be cared for here." Knowing that a refusal would force him to return the girl to her hogan—in essence condemning her to death—Marble pressed his case, but to no avail. Duclos flatly rejected the transfer because the sanatorium was "filled to capacity."[6]

Such tragedies encouraged Duclos to propose the construction of a new tuberculosis hospital at Fort Defiance. Realizing that the Indian Office might be more receptive if costs could be kept down, in early 1927 he suggested building a one hundred–bed facility from logs supplied by the tribal sawmill. If located next to a planned new sixty-bed general hospital, Duclos believed that additional economies might be gained through the sharing of X-ray, laboratory, kitchen, and heating equipment. The commissioner's office initially approved this proposal, agreeing to spend fifty-five thousand dollars on a new sanatorium and to request thirty thousand dollars for a new general hospital. Blueprints for the new sanatorium included wards for male and female patients, modern toilets and showers, a laboratory, office, and receiving area for screening new patients.[7]

Despite elaborate planning, the new sanatorium failed to materialize. As funding became available the Indian Office, supported by Duclos, shifted its focus to enlarging the general hospital and opening small satellite school hospitals at Totatchi and Chinle. Construction soon began, and by the end of 1929 an expanded one hundred–bed general hospital had been completed, although a lack of equipment kept it from opening until February 1930. The remodeled facility included a "well-equipped operating room" capable of handling all reservation surgical cases. The two sixteen-bed school hospitals were also opened the same year. All this construction, however, left the sanatorium in limbo.

Although desperately in need of repairs, Duclos finally decided that the old sanatorium would have to continue pretty much as in the past. Because of an inadequate water supply, Fort Defiance could not support two large hospitals. Instead, the superintendent advised that a one hundred–bed sanatorium be constructed at Gallup or Fort Wingate.[8]

Meanwhile, the Indian Office decided to experiment with a tuberculosis hospital on the western side of the reservation. Unfortunately, this satellite facility strayed from recommendations that new sanatoriums be specifically designed for medical purposes and that they focus primarily on curable patients, to avoid the stigma of frequent death. These discrepancies stemmed from the fact that the Indian Office hoped to save money by utilizing abandoned school buildings. The site in question, the Marsh Pass boarding school at Kayenta, had not been an educational success. Opened in 1914 and substantially remodeled in 1923–24, the school closed in 1927. This left a large government facility, with two large dormitories, available for other purposes.[9]

As early as November 1927 officials recommended converting the Marsh Pass school into a sanatorium. Dr. Guthrie agreed to consider the proposal, primarily because a hospital at the remote location might be very beneficial. Nevertheless, a number of obvious problems existed. Guthrie questioned whether a sufficient number of potential patients existed in the region to support a sanatorium. He also expressed concern about Kayenta's isolation: almost two hundred miles from the railroad, accessible only by a road so bad it required five thousand dollars worth of repairs. The Chief Medical Director thus hesitated to establish an institution solely on the basis of available space. "It is a great mistake to my mind," he observed, "to establish a hospital or sanatorium at a particular place because of the physical plant at such place becoming available."[10]

Mindful of these concerns, Guthrie let plans for the sanatorium languish. Shortly after the publication of the Meriam Report, however, the idea was resurrected, and in the fall of 1928 the Indian Office secured a thirty-thousand-dollar appropriation to remodel the school buildings. Dr. Christian H. Koentz was soon dispatched to oversee the remodeling and set up operations. Although Koentz believed that the school buildings could easily be converted, the area's staggering isolation presented the specter of major staffing problems. Comfortable, convenient, and cheerful quarters thus seemed absolutely necessary. So did a reliable supply of coal. Despite these substantial obstacles, Koentz expected the hospital to be successful. Writing to Commissioner Burke in December 1928, he remarked that there "have been great criticism of the hospitals in the Indian Service and of the personnel operating them. I feel that I am to be classified as another failure if the Kayenta Sanatarium fails to function."[11]

Problems surfaced almost immediately. As the remodeling progressed during the winter of 1928–1929, confusion over funding brought work to a halt on several occasions. These delays stemmed from the fact that Dr. Koentz possessed no authority to make financial decisions. Instead, all judgements originated at the agency's Tuba City headquarters, seventy miles distant. In addition, construction materials came by wagon from Flagstaff to Tuba City and to Kayenta over unreliable roads. These logistical problems led to "lost motion and additional cost." As a consequence, District Medical Director H. J. Warner suggested that the sanatorium be operated as a separate jurisdiction under the superintendency of Dr. Koentz. This arrangement was approved, creating the unusual circumstance of a reservation hospital operating independently of agency administration.[12]

The forty-bed Kayenta Sanatorium opened April 1, 1929. It reached capacity almost immediately, with many of the patients being children transferred from Tuba City. Although pleased by this result, Koentz recognized his precarious situation. From the beginning, staffing and resources failed to meet demand. During the extremely cold winter months, for example, it proved impossible to keep the buildings warm. With only one employee assigned to tend the furnace, it became so cold in the wards that physical examinations could not be conducted. As Koentz remarked, "I can't do good work this way. One radiator would not work at all and the engineer could not leave the boiler long enough to fix it." Nor were the old school buildings properly arranged. The kitchen was situated so far from the wards that "the transportation of food must be made to bed patients thru dust storms, snow storms, and in the winter the temperature gets as low as four or five below zero." Despite the remodeling, roofs leaked, plaster fell from the ceilings, and "we are sadly in need of furniture." In contrast to his earlier call for a "cheerful" atmosphere, employees' rooms looked "deploringly bare." Finally, although intended to accommodate curable tuberculosis patients, the hospital's remote location required that terminal patients be admitted along with general medical and surgical work. In fact, as the only local doctor, Koentz frequently found himself visiting remote camps to treat all kinds of ailments. He even dug graves and buried the dead, all of which took time away from his main responsibilities. Without additional staff, furniture, equipment, and repairs, the future looked uncertain.[13]

Dr. Koentz grew disillusioned. A year after the sanatorium opened, he expressed hope that the Indian Service Medical Corps could be placed on par with the military and public health services. Like other Indian Service doctors, he felt isolated and in need of communicating with his colleagues about common problems. To accomplish this goal, Koentz put forth an elaborate plan to consolidate and centralize medical services on the Navajo reservation. In particular, he advocated the construction of a chain of field hospitals radiating out from a core facility, so that equipment and laboratory technicians could be shared, expenses kept to a minimum, and communications facilitated. An ambulance service, he thought, might then shuttle between the field hospitals and "a central station of sufficient size that has a medical personnel, technicians, nurses, equipment and a trained force of employees." In this fashion, the professional and personal isolation of government personnel stationed at remote locations might be lessened.[14] Although this idea met with no immediate response, it would surface again during the New Deal. In the interval, the Kayenta sanatorium continued to struggle, filled to overflowing.

Meanwhile, the Indian Office received an appropriation of sixty-five thousand dollars for the construction of a sanatorium to serve the Leupp and Hopi jurisdictions (about twenty-five hundred Hopis and five thousand Navajos). Initial plans called for the hospital to be placed at Oraibi in the Hopi country, yet few officials seemed to be enthusiastic about this location. Enthusiasm was further dampened in March 1929, when the Winslow, Arizona, City Council passed a resolution offering to provide the government with a sanatorium site. Although obviously motivated by the prospect of federal spending, the city presented a number of logical reasons why Winslow would be a better location. A division point on the Santa Fe Railway situated just south of the reservation, the town offered an abundant water supply, regular electric and natural gas service, a first-class fire department, an ice plant, and a sewage system. By way of contrast, noted the resolution, none of these amenities existed at Oraibi. In addition, the cost of transporting supplies sixty-five miles to Oraibi would be excessive, roads were unreliable and frequently washed out, and coal supplies in the Hopi country were undeveloped. Therefore, the council argued, the government could save over five thousand dollars per year while meeting the needs of Navajo and Hopi patients.[15]

The Indian Office procrastinated for over a year before responding. Finally, in March 1930, District Medical Director H. J. Warner asked Dr. Lon G. Lynwalter, the Hopi agency physician, to prepare a detailed report, "in your usual forceful and lucid style," on the advantages of constructing a sanatorium along the railroad. Obviously aware of the negative impact of isolation at the Kayenta facility, the subsequent report favored the urban convenience of Winslow. Repeating much of the city council's argument, it confirmed that a "sanatorium in the interior of the Hopi reservation would be at a marked disadvantage." Warner added that qualified medical personnel would be much more willing to work in a town such as Winslow, with all its conveniences. Local doctors and laboratory facilities were also available to help deal with complications associated with tuberculosis, as was an abundant supply of fresh milk and vegetables. Nor did Warner anticipate that the Indian Service would have difficulty in attracting patients, since they "will go where they get the best service." An off-reservation hospital also promised to limit the disturbance caused by the usual parade of visiting relatives. In all, both Lynwalter and Warner regarded Winslow to be an ideal location for the construction of a forty- to sixty-bed sanatorium.[16]

Despite what seemed to be a logical argument, criticism quickly surfaced. Edgar Miller, superintendent of the Hopi reservation, wrote that Winslow's argument was "bunk." Few residents, he suggested, wanted the sanatorium, believing that the Indians should stay in their own country. Nor did the Indians themselves want the hospital in Winslow: "since seeing the one at Fort Defiance our Navajos are more anxious than ever to have one on this reservation." A short time later, the Indian Office took its first look at the actual site, which turned out to be located near the Santa Fe roundhouse and shop complex. Commissioner Rhoads immediately raised questions as to whether smoke and noise, as well as frequent sandstorms, might be a nuisance. He asked for additional information. Fourteen months later, the Indian Office accepted Winslow's offer. Nevertheless, concerns about environmental conditions persisted. When the new District Medical Director, Dr. Paul Mossman, visited the site in February 1932, he encountered smoky conditions on three of six days. Although it involved the extra cost of extending utility lines, Mossman suggested moving the facility to higher ground several hundred yards west in order to "avoid smoke and dust from the shops."[17]

Dr. Guthrie responded to Mossman by stating that the deal with Winslow had been closed. He emphasized that Mossman's predecessor, Dr. Warner, had approved the site, suggesting that the smoke and noise would not be objectionable. Therefore, the Indian Office would not consider another location. In response to a critic who wrote "that an uglier view could not be selected in the State of Arizona," Guthrie offered to plant some quick-growing trees. Officially named the Hopi-Navajo Sanatorium, construction began during 1932. A year later the hospital opened for business.[18] By this time the nation was mired in the Depression and the Winslow sanatorium, like the one at Kayenta, was faced with an uncertain future.

The attempt to provide additional hospital beds in the Navajo country thus met with only limited success after 1928. Poor site selection, logistical problems, and employee dissatisfaction plagued the Kayenta hospital, Winslow's location was dubious, and Fort Defiance remained overcrowded and outdated. As the New Deal began, less than one hundred tuberculosis beds were available to the thousands of Navajos suffering from that disease. Nor were the number of general hospital beds sufficient. Despite the efforts of Dr. Guthrie, the development of modern hospital facilities and services fell far short of the Meriam recommendations.

TRACHOMA SCHOOLS

The Meriam Report endorsed segregated trachoma schools as a temporary replacement for the discredited Southwestern Trachoma Campaign. At these locations physicians and specially trained nurses might focus on treating children—primarily with the old copper sulfate method—while they waited for the development of a more effective way to reach the adult population. The boarding school at Fort Defiance became a prototype institution when it was set aside as a trachoma facility in December 1926. It functioned as a regular school, with the only difference being the limitations imposed by the fact that all students suffered from vision problems. To the extent of their individual capacities, each student attended class while undergoing an extended regimen of supervised treatment. To maintain isolation, the school operated year round. Students regarded as "cured" could be released at the end of the school year, but "uncured cases most certainly should not go home [for the summer] to infect the younger children in the camps."[19]

It required some months for the school to become fully functional. The buildings were modified as necessary, and by the end of 1927 some four hundred children were housed there. Pupils, divided into four groups by age and sex, received a daily treatment (applied under the eyelid by means of an ointment or pencil-like stick) of silver nitrate, copper sulfate, or argyrol. A small number of surgeries were also performed. After visiting the school in December 1927, Assistant Commissioner Edgar Meritt came away "convinced that this school has proved to be a success equal to our greatest expectations." Nevertheless, he found that other schools had yet to be segregated. A side trip to the Northern Navajo (formerly San Juan) Agency confirmed that its three boarding schools housed a large number of trachomatous children. Meritt thus ordered that one of the schools be set aside solely for infected students in order to "lessen the chance of transmission of this dreadful eye disease." Eventually, schools at Shiprock, Tohatchi, and Crownpoint became trachoma facilities during 1928.[20]

Although the plan for separate trachoma schools may have been advisable, given the circumstances, problems quickly surfaced. The Indian Office blundered badly by failing to inform parents of the plan or to secure their consent to transfers. This caused considerable Navajo dissatisfaction as children were moved to different schools without notice. Parents wanted their children at the local school. In many cases they did not learn until after the fact that their children had been transferred to Fort Defiance or elsewhere for treatment. Some parents became so angry that they refused to send their children to school without some assurance that they would not be moved. When the Navajo Tribal Council seconded this concern, some superintendents proposed the unsatisfactory alternative of sending trachomatous pupils home if parents refused a transfer. Another problem appeared when it became evident that Indian Service doctors were unable to detect all cases of trachoma, thereby assuring that some infected children remained in the supposed trachoma-free schools.[21]

Insufficient staffing presented a special problem at the smaller schools. Dr. William L. Davis noted that a lack of nurses prevented the trachoma schools from providing continuous care. In the past, he remarked, physicians might visit a location once or twice a year. When the schools were "left to shift for themselves [without nurses] until the next visit of a special physician, as has been the practice heretofore, . . . in many instances all the good effects of previous treatment are lost, and the effort wasted, as the granules return in many cases, just as numerous as ever." Davis wanted a full-time nurse stationed at every school. Though this suggestion was not acted upon, the situation seemed to ease a bit. By the end of 1928 Dr. Richards reported a drop in the number of cases entering school, which he attributed to segregation and intensive treatment. This development permitted him to transfer all fifty-three "cured or arrested" pupils at Fort Defiance to Tohatchi, which temporarily reverted back to a "trachoma-free" school when its seventy-eight trachomatous students were sent to Fort Defiance.[22]

Although the Indian Office thus switched schools from time to time, Fort Defiance remained the primary trachoma unit for five years. The problems surrounding this institution illustrate the operational difficulties confronting segregated schools. Retaining a sufficient medical staff, for example, frequently proved difficult. Because of heavy administrative responsibilities, a large caseload, and the tendency to accept other employment, the Fort Defiance school found itself without ophthalmological services for extended periods.[23] Problems related to the transfer of pupils also created headaches. Physicians objected to the government's tendency to move students from one school to another at will, disrupting both treatment and academic programs. Even with the frequent transfers, it proved impossible to fully segregate the children. Agency Superintendent John G. Hunter observed during the summer of 1929 that the Indian Office was finding it difficult to make schools trachoma free. "It is true," he wrote, "that there are one or two full trachomatous schools; on the other hand, it is also true that there is no school in the Navajo Country that is trachoma free." Knowing that Navajo parents were unhappy about sending their children far from home, Hunter asked without success that each school be given permission to treat its own trachoma pupils. As it turned out, even the Fort Defiance school failed to maintain strict separation. When Dr. Paul G. Eilers examined the school's pupils in October 1929, he found a third of them trachoma free. This discovery outraged Eilers, who complained that "there is no excuse for enrolling children in the school who do not have trachoma."[24] The segregation program, he knew, stood no chance of success unless strictly enforced.

Government physicians were also upset with the perpetual lack of resources. Unable to cope with the magnitude of the contagion, they complained about inadequate facilities and staff. One doctor remarked that if the children at Fort Defiance were to receive proper treatment, "it does not seem too much to ask that they be examined and treated by a physician as often as three times per week." With daily responsibilities involving the examination and treatment of two hundred children as well as visits to other schools, the physician could draw on the help of just two nurses. Two additional nurses, he argued, would permit more effective treatment, "as the majority of cases should have some medication from two to four times daily."[25]

The flood of complaints sparked a meeting of all six special physicians assigned to the Southwest (Hailman, Perkins, Richards, Richardson, Wood, and Eilers). Gathering at Albuquerque on August 17, 1931, the field medical staff expressed their mounting frustration in dealing with trachoma. Noting that current staffing needs made it impossible to reduce trachoma rates, the doctors asked that at least one special nurse be placed at every boarding school experiencing a significant number of trachoma cases. The doctors also shared their concern that the boarding school environment continued to actively spread the disease. Dr. Richards, in particular, insisted that conditions at the schools fully justified a continuation of special trachoma facilities. Although parting on a note of optimism about ultimately conquering the disease, the doctors closest to the problem were clearly stymied.[26]

Two months later Guthrie accused the field physicians of defeatism. Citing statistics showing a decline in the number of positive findings between 1925 and 1931, the medical director claimed that trachoma was being controlled. It would be cured even faster, he implied, had the special physicians not let up on their commitment. Guthrie specifically charged the doctors with not treating enough cases. To confirm his opinion, Guthrie asked Dr. Mossman, Southwest District Medical Director, for a backup opinion on the current status of trachoma in the Southwest.[27]

This request permitted Mossman to defend his doctors and inform Washington officials that trachoma was not being controlled. The percentage of positive findings had decreased, he noted, because trachoma work was largely confined to schools. Reported new cases, therefore, came almost entirely from children entering school. In addition, the doctors were so overworked they were often unable to visit all their assigned areas. "These factors, it seems to me, have contributed to prevent a true showing of trachoma prevalence," noted Mossman. The high incidence of the disease among the non-school population did not show up in the statistics. Mossman advised Guthrie that the government needed to determine accurately the prevalence of the disease among reservation Indians and get them treated. "Our present force of special physicians have too large districts to be able to do much work outside the schools."[28]

The growing realization that trachoma remained out of control prompted a reorganization of the program in the summer of 1932. Indian Commissioner Charles Rhoads (1929–1933), reacting to criticism from reformers such as John Collier, ordered a shake-up in the field staff. In July 1932, Dr. Mossman was named Medical Director in Charge of Trachoma Activities. He seemed an ideal choice, having been in charge of Public Health Service trachoma activities prior to joining the Indian Service. Known as an advocate of conservative treatment and faced with an expensive and impractical system that did not work, Mossman abandoned the use of special trachoma schools. He also closed down the portable clinics. To maximize resources, Mossman divided the Southwest into four equal districts, each supervised by a special physician. Three of these assignments included Navajo jurisdictions: Polk Richards for Eastern Navajo (Crownpoint); L. S. Lloyd for Southern Navajo (Fort Defiance) and Northern Navajo (Shiprock); and B. M. Richardson for Western Navajo and Leupp. Under this program all areas of trachoma infection, not just schools, were to receive attention. Nevertheless, primary attention continued to be aimed more at active cases than prevention.[29]

Thus, as in the case of the hospitals and sanatoriums, the trachoma program had failed to make significant progress by the time of Roosevelt's election. The concept of segregated trachoma schools on the Navajo reservation had obviously provided some help to schoolchildren, especially through the capability of enforcing sanitary measures, but it failed to reach the general population. Segregation, moreover, was almost impossible to implement, given the inability to provide full-time medical supervision and the concern of Navajo parents. More important, even when sufficient treatment was present, nothing really worked. Neither radical surgery nor grattage guaranteed that the disease would not reoccur. Treatment with "prophylactic drops" or ointments also failed to provide permanent results.[30] As a consequence, trachoma continued to haunt the Diné.

NURSES AND MISSION HOSPITALS

The Meriam committee strongly endorsed Guthrie's interest in increasing the use of field nurses and cooperating with philanthropic organizations. Like Guthrie, the Meriam Report regarded public health nurses as preferable to field matrons because they were highly trained medical professionals capable of making "a very definite contribution to the health of the Indians." If permitted to operate independently from agency physicians, their special training promised to advance the cause of disease prevention, personal hygiene, and sanitation in Indian camps. The Indian Office accepted this recommendation, and under Guthrie's direction it used the report as a springboard to expand the number of field nurses. To a degree, this effort also coincided with the hopes of Indian Commissioner Charles Rhoads that Indian health-care responsibilities, if they could be sufficiently upgraded, might eventually be assumed by the individual states.[31]

It is doubtful that any government field nurses were initially assigned to the Navajo. However, officials in Washington recognized the potential for such services and this eventually encouraged them to enter into an experimental cooperative program with the New Mexico Association of Indian Affairs (NMAIA). Founded in 1922, this private charitable organization had become involved in promoting Indian health-care issues. In 1924, the association initiated a program of providing field nurses, at its own expense, to the Pueblo Indians. Encouraged by the success of this effort, in 1928 the NMAIA dispatched nurse Elizabeth Duggan to the Navajo community of Nava. Having previously worked among the sedentary Pueblos, Duggan found the scattered, semi-nomadic Diné residents difficult to reach. Despite dispensing medicines out of several trading posts, she grew discouraged over her lack of success and left the reservation. A successor, appointed in May 1929, did little more.[32]

Meanwhile, the Indian Office authorized the employment of its own field nurses among the Navajo. In an effort to ascertain Navajo attitudes about white medicine, agency physicians attended a number of tribal chapter meetings in 1930. The results of this effort suggested that field nurses would be well received. As a consequence, two staff nurses from Fort Defiance general hospital were assigned to field duty, one near Tohatchi and the other at Chinle. The nurses were so well received that Superintendent John G. Hunter concluded that their success showed "conclusively that the Navajo Indian is not only willing to accept, but is reaching out for the white man's teaching, not only along agricultural lines, but medical as well. It is felt the time is at hand to inaugurate a system of intensive teaching through field dispensaries, field nurses supervised by a field physician by which the Navajo can be shown that disease can not only be cured but can also be prevented. . . . It cannot be too strongly urged that field dispensaries containing liveable quarters for field nurses be placed at advantageous points throughout the reservation and an organized system of health teaching begun." Perhaps encouraged by these remarks, in late 1930 a second cooperative effort was launched when the Indian Office agreed to permit two more NMAIA nurses to work at remote communities within the Northern Navajo jurisdiction. Soon thereafter Elizabeth Forster arrived at Red Rock trading post, about thirty-five miles west of Shiprock, and Mollie Reebel set up camp at Newcomb, fifty miles south of the agency.[33]

Both women worked under extremely primitive conditions. Forster, a truly dedicated and compassionate individual, was forced to live in two small rooms at an abandoned medical outpost. Nevertheless, she quickly set up clinics and began treating the sick. Within a short time she managed to establish a good rapport with local residents, her success stemming largely from the fact that she readily accepted Navajo ways and recognized her own limitations. In particular, she willingly acknowledged the value of healers and their use of natural remedies, writing on one occasion that "I soon realized that the Navajos hereabouts expected to find me antagonistic to their religious customs and were slow to consult me about illness until their medicine man failed to help, but gradually they are showing more confidence in my good will and often notify me that they are having a sing and invite me to attend."[34]

Foster's routine involved visiting remote hogans to help at times of childbirth or epidemics and in dispensing medicines. She also worked with the agency physician to assure that he examined the most serious cases during his periodic visits. In a few instances, she even drove patients to the hospital at Shiprock. Her reports, made to the NMAIA, indicate that she treated the Diné for everything from tuberculosis and trachoma to frostbite. Unfortunately, Forster's willingness to accept traditional medical practices irritated the Indian Office. Agency Superintendent E. R. McCray and head physician Dr. Fred Loe apparently became upset with her friendly relationship with traditional healers, believing that she encouraged the very practices they hoped to eliminate. Forster's personality, and not the value of field nurses, thus became an issue. In fact, McCray energetically advocated the use of government field nurses, believing that these women would advance outreach efforts by steering doctors toward the most needy cases. In 1932 he asked the commissioner for two more government field nurses. With regard to Forster, however, he apparently believed that he could not control her actions since she was not on the federal payroll and did not represent the government. This attitude translated into a lack of support for Forster's activities. Eventually, McCray informed Forster that her living quarters were needed for other purposes, leaving the nurse with no place to live. She resigned in early 1933, and was not replaced with another association nurse.[35]

Mollie Reebel, the other NMAIA nurse, was more successful. Working first in the Newcomb vicinity, then at Navajo Mountain, she visited remote communities and operated field clinics. Equipped with a bedroll, tent, and wagon, she provided as much individual care as possible. She too reported that the Diné were usually receptive to her visits. Nevertheless, there were many difficulties. Impassable roads, severe weather, and a lack of resources made it difficult for her to do much more than dispense medicines and provide basic remedies. As with Forster, hopes of educating the Navajo people on issues of hygiene and causing them to alter their lifestyle soon fell by the wayside. In this sense, the anticipation that field nurses would promote prevention failed to materialize. Nor did there seem to be much benefit in working with privately funded field nurses. Nonetheless, Mollie Reebel continued her efforts until 1935, when the NMAIA pulled out altogether.[36] She then joined the Indian Service as a field nurse.

Another area of potential cooperation between the Indian Service and private charitable organizations involved mission hospitals. Church-run hospitals had been part of the reservation since the Episcopal Good Shepherd hospital opened near Fort Defiance in 1897. Indeed, this institution set a precedent for cooperative relationships with the Indian Service by relying on part-time help from government doctors. Moreover, it functioned as the major trachoma clinic at Fort Defiance until closing in 1929 to focus exclusively on missionary activities. Meanwhile, several other church hospitals and clinics had opened. By 1930 the two most significant denominational medical facilities on or near the reservation were the Rehoboth Hospital operated by the Christian Reformed Church near Gallup and the large Presbyterian hospital at Ganado. These facilities reached elements of the Navajo population in areas of limited government service.[37]

The existence of these church hospitals presented the government with an opportunity for cooperation. The Indian Service obviously needed all the help it could obtain. Although some medical facilities had been upgraded in the wake of the Meriam Report, others were totally unfit. The agency hospital at Shiprock, for instance, was depicted in 1932 as "poorly constructed and wholly inadequate. . . . The equipment is poor, and the condition of the building would not justify any repairs or enlargement. The foundation is bad, and the building itself, being a wooden structure, is virtually a fire trap." Other reports indicated that more hospitals, physicians, and nurses were necessary for the government to get a handle on reservation medical problems.[38]

Despite the obvious advantages of encouraging the expansion of privately funded hospitals, which brought needed resources to the reservation, the Indian Service expressed a mixed reaction to these institutions. There appears to have been a rather strained relationship with the Rehoboth Mission Hospital. Founded in 1910 by the conservative Christian Reformed Church, the poorly funded and ill-equipped facility was looked upon by its staff primarily as a vehicle for religious conversion. This created some friction, particularly after Dr. Richard H. Pousma became the medical director at Rehoboth in 1927. A man of strong religious views, Pousma criticized the government for not doing more to support missionary efforts. Totally opposed to traditional healing ceremonies, he expressed anger that such events continued to be tolerated. Perhaps what galled him the most were indications that agency officials might be moderating their opposition to traditional ceremonial events. In 1931, for example, Southern Navajo Agency Superintendent John G. Hunter had written to Washington that "under present conditions I do not believe that the Navajo dances retard, to any extent, the advancement of the Indians." Although Hunter had not specifically endorsed healing practices, Pousma believed otherwise. Testifying before a Senate investigative subcommittee in May 1931 (see below), Pousma stated that Navajo ceremonials always related to healing and that these gatherings accomplished nothing more than the spread of communicable diseases. In Pousma's opinion, anyone encouraging "religious dances" should be regarded as "idiotic, exceedingly stupid, and ignorant of conditions among the Indians."[39]

If these complaints were not enough, government officials were also irritated by Pousma's criticism of their medical practices. In contrast to the federal desire to get more doctors into the field, Pousma believed this activity to be a foolish waste of time. "One of the greatest griefs the doctor has to put up with," he argued, "is to be called out on a very hard field trip of 30 to 50 miles to an Indian who needs nothing but an aspirin tablet, and if the Indians know that a doctor will answer they will make many unnecessary calls. . . . If they need hospital care they can come along to the hospital." The missionary physician also believed that the government ought to devote more energy to dealing with venereal disease. Not only did he regard this as a growing problem, but he believed that the Indian Service ignored the situation. While he correctly realized that the disease was again increasing, he proposed rather draconian remedies, urging the government to crack down on the Navajos, even to the point of invading their privacy. He insisted that infected individuals be forced to remain hospitalized until cured, and while confined be compelled to do manual labor. In fact, he wanted the Indian Office to compel Navajo males to identify their sexual partners, so that the women might "be apprehended and compelled to undergo hospitalization."[40] These unrealistic attitudes and criticisms rankled government doctors.

A much better relationship developed with the Presbyterian hospital at Ganado. This operation dated back to 1906, when the church approved the construction of a twelve-bed facility. The small hospital struggled until Dr. Clarence Salsbury became medical director in 1927. Having previously served as a medical missionary in China, Salsbury possessed a great talent for fundraising and innovation. Like most missionaries, he rejected the validity of traditional healing practices, at one point stating that "old, ignorant, superstitious medicine men" presented the greatest obstacle to progress. If nothing else, however, Salsbury was a practical man and he quickly began to work with prominent Navajo leaders and healers, at one point convincing a group of healers to enter his hospital, then publicizing the event in order to persuade the community that he could be trusted. He also used this success to solicit gifts, always being careful to indicate that some patients "have accepted the Lord as their Saviour and come out of heathenism."[41]

In 1929 Salsbury obtained funding to construct a large modern hospital. Dedicated on May 1, 1930, Sage Memorial Hospital was a state-of-the-art facility. Able to house seventy-five patients, the two-story stone building also contained a surgical unit, X-ray department, laboratory, modern kitchen, and an "excellent Buick ambulance." The most advanced medical facility on the reservation, Sage Memorial was only slightly smaller than the Fort Defiance hospital. It drew immediate praise. Among the dignitaries attending the dedication were Navajo leader Henry Chee Dodge, who donated five hundred dollars to Salsbury's cause, and Reuben Perry, superintendent of the Albuquerque Indian School. Commissioner Rhoads sent a letter of congratulation. Completion of this impressive structure enabled Salsbury to bring additional physicians to the Navajo country. To reach patients in the surrounding thirty-five hundred square miles of territory, the hospital established five scattered community centers, "staffed partly by graduate nurses [which] serve as miniature medical centers and feeders for the central medical plant." Salsbury also recognized the need for Indians to be involved in the practice of medicine. To this end, in 1930 he opened a training program for Indian nurses. The only program of its type in the country, Salsbury explained that "I have become convinced that what Ganado needed, and what the whole Navajo tribe needed, was its own Indian nurses, [who] would be able to understand the patients as no white personnel ever could." Despite a warning by some Indian Service officials that this program would fail, the Training School for Nurses flourished.[42]

Sage Memorial Hospital quickly became a showpiece in the field of Indian health care, accredited by the American College of Surgeons. Although Sage Memorial had received much more favorable publicity than government hospitals, the Indian Service initially offered its cooperation. In the fall of 1930, for example, Dr. Paul Mossman, one of the government's top trachoma specialists, presented a two-day clinic and performed over twenty surgeries. The following year, Southern Navajo Agency Superintendent John Hunter observed that the "service rendered to the Navajo people at the 75-bed hospital is of extraordinary worth, and is highly appreciated by the Navajos and by the Government force." Sage Memorial even provided laboratory work for the government. Nevertheless, an element of jealousy lay beneath the surface. Reports indicating that Indians preferred Sage Memorial because it was better equipped and administered did not always sit well with government employees. Although the competition presented by Salsbury's hospital did not immediately cause problems, competitive pressures would surface during the New Deal. Meanwhile, the mission hospitals did not always get along with each other. Jacob C. Morgan, a noted Navajo advocate of assimilation and friend of the Rehoboth Mission, criticized the moderate philosophy of Salsbury, remarking that "I think Dr. Salsbury is a man full of hot air. A poor example for a christian, if he is such."[43]

THE SENATE HEARINGS

During April and May 1931, the U.S. Senate Subcommittee of the Committee on Indian Affairs staged a series of hearings in the Navajo country. Comprised of Senators Lynn J. Frazier (chairman, North Dakota), Burton K. Wheeler (Montana), Elmer Thomas (Oklahoma), Henry A. Ashurst (Arizona), and Assistant Commissioner of Indian Affairs J. Henry Scattergood, the subcommittee took testimony at a number of locations, including the agency communities of Crownpoint, Fort Defiance, Leupp, Shiprock, and Tuba City. The hearings represented part of a continuing survey of reservation conditions backed by John Collier and other vocal critics of the Indian Service. Senator Frazier, in particular, worked closely with Collier. Although the reform leader was present for only one session, the hearings focused on Collier's concern about the ineffectiveness of federal Indian programs. Medical care thus received considerable attention.[44] The resulting 940 pages of testimony included statements from agency officials, physicians, missionaries, individual Navajos, and others. What emerged was a picture of medical failure in spite of the sincere effort of many government employees to improve conditions.

Perhaps realizing that the Senate hearings were partly motivated by politics, some Indian Service employees seemed hesitant to express overt criticism. Still, they eagerly sought more financial support. Most comments therefore began with the caveat that health conditions were either good or improving before launching into an attack on current conditions. In any case, the plethora of health problems and lack of resources became public. Overall, observers believed that tuberculosis and trachoma remained out of control and that in some locations venereal diseases "are also becoming more common and constitute a serious menace to the general health of the Navajos."[45]

Tuberculosis appeared epidemic at many locations. Dr. William B. Hagerty from Shiprock presented a blistering criticism of government efforts; focusing on the lack of a local sanatorium, Hagerty told the subcommittee that "the tuberculosis conditions on this reservation are very unsatisfactory. . . . We are doing nothing for tuberculosis." Terminal patients could not be cared for because of a lack of facilities, although the general hospital might admit a few cases who had come miles for help "and we have not the heart to send them home to die." Dr. Koentz at Kayenta reported that his facility had encountered great difficulty in successfully treating adult Indians because they appeared too late for treatment or insisted on going home if their condition seemed to improve. When asked what the government might do to control tuberculosis, all the medical personnel suggested the expansion of existing sanatoriums and the construction of new ones.[46]

Trachoma drew fewer comments. Nevertheless, physicians and superintendents stressed that many adult Navajos suffered from the blinding eye disease and that the best chance to control the disease remained with isolating school-children, although this had not proven terribly effective in the past. The majority of pupils in some jurisdictions remained afflicted with trachoma. The subcommittee also raised questions about the methods of treatment in use, expressing concern over some of the painful methods reportedly used on other reservations. Members were gratified to learn that most doctors preferred the use of copper sulfate and argyrol ointments in order to avoid the extreme pain commonly encountered when copper sulfate pencil was rubbed on the inside of the eyelid. Doctors from all five jurisdictions confirmed that trachoma remained a problem, despite some hope that the disease might soon be controlled.[47]

Witnesses also emphasized the need for more doctors, expressing an opinion that the lack of effective medical care could be blamed on the inability of physicians to reach the general reservation population. Hospital work, despite a general lack of resources, seemed to be doing relatively well. At these facilities, doctors could practice the methods of modern medicine and observe some positive results. Fieldwork, however, presented another story. Dr. W. A. Fahy told the subcommittee that every request for service was answered, but that few camp Indians wanted help. Maternity cases were typical. Women living near a hospital readily used its birthing services, but the great majority of newborns continued to be "delivered in the field," with no doctors available. Because of the persistent lack of personnel, few field clinics could be offered and educational efforts remained almost nonexistent. Dr. H. E. Scoles remarked that the Navajos seemed to be more willing to accept western medicine and hospitalization, yet the "magnificent distances" involved and the migratory nature of the Diné made it impossible to deliver medical care to much of the population.[48]

In addition, considerable enthusiasm surfaced for the hiring of more government field nurses. Dr. Fahy told the subcommittee that "I believe that the time is here now for field nurses and field dispensaries. I feel that the Navajo is in a very receptive mood for teaching and it should be the duty of the field nurse to do more teaching and demonstrating than dispensing." Dr. Hagerty noted that field nurses were absolutely necessary, suggesting that they were needed in his jurisdiction (Northern Navajo) to educate the Indians in personal health care, to be available for home calls, and to bring the sick in for hospital care. These women appeared to be the best vehicle for reaching remote communities, convincing the Indians to accept modern medicine, and improving the standard of living. Dr. Koentz reported that his part-time field nurse arranged her trips to coincide with chapter meetings, where the Navajo gathered monthly to discuss tribal business and socialize: "Our nurse gets to meet a lot of these Indians at the meetings and visit with the mothers, telling them how to take care of their babies, give them talks, and so forth. She meets a lot of them and treats them at the time, picks up the serious ones, and, if possible, brings them to the sanitarium." From these and similar comments it became apparent that both the subcommittee and government employees believed that the use of additional field nurses would be necessary for the Indian Service to effectively reach the Navajo population. Indeed, superintendents did not hesitate to ask for the immediate employment of ten to fifteen trained nurses.[49]

Despite improvements made to hospital facilities since 1928, conditions at some locations shocked the subcommittee. Dr. Scoles informed the hearings that his thirty-two-bed facility at Crownpoint was in fact a converted school dormitory suffering from such overcrowding that as many as three patients shared the same bed. Admitting that this "condition is intolerable for proper medical service," he described other problems. The hospital laundry, for example, occupied space in the operating room. Indeed, the washing machine chugged along just six feet from the surgical table. Scoles also articulated the need for a tuberculosis sanatorium. Under current circumstances, tubercular patients had no place to go because the hospitals at Laguna and Fort Defiance were full. As a consequence, they remained at home, "a menace to other members of the family." Administrators from other hospitals also expressed the need for enlarged facilities, pleading for more beds and basic equipment such as X-ray machines. Dr. Scoles passionately asked the subcommittee for congressional support in improving the hospitals.[50]

Surprisingly little criticism was expressed about the activities of traditional healers. A number of officials seemed to feel that the influence of "medicine men" was slipping as federal medical activities expanded across the reservation. Dr. Scoles told the subcommittee that healers still presented a source of competition, but the availability of new health services provided "an entering wedge to separate the Indian from his superstition." Leupp Superintendent John Balmer agreed, remarking that while healers remained a force among the Diné, he believed attitudes were changing. Nevertheless, he still felt that the only way to overcome the "problems" presented by traditional practices was to increase the size of the government's medical staff.[51] In general, however, there were few expressions of concern about Navajo medical practices, apparently under the assumption that "medicine men" were becoming obsolete.

Individual Navajos were also permitted to address medical conditions, but only a few came forward. These speakers hardly represented the full range of tribal opinion, with none of them defending traditional medicine. Nonetheless, unhappiness with the government clearly existed. Some residents at Northern Navajo expressed anger toward government practices at the Shiprock hospital. In particular, they resented being turned away after long trips to seek care. They also disliked the attitude of doctors, who appeared to be overbearing and unsympathetic. Speaking through an interpreter, one Navajo man stated that "those people that work in the hospital don't take any special care. They handle them roughly and scold them and so on, and that does not seem right." Comparable complaints about hospital food also surfaced, with some patients feeling that they were being starved because they could not eat their normal food, which doctors refused to provide. Among those who expressed concern about government medical care was Dashine Chischilege, chairman of the Tribal Council.[52]

Another Navajo observer expressed appreciation for government efforts, maintaining that doctors were doing everything in their power to help the Diné. Owing to long distances and bad roads, however, isolated population centers remained neglected. This particular woman argued that the addition of doctors, nurses, and field clinics was urgently needed to prevent unnecessary deaths. To make her point, she described several tragic incidents, including one where a sick boy could not be reached for days because the doctor's "so-called ambulance" broke down. By the time the lad reached a hospital, it was too late for surgery, and the boy perished. This Navajo woman hoped that future incidents of this nature could be prevented by enhanced government funding.[53]

The subcommittee hearings ended on May 21, 1931. Although the testimony did much to document the medical condition of the Navajo and emphasize the need for more money, few immediate changes occurred. Still, the Indian Office, aware of the unfavorable publicity, made some effort to determine if economical modifications could be undertaken. In the summer of 1932, Rhoads ordered a survey of medical conditions in the Southwest, particularly with regard to the possible standardization of methods, personnel, and facilities. And indeed, a few limited improvements could be detected by mid-1932. At Fort Defiance, Superintendent John Hunter found the money to hire a field nurse and field physician to work with the off-reservation Navajos living south of Gallup. Hunter believed that the nurse was especially effective in immunizing preschool children and instructing mothers in basic hygiene. Impressed with this success, the superintendent unsuccessfully suggested that the government hire six field nurses to work on the reservation. Meanwhile, physicians from Fort Defiance, Tohatchi, and Chinle enhanced their visits to chapter meetings by giving talks on disease prevention, performing medical examinations, and occasionally persuading an individual to enter the hospital. The Navajos appeared to appreciate such attention, although the government viewed these visits as a temporary expedient until "dispensaries connected with the chapter houses" could be opened.[54]

Despite these advances, major problems obviously remained. During the 1932 fiscal year both the Tohatchi and Chinle hospitals suffered through lengthy periods without a physician, undoing "the good work of several months of teaching Navajos to utilize our hospitals." In another instance, the Fort Defiance general hospital received a new X-ray machine, which greatly facilitated the diagnosis of tuberculosis, yet it employed no technician to operate the machine, forcing doctors to handle that task themselves. Nor did a dietitian work at the hospital. Although the Fort Defiance general hospital was considered "quite well equipped," the smaller reservation facilities suffered from numerous inadequacies. At Chinle, where a bad boiler prevented the sterilizer from working, the electricity shut off at 10:00 P.M., "making it necessary to use kerosene lamps that are a menace to the patients and the building."[55] Such problems typified conditions at hospitals across the Navajo country.

The Meriam era ended in 1933, with the beginning of the New Deal. Without question the report prompted some changes in the medical services provided to the Navajo people. Yet these improvements consisted of little more than opening two sanatoriums, the employment of additional staff, and some enhancement in hospital facilities. More important in some respects, the five-

year transitional era brought to light the enormous medical difficulties facing
the Diné. In particular, the need to provide public health services and involve
the Navajo people more actively in health issues became evident. These services, of course, could only be provided by a significant influx of financial aid.
In 1932 this seemed remote indeed without aggressive national leadership and a
commitment to move in new directions.

CHAPTER NINE

NEW DEAL

Among the pre-Columbian religious functionaries, in the Navajo tribe, are the medicine men. Their functions in the sphere of mental healing are important. They do not offer any significant resistance to modern medicine.

JOHN COLLIER, INDIAN COMMISSIONER

We are also much concern[ed] about health conditions among our people. We have very little help in this matter. Mr. Collier promised our people that he will establish a field nurse at every day school and a doctor to hold clinic at all day schools. Where are they, we do not see them.

ROBERT MARTIN, TRIBAL COUNCIL

John Collier became well known in Navajo country during the New Deal. As the generation's most vocal and colorful advocate of Indian policy reform, he wanted to change the way the Indian Office operated. A champion of Indian causes during the 1920s, the outspoken and volatile native of Georgia brought radical new ideas to the commissioner's post in 1933. Committed to the concept of "cultural pluralism," he inaugurated a new era in Indian policy by advocating the preservation of native culture, a local educational system, restoration of tribal lands, self-rule, and direct economic aid. Although hampered by budget restraints, Collier energetically pursued these goals during the administration of Franklin D. Roosevelt.[1]

Despite his determination to improve the lot of Native Americans, the aggressive and paternalistic nature of Collier's reforms created almost as many problems as they solved. As a consequence, some of his New Deal policies caused an adverse reaction among the Diné, which left them bitter and suspicious of the government. Even passage of the Wheeler-Howard bill, the centerpiece of Collier's Indian New Deal, rankled many Navajos. The 1934 legislation ended the allotment era, authorized the creation of tribal constitutions, and focused heavily on permitting the tribes to preserve their cultural identity. Although well intended, some of the bill's provisions, especially the one reorganizing tribal government, were effectively opposed on the reservation. Past injustices, including a feeling that the government had not lived up to its treaty obligations in the areas of health and education, partly accounted for the negative vote. As one Navajo put it, "Why trust [the government] now."[2]

Navajo opposition to the Wheeler-Howard bill must also be understood in light of Collier's hated livestock-reduction program, launched in 1933 over tribal objections. Intended by the Indian Office to reduce soil erosion, improve the value of Navajo herds, and preserve tribal society, the program was carried out in a brutal and heavy-handed way that ended up with some families seeing their animals slaughtered before their eyes. Completely ignoring the central role played by livestock in tribal culture, Collier tolerated no opposition. This spectacle, which lasted on and off until 1941, embittered most Navajos and turned them against the government. Individual reactions were similar to that of Chee Carroll, who blamed the whole thing on Collier "and his weird ideas." Particularly frustrating for the Diné was their inability to convince the government that reduction plans did not work. As Kayenta resident Buck Austin noted, "he [Collier] was stubborn as a mule and did not listen to the voice of the people." Many other Navajos believed that the episode left them destitute, and some even expressed their outrage by attacking government employees.[3]

The highly charged livestock issue impacted other government programs on the reservation. Howard Gorman, tribal vice-chairman, was roundly criticized by his own people when he agreed to become a government interpreter in 1936. Indeed, any association with government seemed to taint tribal leaders. Gorman himself later summed up tribal opinion: "I think a lot of injustice was done to the Navajo people during the stock reduction. I think the government could have done the whole thing differently and more effectively, on the basis of a high-class manner instead of the way it was—creating a lot of antagonism on the part of the people." As a result, the Navajo people often harbored negative feelings toward any New Deal program, including medical improvements. Peter Iverson observes that "while the stock reduction program took place, it affected everything on the reservation, not only the daily lives of the people, but the tribal government and other programs of the federal government as well."[4] As a consequence, the unfolding of Collier's medical program and the Navajo response cannot be divorced from the underlying tension produced by the socioeconomic disaster then dominating Navajo life.

CHANGING PRIORITIES

Collier's preoccupation with crafting the Wheeler-Howard bill during his first year in office kept medical concerns somewhat in the background. The new commissioner, however, was well informed about the Navajo medical situation as a result of the 1931 Senate subcommittee hearings, which clearly demonstrated the need for more hospitals, doctors, and nurses. As soon as time permitted, Collier committed himself to a complete overhaul of reservation medical services, blaming the rampant tuberculosis, trachoma, and high infant mortality on a lack of federal resources. Problems related to poor sanitation, malnutrition, and a lingering Navajo mistrust of government medical services also seemed to need attention. Enamored with the then popular public-health movement, the New Deal reformer proposed dealing with these obstacles through education, field care, and prevention, all supported by a significant improvement in the medical infrastructure.[5]

Navajo medical services obviously needed consolidation. In 1933 nine government hospitals, each handling its own affairs, operated on or near the Navajo reservation. Centralization, an idea previously circulated among reservation officials, appeared to offer significant benefits, and it blossomed under Collier, who made it part of an overall administrative reorganization of the reservation. To this end, in May 1934, Collier appointed Dr. W. W. Peter, a prominent member of the national public-health movement, to the newly created position of Medical Director, Navajo Area, with offices at Albuquerque. This position was then folded into the 1935 consolidation of reservation administration. Under the new system, the five existing jurisdictions were combined to form one central agency, headquartered a few miles south of Fort Defiance, at Window Rock. When Chester E. Farris became General Superintendent of the United Navajo Reservation on May 20, 1935, the old Eastern, Northern, Southern, Western, and Leupp subagencies disappeared. The new structure promised to be more efficient and reliable (although some Navajos expressed concern because it became more difficult to gain the ear of a government representative). One anticipated benefit was a more effective health program.[6]

During an exchange of views with reservation officials in November 1934, Collier and Peter suggested a general strategy for dealing with the Navajo medical situation. Collier indicated that he would support the creation of a unified medical system "with one strong central hospital at some agreed upon central location, and with all other existing institutions closely affiliated." A unit of this nature permitted the use of centralized supply-office and laboratory facilities. It also allowed the Indian Service to provide its staff with such professional amenities as a circulating medical library and the flexibility to shift personnel from place to place as needed.[7]

Collier also wanted government doctors to show more sensitivity toward Navajo tradition. "Cultural pluralism," a significant aspect of his reform agenda, included the acceptance and preservation of traditional beliefs. From the begin-

ning of his administration, Collier stressed what Elinor Gregg called "an anthropological approach . . . to the conduct of the Indian Service." With regard
to medicine, Collier acknowledged that modern medical practices were necessary for the elimination of disease. At the same time, he understood the importance of preserving traditional culture. Accordingly, in 1936 he announced that
Navajo "medicine men" deserved to be recognized for their contribution to
mental health and that they posed no threat to modern medicine.[8]

Indications of this philosophy quickly appeared on the Navajo reservation.
Instead of the emotional, embittered opposition expressed by earlier physicians, Dr. Peter suggested that "medicine men" possessed the advantages of
familiarity and proximity: "He understands the language and the customs of
the patient and the patient's family. He is the beneficiary of tradition." Although Peter lamented that healing ceremonies sometimes prevented patients
from seeking timely medical attention, he admitted that healers were becoming more adept at recognizing grave problems and referring them to hospitals.
Such practices benefited both the patients and the healer, who often took credit
if the patient recovered.[9]

As might be expected, any suggestion that they tolerate traditional ceremonies and practices upset some government doctors, who charged Collier
with preventing the Navajo from receiving proper medical care. The idea drew
similar criticism from non-government sources. Jacob C. Morgan, the outspoken Navajo political leader and opponent of New Deal policies, publicly
attacked Collier's plan, stating that "Mr. Collier is very strong for the continued performance of the medicine man of the tribe. He says that a white man
learns and is being educated thru Indian ceremonials." Morgan disagreed,
calling the healer "a judge, loafer, a gambler and often time a drunkard." To
support this argument, Morgan recounted several tragedies he blamed on
healer malpractice. In one instance, he noted, a young boy had "died as the
direct result of pagan surgery," having been taken to a hospital too late to do
any good. "After the boy died at the hospital the Indians blamed the white
doctors for it." Collier considered Morgan to be misinformed. "I am strong
against the indiscriminate condemnation of Indian native ways," he wrote in
response, "and against that form of blindness which sees no virtue except in
one's own doctrines, conventions and superstitions. The Navajo religion is a
lofty one—lofty in the ethical and in the esthetic meaning."[10]

Another indication of Collier's perceived tolerance of traditional medicine
appeared with the growing antagonism between himself and Dr. Clarence
Salsbury, director of Sage Memorial Hospital. Despite Salsbury's willingness to
accept the endorsement of Navajo healers, he publicly linked medical care to
religious conversion. As one of his physicians observed in 1933, "To-day there

are two outstanding needs among the Navajo people. The greatest is a saving knowledge of Jesus Christ. The other is an understanding of the opportunities offered them by medical service. . . . The medical missionary with a heart full of the love of Jesus, his mind and hands trained in the art of medical science, has the privilege of executing the last command of the Great Physician." Salsbury believed that Collier's approach contradicted this goal. The commissioner, in turn, did not want the government to participate in religious proselytizing.[11]

Tensions came to a head when Salsbury began staging an annual Navajo "Chautauqua" in 1934. A revival meeting, medical clinic, and country fair all rolled into one, the Ganado event attracted prominent doctors from across the country to hold clinics and workshops. For two days prior to the Chautauqua as many as twenty-five doctors and fifteen nurses treated the medical needs of "our Navajo people." When combined with free meals, the event drew in hundreds of Navajos "who would not come primarily to hear the Good News of a Saviour, but who, having come to the Chautauqua from other motives, will follow the crowd into the big Tent anyway." As useful as these services proved to be, Collier objected to the obvious religious atmosphere and discouraged Indian Service personnel from participating. A total of five Chautauquas were held, all very successful from Salsbury's viewpoint, but Collier's opposition led to their demise in 1938, once the Indian Service inaugurated a competing tribal fair at Window Rock. At this event, government doctors offered clinics without religious overtones. Overall, the tiff between Collier and Salsbury did little damage to reservation medical services despite highlighting the contrast between the commissioner and missionary doctors regarding the place of native tradition.[12]

DOCTORS

Many of Collier's ideas were incorporated in the reorganization of Navajo medical services carried into effect during 1934 and 1935. Peter formalized a "Navajo Health Plan" in early 1935. In general, it sought to improve professional standards among doctors and nurses, train Navajos for medical jobs, and create a Navajo Board of Health to directly involve the Diné in understanding their health needs and cooperating with the government. Peter also committed the government to opening modern new hospital facilities. At the core of the plan was a 145-bed medical center located at Fort Defiance, which would serve the entire reservation with diagnostic, laboratory, and research services. To make room for the medical center, the old sanatorium would be demolished, with the current general hospital becoming a tuberculosis facility. Peter also suggested the construction of new hospitals at Crownpoint and Shiprock, and the opening of smaller clinics, beginning at Gallup and Window Rock.[13]

Collier and Peter emphasized upgrading the medical staff. Realizing that doctors suffered from isolation, the new health plan proposed the establishment of regular "refresher courses" and workshops "in order to achieve continuous professional growth." Implied, if not specifically stated, was the intention to send more public-health specialists into the field. Additionally, Peter sought to upgrade dental services (seldom provided in the past) by stationing a number of mobile dental clinics among the Diné. These proposals were reinforced by statistics demonstrating a sad state of neglect. Peter noted, for instance, that for every fifty thousand people, the general population was served by sixty-three physicians, eighty-seven nurses, and twenty-eight dentists. The Navajos, with approximately forty-five thousand people, could call on only eighteen physicians, fifty-one nurses, and two dentists. Peter hoped that the reorganization plan would enable him to render to the Diné the kind of health services available elsewhere in the country.[14]

Thus committed, Peter upgraded the quality and number of reservation medical personnel as much as possible, lobbying for salaries comparable to those of the Veteran's Bureau and Public Health Service and adopting recommendations that the Fort Defiance general hospital make every effort to secure American College of Surgeons accreditation. Unfortunately, his efforts ran headlong into financial limitations dictated by the Depression. Although government jobs did attract a number of capable young doctors, it still proved difficult to fill vacancies, especially at the senior level. Faced with constant personnel shortages, the Indian Office regularly transferred doctors and nurses from place to place, leaving positions unexpectedly vacant. In August 1933, Superintendent John Hunter complained that doctors in the Southern Navajo jurisdiction were overworked: "Never was [there] greater need of medical assistance and never did we have so little help." Collier acknowledged that administrative problems caused vacancies to go unfilled. Nevertheless, he remained optimistic that things would improve, reaffirming his commitment to improving the number and quality of Indian Service physicians. He expressed hope that forthcoming Civil Service examinations "will be able to materially improve the personnel over what has been possible for the past number of years."[15]

By the summer of 1936 a number of new physicians were in the field doing public-health work at community centers and day-school clinics. From these locations they also made some attempt to visit individual homes. One observer concluded that "the younger, more energetic and more liberal men coming into the Service in late years, are showing results." Nonetheless, this effort failed to reach many Navajos, who still showed a pronounced "disinclination" to patronize government doctors. After three months in the field, one doctor concluded that the job was expensive, useless, and worthless, doing more harm than good: "The [field] physician cannot leave medicine to be taken at certain specific times because most Indians tell time by the sun; the Indian cannot be trusted with patent drugs because he is easily tempted to try getting well quickly, . . . As a physician, the field man can do no more than an intelligent field nurse, which is to encourage the really sick Indian to accept hospital care." Another doctor, C. D. Hopper, wrote in 1935 that fieldwork would be unsatisfactory to anyone needing the inspiration of visible accomplishments. Although admitting that field efforts had improved over the past five years, Hopper realized that for some time to come field physicians must be motivated solely by "the call to duty." A lack of money to hire Navajo interpreters compounded the frustration. Without an ability to ask questions and secure answers, fieldwork did not seem to be particularly efficient, especially when so many Navajos distrusted the government.[16]

On the other hand, doctors on the Navajo reservation were encouraged by the creation of a professional organization in 1937. Composed of physicians from the entire region, the Southwestern Indian Service Medical Society met twice a year to discuss current research, hold workshops, present papers, and socialize. By 1940 the Medical Society had become thoroughly professional, representing over fifty physicians, six dentists, and two hundred nurses. Visiting experts from the Arizona State Public Health Service, National Tuberculosis Association, U.S. Public Health Service, and the Indian Office participated in their meetings. Without doubt, these semiannual gatherings improved morale and made working conditions more tolerable.[17]

Overall, by the time the United States entered the Second World War the efforts of Collier and Peter to recruit better physicians had paid limited dividends. The quality and competency of physicians had improved. Hospitals were better staffed, and more physicians worked in the field. Nonetheless, doctors remained overworked and underpaid. Most physicians, including senior surgeons, were bogged down with work. And despite the strong efforts of the Indian Office, not enough qualified doctors wanted to work on a remote and uncomfortable reservation.

NURSES

Collier also attempted to enhance nursing services through the improvement of hospital living conditions, expanding the number of field nurses, and creation of a group of Navajo nurse-aids. This last idea received considerable attention in 1934 after Collier hired Sally Lucas Jean to become his Supervisor of Health Education. Founder of the American Child Health Association and a public-health activist, Jean agreed that more Navajos should be involved in providing health care. Perhaps spurred on by the success of Salsbury's Indian Nursing School at Ganado, Jean proposed stationing nurse-aids at various community centers and boarding schools. Recruited from the boarding schools, where they had received some health training, these young Navajo women, "who understand both languages and the various phases of medical service having to do with the conservation of health, can be given a very vital place in the integration of the health and education programs of the Service." Inspired by the possibilities of employing more Navajos, Collier permitted Jean to plan a four-week summer institute to educate these women in the care and prevention of trachoma, infant health, social problems, and health teaching.[18]

The nurse-aid concept assumed that superficially trained young Indian women would be able to assist doctors and nurses as well as work independently. The first training institute, held at Santa Fe Indian School during June and July 1934, attracted a total of ninety-eight young Navajo women representing all parts of the reservation. During the month-long course the trainees maintained two specially constructed hogans as "fresh, clean, beautiful structures." Each girl also became a "mother for a day," caring for a small infant over a twenty-four-hour period. In addition, they learned basic first aid, how to eliminate flies, the proper use of soap and water, and ways to prevent eye disease. Polk Richards and other prominent Indian Service physicians lent a hand, providing such helpful hints as how to sterilize muddy ditch water for use in cleansing eyes. Although this training was extremely basic, Jean hoped that her young women might be quickly put to work.[19]

Unfortunately, the nurse-aid program failed to meet expectations. The first class got off to a bad start when physical examinations revealed that a quarter of the trainees had active trachoma, seven suffered from tuberculosis, and twenty-eight needed other medical attention. This situation led to serious concerns about the screening process. It was also embarrassing that many of the girls had to be excused because of poor health. More important, perhaps, most of those completing the course could not find employment. Although fifteen women were assigned to help field nurses, Jean's proposal to station nurse-aids across the reservation floundered on the rocks of financial retrenchment. In addition, Peter hesitated to employ trainees unless they were accompanied by a doctor or a nurse. As a result, the 1935 summer institute looked very different. This time most participants came from other tribes, only 30 of the 103 girls being Navajos. Expectations were lowered. A few of the trainees still planned on becoming nurse-aids, but most studied home economics or prepared to enter a regular nursing school. Despite a lack of employment opportunities, Jean hoped to continue the institutes, maintaining that if nothing else, "all of [the girls] will be better prepared to live healthfully, and to help prevent disease among their people."[20]

The nurse-aid program slipped even further after 1936, when Edna A. Gerken replaced Jean as Supervisor of Health Education. Although Gerken adopted some of Jean's ideas, she focused primarily on instructing school-teachers and their Indian assistants in basic medicine during a two-week summer school held at Fort Wingate. Here too a hogan was used to provide home-care lessons. Attendees also witnessed surgeries, received practical lessons in the detection and treatment of trachoma, and learned infant-care techniques. Navajo employees, such as housekeepers and school assistants, received special information on what the Diné called "invisible worms," or bacteria. Whatever the value of this training, the nurse-aid concept had run its course. With superficial training, insufficient funding, and opposition from some doctors, an independent corps of Navajo health workers never gained ground. In 1939, the new Fort Defiance general hospital employed six nurse-aids, probably the only ones on the reservation.[21]

The field nursing program fared much better in the early New Deal years, although it too eventually collapsed. By the time Collier became commissioner the benefits of field nursing seemed irrefutable. Collier himself actively promoted this approach through *Indians at Work*, a public-relations magazine started by the Indian Office in 1933.[22] Under such titles as "Drama in the Life of Field Nurses" and "Tenting on the Western Navajo," stories about field nurses appeared frequently. Peter and Edna Gerken also wrote articles explaining the concept of public-health work and what the nurses actually did. Peter praised these dedicated women for their extraordinary versatility and resourcefulness: "Her time is spent 'in the field' and with us that means desert mostly. She must be able to drive a car of uncertain vintage and reliability over roads that are tracks or less. In the dry season she and all she carries gets covered with dust. In the wet season, with mud. She must be able to live with herself for company, for much of her time is spent alone."[23]

In general, field nurses were expected to handle everything that came their way, usually without outside help. During the course of a year a field nurse could anticipate helping with school physical examinations, providing bi-weekly trachoma treatments, training a nurse-aid, making home visits for maternity and prenatal care, educating the Diné about the spread of tuberculosis, instructing mothers in infant care, arranging for dental services, and attending an occasional nursing convention. Registered nurse Mollie Reebel recounted some of these experiences for *Indians at Work*. In one typical case, she and her Navajo nurse-aid, Mary, responded to a request for help from the Navajo Mountain area. Not having an automobile of her own, she borrowed a trader's car, secured general directions, then "started out across the sage-brush to find the hogan." After a ten-mile journey, Mollie arrived at the home, examined two sick children, and "doctored them up." Though not an extraordinary feat, Mollie's respect for the Navajo reveals why she succeeded. Before examining the children, she secured the confidence of the family by accepting a meal. Only then did she request permission to give the patients some medicine. As a consequence, the family expressed satisfaction with her visit and "cordially" invited Mollie and Mary to visit again.[24]

Encouraged by such responses, Collier sought to increase the number of field nurses. It was also important that field nurses not be distracted by other duties. At Kayenta, for example, the field nurse spent more time in the sanatorium than in the field. The Indian Office struggled to improve this situation, and by 1936 it had secured enough money to increase the number of reservation field nurses from four to nine, with another three to five positions under consideration. This compared favorably to the increase in hospital nurses, which rose from twenty-nine in 1931 to thirty-one in 1936. As the number of reservation day schools increased under the New Deal education program, Peter expected field nurses to work more effectively with children.[25]

The Navajo field nurse program remained popular through 1937. Signs of trouble, however, appeared on the horizon when Peter decided to analyze the effectiveness of his nurses. Along with District Medical Director Estella Ford Warner, he reviewed the records and reports of sixteen field nurses who had worked on the Navajo reservation between 1932 and 1937. The results proved both surprising and alarming: 40 percent of a nurse's time was spent in travel and 15 percent in record keeping. Another quarter of her time involved clinic and dispensary work, leaving only 20 percent for visiting patients. During the five-year period, nurses visited nearly fifteen thousand homes, seeing about thirty thousand patients. In order of frequency, they dealt with "child welfare (infant, preschool, and school), medical, communicable diseases, tuberculosis, and surgical." Of particular note, the nurses found 70 percent of the cases on their own, while Navajos asked for help only 27 percent of the time. These figures led Peter to conclude that "the type of service, under the guise of field nursing, is perforce, ineffectual, inefficient, and expensive." Indeed, "only about 20% of the nurse's time was devoted to activities considered a legitimate part of a public health nursing service."[26]

In December 1937, Peter, Warner, and reservation superintendent E. R. Fryer sat down to review the program. At that time, only six of the eleven authorized field nursing positions were filled. A survey of conditions revealed a number of specific problems. Field nurses at many locations occupied no separate living quarters, often being required to reside in spare rooms. The areas assigned to these women were too large, with some requiring twice weekly visits to seven or eight separate locations. Bad roads and severe weather conditions hampered access in many areas. The nurse stationed at Pueblo Pintado, for example, drove 450 miles per week over dirt roads just to visit the schools in her area. Some Indian Service employees, including more than one school principal, caused additional problems by failing to cooperate with field nurses. The review committee agreed with Interior Secretary Ickes that "Super-women" filled these jobs. Nevertheless, if their work were to continue the government needed to fill the five vacant positions as soon as possible and establish a new position at Fort Wingate. Furthermore, "a well functioning public health nursing program" required that each nurse have a reliable car, a driver/interpreter, adequate teaching materials, and proper living quarters and office space.[27]

Given such problems, Peter and Warner unilaterally developed a plan to reorganize field nursing in the Navajo area, fundamentally changing the nature of fieldwork. To promote efficiency, some of the most appreciated practices, such as transporting patients to hospitals and dispensing medicines, would be eliminated. Peter also wanted to place the program directly under his control (through the office of a public-health nurse supervisor) in order to ensure better supervision. In addition, he hoped to create a board comprised of representatives from the tribal council, the superintendent's office, and the educational division to review current practices. The real change, however, lay in the suggestion that field nurses should primarily serve as teachers instead of healers. Although education had always been a part of their job, in practice it took a backseat to direct medical care. Under the new plan field nurses would help establish a health-education program, assist in teaching the Diné to protect their health, and aid Indian people in assuming responsibility for their own health. In the future, therefore, field nurses would focus on education, thus maximizing their time and energy. To compensate for the loss of service in remote areas, Peter and Warner advocated the opening of a series of clinics, staffed by physicians and assisted by a public-health nurse. "It is desired," they stressed, "that [the Navajo] come to the physician for medical service rather than for the physician and nurse try to find him." Home visits (probably the most popular aspect of the program) would be discouraged, though not entirely eliminated.[28]

These changes were completed by 1940. A memorandum prepared that year by Estella Ford Warner and Gertrude Hosmer, District Supervising Nurse, defined Navajo field nursing as "the interpretation, application, and teaching of sanitary, medical and social procedures to promote health, prevent diseases, and correct defects." Actual care of the sick in their homes was no longer considered an essential part of their work: "Doing things to people is often easy, but is expensive and of temporary benefit. Showing people how to do things for themselves may take a little more time, but it is relatively inexpensive and its results are lasting." Shortly thereafter funding for most field nurses on the reservation was withdrawn. This marked the end of the field nursing program as originally conceived in the 1920s and practiced in the 1930s. A few field nurses remained for school, tuberculosis, and trachoma work, but the outreach medical portion of their work largely disappeared.[29]

Though not as dramatic as fieldwork, other nursing activities slowly improved during the New Deal. A survey at the beginning of Collier's administration indicated that the Indian Service (because of a turnover rate of nearly 80 percent) was losing more nurses than it could hire. The reasons for this unsatisfactory situation were clear: "long hours, overwork, physical breakdown." The Indian Office soon began a campaign to relieve the understaffing, including the employment of additional Navajo nurses. To secure more trained native women for this endeavor, the government offered a number of nursing scholarships with a guarantee of employment upon graduation. This program worked well enough that by 1936 ten of the fifty-one hospital nurses on the Navajo reservation were Indians. By then the staff also included several specially trained surgical, trachoma, and tuberculosis nurses. Most of them lived in decent quarters, were well trained, and maintained professional standards. In 1940 these nurses joined with other U.S.I.S. nurses in the Southwest to form an association for the exchange of ideas and "an ultimate high standardization of nursing procedures and techniques." The first annual meeting drew sixty-four nurses, who discussed such timely questions as the "Cause of 'Turn-Over' of Nurses in the Indian Service." In a related development, the Indian Service resurrected a version of the nurse-aid program, this time focusing on young Navajo men and women to serve as hospital orderlies and attendants, with a primary focus on translating.[30]

THE NAVAJO MEDICAL CENTER

Despite the attention given to doctors and nurses, the focal point of New Deal plans for the Navajo always came back to a centralized medical center at Fort Defiance. Although enlarged in 1929, no one questioned that the old general hospital needed replacement. A report in April 1933 condemned the building's electrical plant as so obsolete that it could not handle 110-volt A.C. systems, thus making it impossible to use most of the electrical appliances essential to a modern hospital. Soon thereafter, S. W. Cartwright, senior physician at the hospital, complained that the facility did not have a separate ward for contagious patients. "At present," he wrote, "we have measles, whooping cough, mumps, erysipelas, and spinal meningitis cases in the hospital and it is absolutely impossible to keep them all isolated." Under such conditions, Cartwright maintained, diseases spread from patient to patient, preventing the government from providing the Navajos with "the service to which they are entitled."[31]

Peter addressed these problems by proposing the construction of a new 145-bed hospital and converting the old building into a sanatorium. Collier endorsed the idea, and by October 1935 plans were prepared. The new medical complex, composed of three units, would feature a separate hospital, nurse's home, and laboratory. The main building was to have several wards, examination rooms, doctor's offices, an operating room, and a pharmacy. In addition, a small emergency room, an out-patient department, and a dental office were included. Presuming an average occupancy between eighty and one hundred patients, Peter expected the facility to employ more than thirty nurses. This dictated separate living quarters, with a reception room "for large social gatherings such as dances and parties," where nurses, for psychological reasons, might experience maximum living comfort. The laboratory was designed to handle all the basic reservation work.[32]

These plans, although modified somewhat to fit economic realities, were basically fulfilled. In 1936 the Indian Office allocated 450,000 dollars for the hospital, a bit less than needed to fully implement the original plan. As a result, Peter scaled back the laboratory, incorporating it into the main building and requiring the smaller reservation hospitals to perform some of their own basic laboratory work. Nevertheless, by mid-1936 Peter expressed considerable optimism: "Here we hope to have facilities and equipment and personnel to do our best medical and surgical work in difficult cases. In addition, this base hospital is to serve as a place for continuous training of medical and nursing personnel through the assignment of newcomers for a short stay while being broken to harness; through the holding of medical and nursing meetings at intervals; through the sending from other hospitals within reach their different medical and surgical cases." He also expected the new medical center to conduct research on health concerns associated with the Navajo.[33]

From its inception the Fort Defiance Medical Center formed the nucleus of Collier's commitment to open new Indian hospitals. By 1936 a dozen other facilities were under construction, with six others being remodeled. None, however, were as large or as modern as the Navajo facility, which became something of an Indian Service showpiece.[34] Expectations ran high as the buildings neared completion. Intended to serve both the Navajo and Hopi population, the medical center would provide health services for the largest Indian reservation in the United States, caring for some 50,000 people scattered across 25,000 square miles of high desert. At the center of a complex of ten hospitals and three sanatoriums employing some 289 people (148 Indian and 141 white), Fort Defiance was designed to receive all difficult cases, perform most laboratory services, train new employees, and organize clinics and refresher courses. With so many modern services, including the ability to perform postmortem examinations, there seemed good reason to anticipate American College of Surgeons certification.[35]

The Navajo Medical Center formally opened June 20, 1938, amid great fanfare. In keeping with Collier's desire to accommodate Navajo tradition (and perhaps to soothe tribal feelings), the opening ceremonies featured several healers, who sang songs, pledged cooperation, and blessed the buildings. Without doubt a significant milestone in reservation medical history, the opening of the new hospital truly represented the beginning of the modern era. Serving as the administrative center for the entire reservation, it employed some of the best doctors and nurses in the Indian Service. Once in operation, the Navajo Medical Center was staffed by 5 physicians, 3 head nurses, 30 staff nurses (including several Navajos), 6 nurse-aids, laboratory and X-ray technicians, a dietician, and 25 ward attendants. In addition to the daily average of 114 bed patients, 55 more received treatment as out-patients. These figures compared favorably with other Indian Service hospitals, which averaged 52 beds in capacity and 67 percent occupancy.[36] By some accounts, the shining new facility made the Navajos more receptive to government care. Few doubted that the medical services offered to the Diné had made a great step forward.

The center was not free from criticism, however. Some members of the Tribal Council complained that Collier was not doing enough to reach the remote population. Robert Martin from Shiprock expressed great unhappiness with Collier for not concentrating more on field nurses and school clinics. "Where are they, we do not seen them," he asked J. C. Morgan. And although the new hospital employed several Navajos, a few felt ill treated. One Navajo woman, Grace McCray, wrote that Peter ran the Medical Center like a dictatorship, threatening to fire unhappy employees. She also objected to the attitude of female supervisors who tolerated no input from their Indian employees, telling them "it is none of your business." Irritated, she defiantly stated that "I think it is every intelligent Navajo's business how things are run out here." The hospital also continued to suffer from staffing problems. Turnover rates continued high, and as World War II approached it became increasingly difficult to attract experienced doctors. Financial problems, moreover, continued to plague the center. Things became so bad that Peter eventually toyed with the notion of having Navajos pay for some of their medical services, as they "do so now with their own Medicine Men." Despite support from several doctors, this idea received scant consideration from Collier, who did not want to give the tribe another reason to complain.[37]

THE CONQUEST OF TRACHOMA

Of all the major health problems among the Navajo, only trachoma seemed curable during the New Deal. Indeed, Collier believed that "trachoma can be cured" as soon as the specific disease organism could be identified.[38] As a consequence, the commissioner's office encouraged its doctors to develop new methods of treatment, hoping that a breakthrough might soon materialize. Much of this effort focused on the Navajo, where trachoma continued to be a major scourge.

Unfortunately, Collier's emphasis on trachoma control got off to a slow start. In the initial atmosphere of Depression-era relief programs and financial retrenchment, lines of communication between Washington and Fort Defiance collapsed. During the summer of 1933, Dr. Jay Nash, director of the Indian Emergency Conservation Work program, set out to relieve reservation unemployment by establishing a series of public-works camps, including several for the Navajo. Unfamiliar with the Navajo and unaware of the existing trachoma program, Nash proposed using one of his Navajo camps exclusively for trachomatous men. To compound the situation, he initiated his program without consulting reservation doctors, showing up at Fort Defiance in August 1933 to open an IECW trachoma camp. Paul Mossman, U.S.I.S. Medical Director in Charge of Trachoma Activities, exploded when he learned of the plan. He immediately drove from Albuquerque to Fort Defiance to head off Nash. In the heated discussion that followed, Mossman declared the camp impractical because it offered insufficient medical care (Nash had assumed that one nurse would suffice). When Nash realized the actual situation, he backed down, although the Indian Office continued to favor the idea. Eventually, Mossman agreed to support a camp if it were located adjacent to the agency hospital. Even so, he showed little enthusiasm for the project, pointing out that the two hundred men living there would require so much treatment time that little work would be possible.[39] Eventually, the camp idea, like so many others, was discarded.

Meanwhile, the Indian Office vacillated over ways to control the disease. In July 1934, for example, Collier called a medical conference in Washington, D.C., to outline a course of action for the Navajo and Apache reservations. As a result, the Indian Office revived the idea of special trachoma schools, deciding to open one to the children of both tribes on the Fort Apache reservation. Six months later, the Indian Office concluded that for financial and other reasons, government-designated trachoma schools for the Navajo were impractical. At the same time, Collier reluctantly ruled that the government possessed no authority to compel treatment of unwilling patients. "I believe that more would be lost than gained," he admitted, "if we attempted to forcibly treat cases now and then who do not wish to be treated."[40]

Fortunately, Indian Service doctors were making advances in other ways. In 1935, Dr. Phillips Thygeson of Columbia University began a research program at Fort Apache to test the theory that trachoma was caused by a virus, an idea supported by such Indian Service doctors as Polk Richards. Meanwhile, Dr. Sidney J. Tillim penned a highly critical paper for the National Society for the Prevention of Blindness. Under the present system, Tillim remarked, government trachoma work was dependent on the twelve special physicians, only three of whom worked in the Southwest. These doctors visited schools once every three or four weeks, operating as necessary, but leaving aftercare to nurses. Although this approach produced some favorable results among schoolchildren, it did nothing for the non-school population. For these unfortunate people, "the diagnosis and treatment of trachoma . . . are left to the willingness and inclinations of the school or Agency physician. Unless the general practitioner has the willingness and inclination—and often he has other leanings— this part of the population is left untreated." Tillim also claimed that present medical facilities were inadequate and that the government failed to fully utilize its doctors.[41]

Tillim's analysis supported the growing conviction among Indian Service personnel that a dramatic new effort would be expedient. As a consequence, the Indian Office agreed to appoint a consulting ophthalmologist to rejuvenate the trachoma program. In September 1936, Polk Richards, who had replaced Mossman as Trachoma Medical Director, offered the job to noted Chicago ophthalmologist Dr. Harry S. Gradle. Although Gradle knew nothing about Indians or reservations, he accepted the appointment. When Gradle asked for a candid assessment of the situation, Richards willingly elaborated. Admitting that no statistics on the extent of the problem existed, he acknowledged that "its epidemiology often has us groping for rational explanations." He also emphasized that most government doctors, including those who specialized in eye work, had learned from experience, not as trained ophthomologists.[42]

Following a lengthy exchange of correspondence and a hasty visit to the Navajo, Gradle submitted a comprehensive plan for controlling trachoma on the reservation. The plan called for a massive and expensive campaign to eradicate the disease within five years. Consisting of three major components that bore a remarkable resemblance to earlier efforts, Gradle first suggested the creation of six segregated boarding schools. These institutions would operate year round and be staffed by a trained ophthalmologist, an ophthalmic nurse, and a nurse's helper. This "Ophthalmic Team" must devote its entire time to treating infected students. A second aspect of the program featured the creation of out-patient clinics at remote trading posts. One of six additional Ophthalmic Teams would visit these locations every two weeks to treat infected adults. Between visits, a field nurse would visit the clinics twice a week to administer additional care. Finally, to reach the most remote families, a "Trachoma Patrol," consisting of Indian and white reservation workers, would visit every hogan and bring all cases of sore eyes to the nearest clinic. In this way, Gradle predicted, trachoma must surely disappear.[43]

Gradle's plan did not sit well with government doctors, particularly Richards. Although he supported the idea of segregated schools, the "Trachoma Patrol" appeared ridiculous. Using force to round up patients guaranteed a hostile reception. He also thought the employment of a dozen ophthalmologists "a bit extravagant." These doctors were expected to replace the present group of special physicians. "Would you discard these experienced men," he wrote Gradle, "who have done and are doing work and replace them with young, inexperienced men, who, in that they know more about the ten layers of the retina, would probably know less about trachoma and the Indian health program as a whole?" Lucy Wilcox Adams, Director of Navajo Schools, also objected. She opposed establishing so many segregated schools because it would disrupt the entire education system. Navajo parents, moreover, were likely to oppose transfers. Considering that Collier was then attempting to force his unpopular stock-reduction program on the Diné, she had little desire to increase Indian anger.[44]

Gradle's idea was formally dismissed just days after its release. E. R. Fryer, reservation superintendent, wrote Collier on October 26, 1937, that Gradle showed an almost total ignorance of the problem. Remarking that the plan did not consider "the fiscal, sociological, psychological, personal, and administrative difficulties which would have to be overcome," the scheme seemed unworkable. Fryer acknowledged that schoolchildren could not be easily uprooted, appropriations were insufficient, and government workers were engaged with more important business than running from hogan to hogan looking for trachoma cases. Then, too, summer–winter migrations and the ceremonial schedule were not factored in. Fryer did not advocate abandoning the trachoma program, but, as he stated, "I am suggesting intelligent caution and wise step-by-step procedure that will oil the water before we launch the boat."[45]

As events soon proved, the Gradle plan was not necessary. By 1937 research conducted by Indian Service physicians began to pay off. The Thygeson studies at Fort Apache led to the conclusion that "trachoma is a virus." Meanwhile, Dr. Fred Loe, then stationed on the Rosebud reservation in South Dakota, began to experiment with orally administered sulfanilamide. The results were startling. In early 1938, Loe wrote that "it was truly wonderful the way those eyes cleared up and they did so in almost two weeks." Although recognizing that his experiments needed confirmation, the excited physician remarked that "I do think it is the most wonderful treatment I have even seen in trachoma." This discovery proved of enough significance for Loe to summarize his field observations at the 1938 meeting of the American Medical Association. Meanwhile, the Indian Office proudly announced that its physicians had discovered an effective treatment for trachoma.[46]

Research into the sulfanilamide treatment expanded once the preliminary results were confirmed. Richards ordered a year of intensive study at eleven reservations and at the Fort Apache boarding school. These studies produced dramatic results. More than a thousand Indians received the experimental treatment, with 43 percent of the subjects having the disease arrested and another 50 percent showing significant improvement. The statistics from Fort Apache were even more amazing. Within a month, 75 percent of the cases were arrested. The remaining cases were arrested after a second treatment.[47]

Reports of these tests set off a flurry of medical activity. Gradle was sufficiently impressed to begin a sulfanilamide treatment program among a group of Illinois whites. He too reported "rather startling results." Other physicians also began to experiment with the sulfa drug.[48] By early 1940 the Indian Office was ready to launch a full-scale trachoma eradication program. Under the general direction of Dr. Richards, special physicians were instructed to organize trachoma clinics throughout the Southwest. Beginning at school sites, these clinics provided a three-week program that included vision tests, blood examinations, and sulfanilamide treatment. Every type of facility was pressed into service as adults and preschool children were treated. In 1941 the Indian Office reported that "the results of our efforts to eradicate trachoma with sulfanilamide have been so encouraging that we feel that the work should be continued with increased vigor until the incidence of trachoma in the schools and among the Indians, as a whole, has been greatly reduced or entirely eliminated as a health problem."[49]

Navajos generally submitted to the sulfanilamide treatment. Although the drug did not actually cure the disease, it relieved the symptoms, caused little discomfort, and dramatically reduced its reappearance. By 1943 the rate of trachoma among Indian groups had been reduced to less than 5 percent. Collier's office claimed well-deserved credit for this advance, the first real success achieved by Indian Service physicians. Drs. Loe and Richards, in particular, received a number of accolades. Fittingly, perhaps, Polk Richards, who had spent thirty-five years in government service, much of it battling trachoma on the Navajo reservation, retired in 1942, pleased that his lifelong commitment of Indian health had been rewarded. Although trachoma was not fully eradicated, the future looked much brighter.[50]

THE TUBERCULOSIS DILEMMA

New Deal efforts to eradicate tuberculosis failed to match the success with trachoma. From the beginning, Collier and Peter recognized the danger that this disease posed to the Navajo. Despite few reliable statistics, the prevalence of tuberculosis among American Indians was believed to be ten times greater than that in the general population. Among the Navajo, some observers estimated that the tuberculosis death rate averaged about fifteen per thousand, or 17 percent above the national level. Aware of these figures, Peter's 1935 tribal health plan emphasized an aggressive eradication program consisting of three basic parts: (1) upgrading and modernizing existing sanatoriums; (2) testing experimental new procedures and treatments; and (3) utilization of new methods to identify existing cases and prevent new ones. Unfortunately, financial and technical restraints prevented any of these ideas from being particularly effective.[51]

The need for additional sanatorium space was obvious. On the day of Roosevelt's inauguration, only the rundown facilities at Kayenta and Fort Defiance served tuberculosis patients. Neither hospital provided state-of-the-art care, their primary function being to separate contagious (often terminal) patients from the tribal population. Kayenta could not even fulfill this objective. In November 1933, the Winslow sanatorium came on line, adding another forty-five beds. Together, the three sanatoriums provided slightly over one hundred beds for the entire Navajo and Hopi population. By Collier's own estimate, this met only 10 percent of the need.[52]

Peter's Navajo medical plan called for the old general hospital at Fort Defiance to become a sanatorium once the new medical center was completed. Because this did not occur until 1938, however, the Indian Service limped along with what it had, doing its best to provide services at existing locations. Kayenta faced the most difficulty. Never intended to function as a hospital, the isolated facility struggled to keep open, with its eighteen-member staff caring for a small number of tubercular patients (only fifty-seven in 1935). Indeed, most of the hospital deaths resulted from epidemics of measles, whooping cough, and scarlet fever. Buildings needed repair, employee working conditions remained spartan, and basic medical equipment (such as an X-ray unit, large laundry machine, and a dishwasher) was unavailable. Superintendent R. J. Enochs remarked that "a five minute inspection of our present Sanatorium buildings has and always will convince the most conservative of the need for a new hospital at this place."[53]

Conditions at Kayenta continued to deteriorate. One 1938 report noted that facilities for isolating communicable patients from general patients, males from females, and adults from children were wholly inadequate. Given these conditions, some reservation officials suggested converting the plant into a home for the blind, aged, and crippled. Despite an endorsement by the Navajo Tribal Council, the Indian Office rejected the idea, directing instead that the sanatorium be improved at the least possible cost. The resulting effort made some progress, bringing in a physician specializing in tuberculosis, hiring a new head nurse, and making efforts "to correct our stinking sewage disposal system." Nonetheless, the government was forced to reduce appropriations, cutting off plans to renovate the wards, to purchase modern equipment, and to improve employee living quarters. As a consequence, the sanatorium continued to provide inadequate service, unable, as one doctor observed, to "give this experiment at Kayenta a fair chance to prove itself a success or a failure."[54]

The Winslow sanatorium seemed destined for a better fate. Relatively modern and well equipped, it opened in 1933 with great expectations. Nevertheless, the site initially encountered difficulty in attracting patients, prompting the superintendent to plead with reservation officials to send tuberculosis cases his way. The initial lack of interest seems to have been caused by the off-reservation location as well as by the superintendent himself, who refused to admit patients without a detailed case history and outline of specific symptoms. He furthermore declined to admit potentially terminal patients, fearing that the hospital would become known as a place of death. When the hospital finally did reach capacity in 1935, a number of defects became apparent. The superintendent, Dr. L. R. Jones, and staff physician, Dr. R. C. Kesler, quibbled over duties, especially after Jones was also appointed a special physician at large for tuberculosis. Frequently in the field, Jones insisted on occupying the hospital's physician's residence, forcing Kesler to live in town and thus preventing him from being available around the clock for emergencies. Even more disturbing was the tendency to crowd too many patients into the sanatorium. One inspector found the second-floor porch overflowing with variously dressed male patients, some sleeping on the floor. Female patients were crowded in a small room, "none having the proper amount of breathing space per bed." In 1936 Dr. William G. Lewis listed the hospital's major liabilities as a lack of permanent employees, totally inadequate living quarters, and dirty and bare grounds. Local smoke and dust also created difficulty, prompting Lewis to describe the facility as the "poorest equipped, poorest staffed, most desolate institution of its kind that I have ever encountered."[55]

With both the Kayenta and Winslow hospitals struggling, the Indian Office placed its hopes in Fort Defiance. As planned, the old hospital became a one hundred–bed sanatorium once the new medical center opened in June 1938. This permitted the assignment of sufficient medical personnel to staff the sanatorium around the clock and have X-ray and laboratory services immediately available. Quickly filled to capacity, the sanatorium offered a variety of regular and experimental treatments. Even so, the reservation's tuberculosis picture failed to improve. Records kept by the Navajo Medical Center showed that between January 1, 1939, and November 1, 1940, a total of 343 tuberculosis patients were hospitalized, 230 of whom died. These figures did not include fatalities occurring outside of hospitals, which appeared to be numerous. Given such statistics, Dr. Breteslav Sedlacek, senior physician at Fort Defiance, classified tuberculosis mortality among the Navajo as "very high." In truth, none of the sanatoriums could do much more than isolate existing cases. As Kayenta's Dr. R. J. Enochs remarked, tuberculosis could not "be efficiently attacked until the general living conditions of the Navajo are improved. To improve conditions the Navajo must have a correct sense of sanitation and hygiene, a desirable appreciation of clean and wholesome foods, and a wholesome appreciation of, and desire to have, a clean home."[56]

Because of the difficulty of rapidly changing Navajo living conditions, Collier encouraged the use of several experimental procedures. Already under development before the New Deal, infant vaccinations and collapse therapy received his endorsement. The vaccination program involved inoculating newborn infants with bacillus Calmette Gruerin (BCG), a controversial treatment first developed in 1906, in hopes that it would prevent the contraction of tuberculosis. The program began on the Navajo reservation in 1935. No figures exist on the extent of the BCG program, but it appears to have been confined to newborns within easy reach of doctors. Nonetheless, the vaccination program produced favorable, if nonconclusive, results on other reservations and was continued among the Diné into the 1950s.[57]

Pneumothorax or collapse therapy received much more attention on the Navajo reservation. This treatment involved collapsing and immobilizing an infected lung, which, it was believed, would stimulate healing. Collapse therapy had been used by reservation doctors before Collier came to office and Medical Director James Townsend enthusiastically continued the practice, believing that this treatment could save a number of lives. In 1935, the Indian Office launched an intensive program of pneumothorax treatment based on favorable results obtained at the Chicago Municipal Sanatorium and the Phipps Institute of Philadelphia. It appears, from the few records available, that collapse procedures among the Navajo were conducted exclusively at hospitals. In fact, both the collapse therapy and vaccination programs appear to have remained experimental and limited, producing mixed results at best. Although offering some promise, they failed to bring the widespread incidence of tuberculosis in Navajoland under control.[58]

Much more encouraging were government efforts in screening the Diné for tuberculosis. After 1936 school physicians provided regular physical examinations and a pair of field nurses, supported by the Phipps Institute, toured selected portions of the reservation giving tuberculin tests. Those testing positive were X-rayed and if necessary hospitalized. In general, terminal cases went to Kayenta, while less severe patients received collapse therapy or became outpatients at Fort Defiance or in Winslow. Because of insufficient funding, however, this program could not be expanded.[59] Even if sufficient funding had existed, the sanatoriums were so overcrowded that they could not have handled the extra patients.

Efforts to educate the Navajo about the cause and spread of tuberculosis also increased during Collier's tenure. Many observers believed that education offered the best hope of defeating tuberculosis. As a consequence, considerable energy went into reaching the Diné with health messages. In 1936, for example, Edna Gerken prepared a packet of materials for teachers and Navajo reservation employees to use in fostering "healthful safe practices." Through simple stories and poems, students learned about proper nutrition, cleanliness, and waste disposal. Another late 1930s program saw personnel from the Phoenix Indian sanatorium capitalize on the novelty of motion pictures by touring the Navajo country with instructional films. And in 1940 the Indian Office enlisted the services of artist Rudolph Modley to prepare a series of posters depicting healthful activities. A typical illustration portrayed the idea "Don't spit on the ground inside. Spit in the fire."[60] The effectiveness of these efforts with the largely illiterate adult population is open to speculation, but at least the Collier administration displayed some initiative in getting the message out.

In retrospect, by the time the United States entered World War II in December 1941, the medical landscape in Navajo country had changed. Without question, the New Deal years witnessed some modernization of the health-care system. Additional doctors and nurses worked on the reservation; the Navajo Medical Center at Fort Defiance, with the ability to perform most modern procedures, would not have been out of place in a mid-sized American city; educational efforts were raising Navajo awareness of disease prevention; and Navajo workers were being recruited as health-care professionals. In addition, the antagonistic attitude toward traditional medical practices disappeared from official policy. Most of all, the scourge of trachoma had been controlled. Nonetheless, an overwhelming array of problems and failures remained. Still, turnover rates frequently left medical positions vacant, a fact largely attributed to inadequate salaries and bleak living conditions. Conditions at some small hospitals and sanatoriums continued to be unsatisfactory, if not appalling. Despite a clear recognition of need, Navajo medical facilities failed to keep up with demand. More significantly, government doctors and nurses were still unable to effectively reach the suspicious and sometime angry adult Indian population in remote areas. Nor had living conditions improved enough to eliminate the spread of contagious disease. Worst of all, the deadly scourge of tuberculosis continued to exact a fearful toll.

CHAPTER TEN

END OF AN ERA

America's entry into World War II devastated reservation health services, as most of the gains so laboriously achieved during the 1930s disappeared under the demand of wartime necessity. Doctors and nurses, especially the younger and more energetic ones, left the Indian country to serve in the military or to perform other war-related medical service. Budgets suffered, hospitals closed, medical supplies dried up, and rationing of gasoline and tires forced travel reductions. Indeed, Indian medical services declined to such an extent in 1942 that Interior Secretary Harold Ickes noted with alarm that "it is impossible to provide Indians with even the most essential medical care." So great were personnel shortages that by 1944 the Indian medical service calculated that it needed 100 physicians and 188 nurses just to provide basic services.[1] Despite such bleak conditions, the wartime crisis highlighted some of the inherent problems within the Indian Service, helping to set the stage of the sweeping reorganization of the Indian medical program carried into effect in 1955.

Although fully committed to the war effort, John Collier did his best to salvage the prewar medical achievements. Odds were stacked against the Indian commissioner from the first, however. A forerunner of the crippling loss of personnel occurred in March 1941, when James E. Townsend, the New Deal supervisor of Collier's medical program, was recalled by the Public Health Service in "the interest of national defense." Townsend's replacement, Dr. J. R. McGibony, also a PHS physician, lacked his predecessor's administrative experience and close working relationship with Collier. Thrust into an unfamiliar position just as the war started, McGibony faced nearly unsurmountable obstacles.[2]

Wartime budget cuts produced some of Collier's biggest headaches. Overall

Indian Office appropriations dropped from 33 million dollars to 28 million dollars. Medical allocations fared a little better, remaining relatively stable during the conflict. Nonetheless, health programs, impacted by increasing prices and scarcity of supply, declined significantly. Between 1943 and 1945 the number of available hospital and sanatorium beds shrank from 4,469 to 4,064. During those same years seventeen Indian hospitals closed. Faced with staggering losses in medical staff, McGibony attempted to recruit and train more Indian medical workers. Although some progress was made in this direction, even these efforts were blunted by wartime conditions.[3]

WARTIME MEDICINE

Historian Peter Iverson notes that World War II changed the Navajo forever. Not only did many patriotic Navajos support the war effort—both through military service and defense-industry employment—they learned more about the outside world, saw their economy altered by an influx of cash, and became aware of the need to understand mainstream society.[4] Medical perceptions proved no exceptions. Many young Navajo recruits failed to pass military physical examinations, primarily because of problems associated with tuberculosis or the lingering effects of trachoma. According to Ruth Underhill, some recruits admitted that they had never heeded or believed the advice of white doctors about avoiding contact with the sick. Thousands of Diné were rejected for military service, an embarrassing event that increased Navajo interest in listening to white doctors. In all, about thirty-four hundred Navajos successfully enlisted in the army or navy. Their contact with advanced medical techniques and effective new drugs served to enhance their appreciation of modern medicine. "Exposed to Western Medicine as never before," the Navajo, always receptive to changes of proven value, became somewhat more respectful of the medical services and therapy provided by government doctors, although they did not necessarily abandon traditional beliefs. Indeed, returning soldiers commonly had the Blessing Way and Squaw Dance performed for them and those with wounds sought the help of healers.[5]

Contact with the outside world did not always prove beneficial, however. With as many as fifteen thousand people working off the reservation, often living in rundown urban areas and mixing with lower social classes, the incidence of venereal disease jumped significantly. Although this problem was somewhat offset by the military's intensive venereal disease education program, these efforts did not reach the civilian workforce, many of whom returned to the reservation after the war, bringing the disease with them.[6]

Collier hoped to use wartime conditions to persuade more Navajos to utilize federal health-care facilities. To further this goal, he continued to advocate an accommodation with traditional medicine. Fortunately, a number of sympathetic scientists had been doing cultural fieldwork among the Navajos since the late 1930s. Among this group, Alexander and Dorothea Leighton, a husband–wife team of psychologists with a strong interest in anthropology, were studying the relationship between Navajo religion and medicine. Their interest in finding ways to transmit modern medical concepts to the Diné attracted the interest of Collier's public-health specialist, Edna Gerken, who in early 1943 alerted her boss. A study of this nature, explained Gerken, might be very useful if circulated among reservation health-care workers.[7]

Recognizing the wisdom of Gerken's suggestion, Collier persuaded the Leightons to prepare a handbook for distribution to government health workers. To be titled "Therapeutic Values in Navajo Religion," it confirmed Collier's opinion about the compatibility of western and native medicine. Among its more notable sections, the study suggested that medical knowledge be presented "in a form that does not do violence to their faith, and medicine men will be encouraged to practice in the fields where they are most effective and will be accorded the consideration given the clergy." Arguing that the Navajo would more readily accept medical treatment if they were not forced to give up their own traditions, the study acknowledged that healing ceremonies reassured and uplifted the patient, providing a sense of security. "If our medicine is to help and not harm the Navajo," it concluded, "we must avoid clean sweeps. We must get them to accept and use our pertinent, practical knowledge without undermining their faith." As a guide to white doctors, health workers were encouraged to look upon Navajo healers as they would a country doctor, who provided good, sound advice based on a practical knowledge of the people being served.[8]

It took until the end of 1944 for the handbook to appear in print. Edited by D'Arcy McNickle (Kutenai-Salish), an employee of the Indian Office, *The Navajo Door: An Introduction to Navajo Life* was directed at the U.S.I.S. medical staff. Its 150 pages provided the reader with a sound background on Navajo religious and medical views, discussing in simple detail how the Diné reacted to white medicine and what doctors and nurses might expect. Acknowledging that tribal members now accepted such western medical practices as vaccination and patent medicines, a large gulf nevertheless existed: "The primary concern of the Navajo is with the illness, and getting rid of it, and he does not demand consistency of theory and treatment as long as the illness is dispelled." Medical workers thus required a sound knowledge of Navajo customs to be effective. To that end, the Leightons provided a wealth of good advice. In relation to hospitalization, for example, they noted that "when a man or woman gets sick, the family takes over the direction of treatment. . . . The family decides whether to call a Singer or a diagnostician or take the patient to the hospital. If the Singer comes they tell him just what they want him to do. A few medicine men take it on themselves to advise the family, but most conform to the pattern of doing as they are told with all the skill they possess." Doctors and nurses were admonished to bear this in mind when discussing hospitalization.[9]

Given the late date of publication and the large percentage of older doctors on the reservation, it appears that *The Navajo Door* had little impact during the war years. Nonetheless, the Indian Office circulated extracts of the study as early as 1943 and, at one point, planned to follow up with a survey of the chief medical needs and preventive medicine problems of the Navajo. Although wartime restrictions cut the survey short, the Leighton study is generally given credit for influencing the generation of younger physicians entering government service after the war.[10]

Meanwhile, staffing and financial difficulties created problems across the reservation. Hopes that the Navajo Medical Center might finally receive accreditation from the American College of Surgeons faded along with the hospital's inability to maintain basic requirements and keep adequate records. Indeed, every one of the reservation medical facilities lost personnel in the wake of Pearl Harbor. By the end of 1943, the Fort Defiance hospital, which usually carried a staff of thirty-eight nurses, could only muster thirteen. Proportional losses were recorded at other locations. Sage Memorial Hospital surrendered fifteen of its staff and students to the armed forces, while for a time Chinle could not find a single nurse. The financial crisis became so acute in late 1942 that Collier abolished the post of Navajo Medical Director, dismissing his old friend Dr. W. W. Peter. Almost all the bright young doctors hired during the 1930s also departed.[11]

A few months before leaving office, Peter began what proved to be a series of hospital closures and reductions. The first significant change came in June 1942, when the Indian Office turned its complex at Leupp over to the army to house Canal Zone evacuees and closed the Leupp hospital. Attempting to find replacement medical services for Navajos in this area, Peter concluded that his most practical alternative involved opening the already full Winslow sanatorium to general patients. He thus decided to make room at Winslow by persuading tuberculosis patients to transfer to other hospitals. Unfortunately, the main sanatorium at Fort Defiance could not accommodate these patients. Thus, aside from a handful of beds at Kayenta, the Indian sanatorium at Phoenix seemed the only alternative. Although Navajo patients were reluctant to leave home and transportation presented a problem, most of the tubercular patients were nonetheless relocated and the Winslow hospital began accepting general patients. Also, "in view of the impending increase in an already existing shortage of cars, tires, and gasoline, the policy in vogue [at Leupp] up until recently of providing hospital transportation for patients from and to their homes will of necessity be abandoned." Once general patients entered the Winslow facility, it became medically impractical to have tuberculars in the small facility and by war's end they were all gone.[12]

Other hospital closures soon followed, as weaker institutions succumbed to national priorities. In all, five hospitals—Leupp, Tohatchi, Toadlena, Fort Wingate, and Kayenta—ceased operations. The Kayenta sanatorium, although receiving a satisfactory rating in May 1943, closed at year's end. Given its isolated location, high maintenance cost, and relatively few tuberculosis patients, reservation superintendent James M. Stewart concluded "that the medical service on the Navajo will be improved by closing such institutions as the sanatorium at Kayenta and the transferring of personnel to bolster the other institutions by providing adequate medical service to the patients." Without question, these reductions adversely affected the Diné. With the loss of half their hospitals and doctors, plus restrictions on travel, it became even more difficult for the Navajo to take advantage of government health services. Public-health personnel all but disappeared, clinics closed, and critical disease rates increased. After reviewing the number of communicable-disease cases reported during 1942, Dr. Ralph B. Snavely, District Medical Director, noted that over five hundred Navajos had been treated for tuberculosis. Despite a lack of reliable statistics, other diseases seemed to be as common.[13]

RETRENCHMENT

As World War II drew to a close, the Indian Office expressed confidence that tribal medical conditions would rapidly improve. In 1945, the Indian commissioner suggested that wartime interruptions were only temporary and a recovery would soon begin. Yet few changes appeared on the horizon. Rather than increasing budgets, Congress reduced federal appropriations for Indian health care by nearly 750,000 dollars in 1946. As a consequence, remarked the commissioner's office, "the serious shortage of physicians and nurses continued throughout the fiscal year with only slight relief."[14]

Another blow to the medical program came with John Collier's resignation in January 1945. Always an advocate of increased expenditures for health purposes, he was replaced by William A. Brophy (1945–48). Although sympathetic to Indian causes, Brophy demonstrated neither the force of character nor the persistence of his predecessor. He quickly indicated a willingness to cooperate with Congress, which by 1947 wanted to dismantle much of Collier's New Deal program.[15]

As Congress began to turn its attention to reducing federal services, the reservation medical situation lapsed into a limbo that perpetuated many of the wartime problems. During the immediate postwar period only six Navajo hospitals remained open—Fort Defiance, Tuba City, Shiprock, Chinle, Crownpoint, and Winslow. The sole tuberculosis sanatorium, also at Fort Defiance, provided a hundred beds. No more than a dozen doctors staffed these facilities and only one public health professional (a nurse) remained in the field. Budget reductions complicated personnel matters to such an extent in 1946 that District Medical Director Donald J. Hunt informed his superiors that he must either conserve money by severely cutting services or continue at present levels until lack of funds caused a complete shutdown. Despite increased appropriations for 1948, the staffing situation barely improved. That year, one overworked doctor demanded an assistant physician to share the workload, threatening to quit if help did not soon arrive.[16] Meanwhile, agency officials optimistically drew up plans to reopen some of the closed hospitals and to remodel or enlarge others.

The Navajos themselves disliked what they saw. Invited to detail conditions on the reservation before a congressional committee in 1946, members of the Tribal Council, led by Chairman Chee Dodge, expressed grave concern. Dodge argued for the construction of new hospitals at such locations as Kayenta and Toadlena. Herbert Becenti from Crownpoint was even more specific, stating that after schools, hospitals represented the most pressing need. "We have very few hospitals available on the reservation and there is a great deal of sickness among our people," he testified. Not only was it difficult for most people to travel great distances for care, but they might not find a doctor when they arrived. "We do get doctors occasionally," he said, "but for some reason they do not seem to stay very long." Becenti's candid comments reflected a strong feeling that the government had failed to live up to its promises.[17]

The deteriorating conditions in Navajo country attracted both congressional and public attention. The Indian Office (which officially became the Bureau of Indian Affairs in 1947) responded by inviting the American Medical Association to survey medical conditions among the Navajo. In late 1947 the AMA selected a seven-member team of physicians from Southwestern Medical College in Dallas, Texas, to carry out the task. To no one's surprise, they discovered that "Navajos receive incomplete and poor health service." Listed among the most serious deficiencies were nutrition (especially among children), the widespread incidence of tuberculosis, and a complete absence of preventive measures. Due to a shortage of hospitals and poor roads, most

"Navajos did not have access to any kind of medical service." Poor care awaited those able to reach a hospital. With the exception of Fort Defiance and Crownpoint, medical staffs remained poorly qualified and inadequate. Most of the doctors were too old, lacking "the advantage of recent medical training and do not know modern methods of treatment and how best to use the facilities of the hospitals."[18]

The AMA team presented the Indian Bureau with recommendations strikingly similar to Collier's New Deal plan. Establishing an adequate field service topped the list. Opposing current administrative thinking, the team advised against the enlargement or replacement of smaller reservation hospitals. In a throwback to the 1930s, they argued instead that effective care must come from teams of physicians and nurses, "preferably with public health training," reaching into remote locations. Once again, the notion that field doctors should forward those needing hospitalization to an appropriate facility while treating others at home received a boost. To handle the increased number of hospital referrals, more beds would be needed at the Navajo Medical Center. Transportation needs might be met with a reservation-wide ambulance service, supplemented by an air ambulance. Recruiting quality young physicians also warranted high priority. Mindful of the problems caused by isolation and meager salaries, the AMA doctors advised that good physicians would continue to avoid the Indian Service unless they could keep abreast of modern methods of treatment. Much of the same reasoning applied to nurses. Should such changes be adopted, the Navajo might finally receive "the health service they deserve."[19]

Without doubt, the Navajo were not receiving the health care they deserved. The issue of substandard and insensitive physicians seemed particularly delicate. Both the Tribal Council and individual Navajos complained about government doctors. In one recorded instance, a pregnant woman suffered severe injuries in an auto accident. Taken to the Shiprock hospital by her husband, she had to wait until the following day to see a physician. When the couple finally met with the doctor, they were advised to return home, the baby would be fine. Four days later, the woman ended up back in the hospital in serious condition after delivering a badly bruised boy, who soon died. Even more troublesome, some government doctors continued to perform postmortem examinations without consent. A point of contention since the 1930s, the issue became increasingly heated following the war. In 1948 Navajo singer Manuelito Begay complained that the doctor at Crownpoint was performing autopsies just to "learn more about the body." When asked to respect Navajo wishes, the physician responded that "it is going on the world over in those big hospitals." Begay retorted that "we the Navajo do not want any doctor to take

Medical practice on dead Navajos, if any doctor wanted to learn more about the body he can go to Medical school." It particularly irritated Begay that the offending physician refused to stop his unauthorized actions after being so ordered, at one point extracting permission for his exams by telling relatives they would have to bury the dead if they refused.[20]

While these episodes illustrate a callous disregard for Navajo feelings, it is equally clear that other government doctors went out of their way to provide sympathetic care. In particular, after the war health-care professionals influenced by the work of Alexander and Dorothea Leighton began to suggest better ways of accommodating Navajo beliefs. In one such study, Flora L. Bailey provided suggestions on how Navajo women might be convinced to accept hospitalization during childbirth. Focusing on aspects of traditional culture, Bailey observed that native women needed to feel secure and comfortable, with their modesty protected. She thus advocated changing standard hospital procedures to incorporate Diné traditions. Use of the traditional delivery position and permission to conduct such rituals as sprinkling corn pollen about the room seemed small but important concessions. If such accommodations did not occur, Navajo women would continue to use the hospital only when faced with complications. "As a result," Bailey observed, "one hears such bitter reports as that which came from an older woman who lost two daughters in childbirth at the hospital after each had successfully delivered other children at home. Obviously, in her opinion, there was only one deduction—the white doctors had killed her daughters!"[21]

Reservation administrators struggled to improve health services. In 1948 they prevailed upon the Interior Department to purchase a mobile X-ray unit exclusively for the Navajo reservation. During its first year in service this unit examined nearly 16,000 people, 1,859 of whom showed evidence of active tuberculosis. Unfortunately, little or no hospital space existed to care for tuberculosis or other patients. In order to maximize hospital efficiency, reservation superintendent Stewart reorganized the system in October 1948. Fort Defiance, much as it had in the late 1930s, would house all the specialists— surgeon, pediatrician, gynecologist, pathologist, eye specialist, and tuberculosis doctor—as well as laboratory personnel. The remaining four hospitals (Chinle closed in 1947) became "field hospitals," each with thirty to fifty beds, a surgical theater, laboratory, and dispensary, usually under the charge of a single physician. Under this system, doctors at the central hospital could focus on problems specifically related to the Navajo and indeed such research paid occasional dividends. One such effort led to a dramatic reduction in infant hospital deaths due to diarrhea.[22]

Because of the persistence of unacceptable medical conditions, in September

1948 the Interior Department sent another team of AMA physicians to the reservation. Like its predecessor, the team reacted unfavorably. Facilities were so insufficient that some preventable diseases were actually increasing. The incidence of tuberculosis continued to rise, as did the spread of venereal diseases, especially syphilis, which had significantly increased since the war. Children's diseases also took a fearful toll. Even trachoma was on the rebound in some areas. In general, the 1948 report endorsed recommendations made by previous observers: concentration of medical services in a new medical center, more fieldwork, better salaries, training Indian women as nurse-aids, better staff living conditions, and prevention. Because many of the current medical inadequacies could be attributed to the remote and primitive reservation environment, improvement of the infrastructure, especially roads, also needed attention. The team additionally offered a warning about Navajo resistance to such common ailments as cancer and heart disease. Here the Navajo lifestyle seemed to provide a distinct advantage. However, even this benefit seemed doomed as "we continue to give them syphilis, gonorrhea, 'firewater,' soda pop, candy bars, and spearmint."[23]

The AMA team viewed Navajo reliance on healers as another obstacle. Displaying the medical community's age-old bias, they depicted traditional medicine as "employing a few herbs and singing, dancing, and drumming the evil spirits away." Nonetheless, the white doctors admitted "that compared with the methods of modern medicine the constant presence of the medicine man and his untiring ceremonial devotions for days and nights have a profound psychological influence." Although rejecting traditional healing practices, the AMA doctors recognized the need to secure the cooperation of healers, suggesting that the Indian Bureau invite them to visit the Medical Center, where they might get a "visual comprehension of what medicine and surgery can do." Nor was the team blind to the insensitivity of white doctors. One healer complained that government doctors regularly failed to keep patients informed and performed postmortem examinations without consent. In response, team leader Lewis Moorman admitted that "we have not fully measured up to our opportunities and our obligations."[24]

Such negative comments drew a response from Michel Pijoan and Charles S. McCammon, the ranking medical officers at Fort Defiance. They acknowledged that past practice had permitted physicians to be drawn from Civil Service lists and sent to the reservation with no training in "colonial field medicine or in the cultural aspects of the problem." And despite some notable exceptions, the average reservation physician had been a poorly qualified graduate of a lesser medical school, who regarded the field program as a "dull, uninspired routine." Yet Pijoan and McCammon believed the tide had turned.

The 1948 reorganization had gone a long ways toward updating facilities and securing a "sound working staff," especially at the Navajo Medical Center, where hospital admissions and out-patient visits were increasing. The field nursing program was also being revived. From only two field nurses in 1948, the number of trained public-health women had increased to eleven in 1949, with plans to add more in the near future. The main problem, therefore, consisted of the persistent lack of resources. "It becomes at once apparent," the government doctors wrote in the *Journal of the American Medical Association*, "that such a number of visits and admissions is beyond the capacity of the staff described." As a result, the bleak picture drawn by outside observers appeared to be somewhat misleading: "the problem of giving medical care to the Navajo Indians is a challenging one and deserves careful study and effort rather than the emotional approach used by many persons."[25]

In spite of such arguments, the immediate postwar period produced a lot of unfavorable publicity about the government's failure to care for the Navajos. This information, including the AMA surveys, bore some fruit in 1950, with the passage of the Navajo-Hopi Long Range Rehabilitation Act. The result of Interior Secretary Julius Krug's 1948 report analyzing all aspects of Navajo life, including the unsatisfactory medical situation, the act provided 88,570,000 dollars for long-term reservation improvements, particularly schools, hospitals, housing, and roads. Of this total, 4.75 million dollars was allocated for the construction and improvements of hospitals and health facilities. Existing sites at Shiprock, Tuba City, and Winslow were all scheduled for upgrades, while clinic services were to be eventually restored at Chinle, Kayenta, and Tohatchi.[26] This infusion of funds, spread over several years, permitted the Indian Service to begin rebuilding much of what had been dismantled during the war. Nonetheless, it remained to be seen if money alone could materially improve Navajo health.

THE SCOURGE CONTINUES

The effort to enhance medical services during the late 1940s failed to have much impact on tuberculosis. The deadly path of this disease prompted Dr. Pijoan to declare in 1949 that the Navajo tuberculosis situation "needs immediate attention." That same year the Interior Department announced that the "situation in regard to tuberculosis hospitals is grave. Large numbers of individuals seeking admission could not be accepted because of insufficiency of beds and operating funds and personnel even for existing beds." Particularly disturbing was the fact that while national death rates for the disease continued to decrease, the same could not be said of the Indian population. Indeed, between 1946 and 1949 the mortality rate for the general population dropped from 40.1 to 34.6 per 100,000, while the Indian rate remained somewhat over 200. As a consequence, the Bureau of Indian Affairs proclaimed an "all-out attack on tuberculosis." Maintaining that only substantial socioeconomic improvement could fully contain the disease, the Bureau nevertheless attempted to maximize its limited resources.[27]

In spite of the obvious inability to alter the Native American's social and economic status, many physicians still believed that much could be done to control the disease. In 1949, Albert Reifel, a young Lakota doctor, penned a particularly insightful essay on tuberculosis among the native population. Strongly arguing for the improvement of economic conditions, he noted that past government policies had created a situation "that was fertile soil for the seeding and dissemination of tuberculosis." Despite what Reifel regarded as a special government obligation to combat the disease, hardly anything was being done. "The Federal Government," he wrote, "hasty to help downtrodden people of foreign lands, allows only a meager appropriation to the Bureau of Indian Affairs for medical services." To combat the disease, he thus urged increasing the number of portable X-ray units and BCG vaccinations (which seemed to be of value in lowering morbidity rates). In addition, "there should be provisions for adequate medical and sanatorium care for all active cases. From a public health point of view, isolation is necessary if the spread of disease is to be prevented." He concluded on the hopeful note that the recent development of antibiotic drugs looked promising.[28]

Doctors directly involved with the Navajo generally seconded Reifel's analysis. Dr. Pijoan, Chief of Medicine at the Navajo Medical Center, believed that a renewed BCG effort could slow the disease among children. He was also interested in resuming collapse therapy and installing fluoroscopic facilities, but frankly admitted that his one hundred sanatorium beds were sadly insufficient. Dr. Lewis Moorman, leader of the 1948 AMA survey team, also endorsed a BCG program. In addition, he argued that the government must provide a bed for every case of tuberculosis detected. After visiting Fort Defiance in 1950, Moorman elaborated on the Navajo situation. He placed the tribal tuberculosis morbidity rate at ten times the national average, attributing it partly to poor diet, which he regarded as "seriously deficient in variety, quality, and quantity." It seemed particularly ironic to have a "Navajo island of sixty-four thousand people" living on unsatisfactory food while the United States fed the world. Rejecting race as a factor, other environmental conditions, such as inadequate health education, poor management, and insufficient hospital space, accounted for the high mortality and morbidity rates. The Fort Defiance sanatorium clearly failed to meet Navajo needs. Moorman remarked that it possessed "virtually no health, educational, or rehabilitation services," resembling a boarding house where the patients came and went at will. This lack of control caused "the Indians to pay with their lives." With recent results from the mobile X-ray unit indicating that four thousand beds could be filled, Moorman recommended that the current Fort Defiance Medical Center be converted into a tuberculosis facility. He justified the enormous cost of this undertaking by explaining that only the very best medical care, no matter how expensive, could solve the problem: "Otherwise there can be no end to the present mounting costs in money, morbidity, and mortality."[29]

Moorman's argument for additional sanatorium space unfortunately ran counter to congressional priorities. Even the Navajo Tribal Council, which urgently requested the construction of a four hundred–bed tuberculosis hospital, could make no headway. Caught up in the popular movement to divest the federal government of its responsibility for Indian welfare (the so-called Termination policy), Congress refused to fund a new sanatorium. Preferring not to operate health-care facilities if state or other services might be utilized, Washington terminationists provided instead 1,315,000 dollars for off-reservation care and treatment, by making additional beds available to the Navajos at non-Indian hospitals. Navajo leaders expressed disappointment with this compromise, knowing that most patients would be reluctant to travel to an urban hospital or to remain there for extended periods of treatment. Thus, while the transfer program did provide more beds, a relatively small percentage of patients elected to go to unfamiliar locations in California, Colorado, or New Mexico. Even sensational publicity charging the government with letting Navajo children die from neglect failed to change congressional attitudes. As a consequence, the Fort Defiance sanatorium remained the sole reservation tuberculosis hospital.[30]

The patient transfer program at least served to reduce pressure on doctors at Fort Defiance. Even so, the mobile X-ray detection unit uncovered many more potential patients than could be accommodated. In an effort to cope with this problem, the Indian Bureau renewed its emphasis on BCG vaccinations. By 1951 enough evidence existed to suggest that "BCG offers a practical means of supplementing the control program." The following year the Bureau authorized its hospitals to vaccinate newborns (with parental consent), which would hopefully immunize the younger generation. Although a long-term and uncertain solution, tests indicated that unvaccinated children were seven times more likely to develop tuberculosis.[31]

A much more encouraging method of controlling tuberculosis appeared in 1951 when a team of physicians from Cornell University's College of Medicine began to treat Navajo children at Tuba City with two recently discovered chemotherapeutic drugs, streptomycin and isoniazid (INH). As the benefits of chemotherapy became increasingly evident, the Cornell team was joined by Dr. Kurt Deuschle, who came to the reservation in 1952 under provisions of the Doctor-Dentist Draft. Prompted by the Korean War, which had again drawn medical personnel away from the reservations, the Public Health Service assigned some of its doctors to Indian service in lieu of military duty. Although most of the doctor draft physicians were young, inexperienced, and disinterested in public health or Indian work, Deuschle proved a notable exception. Recognizing the potential of the new antituberculosis drugs, the young physician was placed in charge of organizing a reservation-wide tuberculosis control program. Thus began a crash effort to treat hospitalized cases with INH. Working with the Cornell doctors, the enthusiastic and sympathetic Deuschle soon began to detect positive results. Between 1952 and 1957 mortality rates dropped significantly. As Deuschle wrote, "it was soon apparent that the extensive tuberculosis problem among the Navajos was yielding to the health measures instituted by the Government and the Cornell University investigators."[32]

In spite of such optimistic results, Deuschle encountered the age-old problem of persuading the Diné to accept treatment and see it through. Fortunately, he understood the necessity of explaining the disease to healers and securing their cooperation. One of his most vexing problems involved hospital patients, both on and off the reservation, who left before treatment could be completed. Homesick and fearful of hospitals, many patients simply refused to follow medical advice. This problem became so serious in 1953 that Deuschle sought advice from the Tribal Council. Here he joined with Annie Wauneka, daughter of Chee Dodge and chair of the Council's Committee on Health and Welfare. Wauneka, a dedicated and energetic woman committed to tribal service, quickly became engrossed with the tuberculosis program, hoping to convince most of her people to utilize government services. Together with Deuschle, she began to suggest ways to counter Navajo fears. Using her intuition as a woman and a mother, she offered numerous suggestions on how doctors might reach the Diné. As a result, the government soon started broadcasting health messages over the radio and showing educational films using Navajo actors speaking their own language. In an effort to make hospitalized patients feel more at home, tape-recorded messages from family members were also permitted. Finally, with Wauneka's encouragement, Deuschle began to permit families to hold sings in his hospital. As one contemporary noted, "When Navajos got upset they were, like anyone else, poor patients. If a sing could clear the air and give him a relaxed patient, Deuschle was all for it." This unusual move caused patient dropout rates at Fort Defiance to decline noticeably.[33]

Although the gains made with chemotherapy and Navajo customs were significant, tuberculosis remained beyond control. Not every patient responded to the new drugs and doctors realized that other discoveries might ultimately prove more effective. Moreover, while Deuschle and the Cornell team achieved considerable success with hospital patients, they acknowledged that only "the visible top of the tuberculosis 'iceberg' had been lopped off." It remained to successfully reach the general population with a viable field program, which did not then exist. Moreover, tuberculosis research, while on the medical agenda, had to compete for dwindling federal dollars with the myriad of other reservation health problems. As a result, Navajo tuberculosis rates remained well above the national average into the mid-1950s. Statistics for the 1955–57 period show a tribal mortality rate of 7.3 percent compared to a figure of 0.9 percent of the general population. Although the actual number of deaths per 100,000 had decreased from over 200 in 1949 to 52.5, tuberculosis remained at unsatisfactory levels. Fortunately, the tide was turning. Deuschle, who completed his tour of duty in 1954, quickly joined the Cornell team and continued to work at ending this deadly scourge.[34] Meanwhile, the adoption of new "wonder drugs" promised even more dramatic results.

THE PUBLIC HEALTH SERVICE TAKES OVER

The notion that the U.S. Public Health Service might be better equipped to operate Indian health facilities dated back to before World War II. In September 1941 the Bureau of the Budget proposed such a move, prompting a negative reaction from John Collier, who had no desire to lose his control of health policy. The idea made sense to others, however. After all, the Indian Office relied heavily on PHS physicians, especially to fill administrative posts. Although the war muted any talk of a transfer, it returned as Congress started to develop the postwar Termination policy. A direct reaction to the radical changes initiated by Collier during the New Deal, Congress now began to favor ending the Indian's special legal status and assimilating them directly into the national mainstream. Given the notoriously poor state of native health, it appeared to many observers that the medical situation could only improve by placing the responsibility elsewhere.[35]

The first concrete recommendations for transferring responsibilities appeared in 1948 as part of the Hoover Commission's report. A general survey concerning how the federal government might tackle the "Indian problem," the report focused on reducing federal responsibilities. Its analysis of health services thus centered on finding ways of assimilating Indian medical facilities into those of the general population. To expedite this change, the committee first recommended that state and local governments assume more responsibility for public-health activities: local welfare offices could assume the care of destitute natives, and wherever possible, the Indians might use off-reservation hospitals. These proposals, suggested the committee, promised to enhance the quality of health-care services. As Stephen Kunitz has remarked, "the clear intent of the Commission was to strip the Bureau of its authority and integrate Indians into the larger society." These proposals, however, placed such a burden on reluctant state and local governments, that it soon seemed more realistic to transfer medical services to the Public Health Service. A number of medical and political organizations endorsed the transfer, primarily because Public Health physicians were better qualified, the PHS might be more effective in obtaining funding, and duplication of efforts could end.[36]

Congress threw its weight behind the transfer. To many legislators, it represented another step in securing full citizenship for the Indians. It also seemed to advance the political objectives of the Termination movement by eliminating the "segregation" of Indian services. Not until 1953, however, at the height of the Termination frenzy, did Congress actually provide the necessary legislation. That year a House of Representatives bill authorized the transfer of all BIA health services, facilities, and personnel to the Public Health Service (then part of the Department of Health, Education, and Welfare). Despite opposition from the Indian Bureau, some native groups, and DHEW, the bill received administration blessing. Many Indians linked the transfer directly to Termination objectives, fearing that the desire for economy might actually eliminate many of their current health services and force them to travel great distances for treatment. Contesting this interpretation, advocates of Termination such as Utah Senator Arthur V. Watkins suggested that the PHS was better positioned to attract capable physicians, provide its doctors with current research, and secure better salaries. Along with other politicians such as Arizona's Barry Goldwater, Watkins effectively used the high rate of Indian disease to argue the issue.[37]

In June 1954 the Navajo Tribal Council endorsed the change. Historian Wade Davies contends that the vote represented an appreciation of the efforts of Kurt Deuschle, the Cornell University doctors, and Annie Wauneka. Nevertheless, some Council members, remembering past government duplicity, remained skeptical, concerned that the transfer would actually reduce government medical services. In this case, at least, it appears that advocates of Termination joined those who desired better health services. Congress passed the transfer bill in July 1954, authorizing the PHS to assume medical responsibilities on July 1, 1955. As Davies notes, "The Navajos had been promised, and surely expected, that the transfer would mean better and more accessible care. Whether the PHS could live up to these expectations . . . remained to be seen."[38]

Thus ended eighty-three years of United States Indian Service responsibility for Navajo health care. As the transfer date approached, most observers understood that the Indian Service had largely failed to do an adequate job in protecting tribal health. Much had changed in nearly a century, but the Navajo were still paying the price of an inadequate and underfunded federal Indian policy. The task facing the Public Health Service looked overwhelming. Existing hospital and sanatorium facilities remained inadequate, with the Navajo Medical Center complex at Fort Defiance offering 250 beds (150 general and 100 tuberculosis), supplemented only by smaller hospitals at Shiprock, Crownpoint, and Winslow. On the bright side, a new 75-bed hospital at Tuba City had just opened with Rehabilitation Act funding. In addition to the mission hospitals at Ganado and Rehoboth, field clinics at Chinle and Tohatchi also provided a few services. The government medical staff remained small. Life at isolated and depressing settlements continued to dampen enthusiasm, occasionally create cultural tensions, and produce unacceptable turnover rates. Nor were field services adequate. As anthropologist John Adair has noted, "If every one of the 24 public health nurses [available in 1955] had worked day and night, it would have been impossible to provide even token public health services to the 75,000 Navajos living on 25,000 square miles of mountain and desert country."[39]

Nor were disease rates under control in 1955. In connection with the transfer to PHS, the chief statistician of the BIA's health division prepared an analysis of medical conditions on the reservation. Concluding that "it is obvious that mortality and morbidity rates for most of the major diseases are far in excess of the rates for the total United States population," he found pneumonia a hundred times the national average, tuberculosis 15.7 percent higher, and trachoma 1,163 times the national average. Venereal disease and dysentery were also above that of the general population. Infant death rates were devastating: "Even on an understated basis the Navajo death rate for infants and preschool children is 5 times as high as the United States average. The infant mortality rate per 1,000 live births for the Navajo is 139.4, also about 5 times the United States average." Only among the older people were death rates equal or lower, accounted for by the fact that none of the leading causes of death nationally—heart disease, cancer, and stroke—were major factors among the Diné.[40]

On a more positive note, relations between doctors and healers seemed better than ever. Admittedly, few Navajos accepted the germ theory and a number of government physicians still refused to accommodate Navajo traditions. Nevertheless, the cooperative spirit of Deuschle and the Cornell doctors, supported by the efforts of Annie Wauneka and members of the Tribal Council, produced some encouraging results. More and more government doctors expressed willingness to consult healers and permit ceremonies as long as they did not directly interfere with treatment. Conversely, a growing number of Navajo "medicine men" recognized both their own limitations and the usefulness of white man's medicine. They proved increasingly more willing to talk with doctors and to advise hospitalization when necessary. In this way, it became evident that the two sides could indeed cooperate in securing better medical care. As Davies remarks, "Navajos did not replace their ceremonials with western medicine; rather, they recognized that doctors could heal the body and that singers could restore harmony." One healer, admitting that he did not accept the western theory of tuberculosis, nevertheless stated that "If I think a person has tuberculosis, I tell him to see a doctor immediately." Perhaps another singer, Sam Yazzie, best summarized the situation by noting: "After all, the medicine man and your doctors are working towards the same goal. They are both trying to cure the patient, so why should there be any feeling of rivalry between them?"[41]

EPILOGUE

The 1950s attempt to dismantle the Bureau of Indian Affairs quickly faded in the face of Indian opposition and administrative problems. By the 1960s much of the Termination rhetoric had given way to a quest for native self-determination. Although most of the Termination agenda has been assigned to the historical scrap heap, the transfer of health responsibilities from the Bureau to the Public Health Service is a notable exception. In the four decades that have passed since that event, federal health services for the Navajo and other tribes have made great strides in terms of quality, availability, education, reduction of infectious disease, tribal input, and the accommodation of native traditions. Problems, to be sure, remain, but in most respects reservation health care has made great progress in catching up with the rest of the nation. At the same time, the Navajos have increasingly come to accept western medicine.[1]

Changes began almost as soon the Public Health Service took responsibility for Indian health. Operating through its Division of Indian Health, the PHS successfully secured an increase in congressional appropriations—the first step in restoring many of the facilities and services lost during World War II. By 1960 government workers had completed a new seventy-five-bed hospital at Shiprock and opened field centers and clinics at former hospital sites (Kayenta, Tohatchi, and Chinle). Just as significant, the number of government physicians increased from 23 in 1955 to 43 in 1960, and to 115 in 1977. Nursing positions increased proportionately. From 64 registered nurses in 1955, the PHS had enlarged the number of authorized positions to 281 by 1978. As these changes occurred, hospital admissions surged between 1955 and 1970.[2]

The creation of a substantial public-health outreach program, advocated by most reservation officials since the war, had never made much progress under the Indian Bureau. Here, too, the Public Health Service brought rapid change. The number of field nurses, for example, expanded from twenty-four in 1955 to forty-seven in 1978. As these public-health professionals took to the field, they were able to bring immunization programs, educational activities, and diagnostic services to even the most remote desert community. Specialists in nutrition and dietetics also began to confront problems associated with malnutrition. By the early 1960s the outline of an effective prevention program, utilizing doctors, nurses, and medical social workers, was in place and expanding.[3]

Not surprisingly, the prevalence of infectious disease began to decline as medical services increased. By 1959 the use of isoniazid, streptomycin, and other forms of chemotherapy were producing such favorable results in treating tuberculosis that sanatoriums became obsolete and the government began to shut them down. Yet, despite the downward trend, tuberculosis rates among the Navajo remained above the national norm. Kurt Deuschle of the Navajo-Cornell Field Health Research Project summarized the situation when he observed that "because tuberculosis is so chronic, the presence of 7 per cent of clinically significant active or inactive disease on the basis of chest films still marks the Navajo as a tremendously high prevalence area." Nonetheless, tuberculosis was slowly being controlled. So too were infant death rates, primarily caused by gastrointestinal and respiratory maladies, although progress in this area seemed excruciatingly slow. As Davies notes, "infant mortality remained two and a half times above the rate for all U.S. races combined." As the rate of infectious diseases trended down, accidental deaths (mostly automobile accidents), often prompted by alcoholism, became the leading cause of death by 1970, setting an upward trend that lasted for a decade. At the same time, cancer and heart-disease rates increased. As a consequence of such changes, Navajo health concerns slowly began to shift from infectious diseases to socially related medical issues.[4]

The improvement in health services was accompanied by dramatic changes in reservation life. A turning point comparable to World War II came with the breakdown of Navajo isolation in the 1950s and 1960s. Although the wartime experience had opened the doors to Anglo influences, most Navajos remained in their own world—few spoke English, nor were they familiar with Anglo-American culture. This isolation began to crumble during the 1950s, and it continued at an accelerated pace. The construction of paved roads and the replacement of wagons with automobiles and trucks not only permitted outsiders to visit the reservation; it created a mobility among the Diné of unprecedented proportions. This development placed medical services within reach of the most isolated community, producing a much greater familiarity with, and confidence in, western medicine. At the same time, trading posts were gradually replaced with western-style grocery stores and a cash economy. Such facilities also brought the tribe within reach of over-the-counter medicines. Meanwhile, off-reservation employment and wage work increased Navajo familiarity with the American economic system. When the opening of Navajo homes to radio and television programming was added in, information about health and medical treatment became routine. All of these developments broke down tribal insularity and many of the barriers to utilizing government health services.[5]

In response, federal appropriations for tribal medical care showed steady growth for about three decades. Reliable funding permitted the Public Health Service to tailor a medical system more suitable to Navajo needs. A number of administrative changes along the way facilitated this process. In 1970 the Indian Health Service (IHS) replaced the Division of Indian Health. For the Navajo, this brought an element of administrative decentralization with the creation of a local service unit, the Navajo Area Indian Health Service (NAIHS), which eventually achieved considerable independence in the operation of federal facilities assigned to the Navajo. Meanwhile, modern new hospitals and clinics opened. In 1961, for example, a new two hundred–bed Medical Center opened at Gallup, thereby replacing Fort Defiance as the reservation's medical focal point. This new facility, located in an off-reservation urban setting, permitted the IHS to recruit and retain a greater number of physicians, although the Navajo were not pleased with the unilateral decision to move the center of their health services off the reservation. Nevertheless, changes of this sort encouraged younger, enthusiastic, and better-trained doctors to serve the tribe.[6]

Relations between the Navajo Tribal Council and the Indian Health Service have ranged from confrontational to cooperative. After being ignored for years, the Navajo wanted more say in medical policy, frequently objecting to IHS programs because they seemed arbitrary or inappropriate. Such concerns prompted the Tribal Council to establish its own Navajo Area Indian Health Advisory Board in 1970 as a vehicle for expressing tribal concerns. Two years later the Council created a Navajo Health Authority to encouraged Navajos to enter health-care professions. Peter Iverson suggests that the Navajo sought to gain control over health-care activities because "now that Navajos, for the most part had become willing to utilize Western medicine for certain purposes, they wanted to determine how that medical care was provided." In response, the Indian Health Service has attempted to be more sensitive to tribal and individual concerns, although the government agency has been reluctant to surrender its traditional autonomy. Even today, tribal health officials occasionally disagree with IHS policies. In November 1995, for example, the tribe announced that its people were tired of being "guinea pigs" for medical experimentation.

This issue flared up in the aftermath of the hantavirus attack that struck the Southwest in 1993. As outside medical teams invaded the reservation to study the virus, they violated traditional customs and attempted to use the Navajos for experimental testing. Other research programs, routinely approved by the IHS, seemed to benefit only doctors and universities. As a consequence, the Tribal Council has recently approved the creation of a new board, controlled by the tribe, to review all research requests.[7]

Despite such controversies, the past two decades have witnessed notable efforts to enlist more native health professionals. Although this has been very successful with regard to nurses, fewer Navajo physicians have thus far worked for the IHS on the reservation. Nevertheless, that number is growing. Recently, Dr. Lori Cupp became the first female Navajo surgeon. Working at the Gallup Indian Medical Center, Dr. Cupp personifies the cross-cultural approach to medicine now employed by native physicians. As she stated in an interview with *The Arizona Republic*, "Before we go into the operating room, I have to know that the patient is comfortable with an operation. His spirit and my spirit have to agree with each other. He will help me. I will help him. If the spirits are against each other, the operation won't work." The slowly growing number of native physicians, combined with the improvement of facilities, the construction of paved highways, and general use of automobiles, have persuaded most Navajos to utilize hospital services and out-patient clinics.[8]

Certainly the most significant development since 1970 has been the continued reduction of mortality and morbidity rates. Today health conditions are close to national levels. Most of the debilitating ailments so prevalent a generation earlier are things of the past. With the continued application of antituberculosis drugs, that dread disease has all but vanished (although the disease appears to be on the rise worldwide again, with the development of drug-resistant strains, and may eventually affect the Navajo population). So to have infant deaths, which dropped from 52 per 100,000 in 1967 to 10 in 1988. Even more notably, gastro-intestinal disease during the same period has been reduced to an average of only 3 deaths per 100,000 Navajos. Unfortunately, the upward postwar trend in heart disease and cancer has persisted as tribal lifestyles have grown more similar to those of the nation as a whole. Other social diseases, such as AIDS, have also made an appearance on the reservation. Overall, the death rate for the Navajo from all causes, including accidents, remains slightly above the national average. As Davies remarks, however, without accidents "the rates would be very competitive. This is particularly encouraging for the NAIHS because it indicates that those areas in which they have a direct influence have been affected very positively since 1955."[9] Indeed, the gains have been significant enough to constitute a medical revolution.

The historically strained relationship between government doctors and Navajo healers has also improved in recent years. Continuing a trend established after World War II, both white doctors and tribal healers have demonstrated more of a willingness to accept each other's area of expertise. Most Navajos still prefer to consult with their "medicine men," although they will also go to the doctor, thereby combining the two into a comfortable treatment program. Without question, many healers still do not believe in the germ theory and some government doctors dismiss native medical skills. Nevertheless, government doctors pay more attention to ceremonial matters, in some cases encouraging them before, during, and after hospitalization (as long as they do not interfere with medical treatment). Such accommodations seem to work rather well in spite of the occasional conflict that irritates one side or the other. Indeed, Navajo healers have recently received credit for helping to identify the deer mouse as the carrier of the deadly hantavirus that struck the Southwest in 1993.[10]

To prevent the erosion of their traditional role, a group of prominent healers obtained tribal permission to form a Medicine Man's Association in 1978. Now called the Dineh Spiritual and Cultural Society, this organization strives to perpetuate Navajo healing practices and to guard against the loss of this important part of tribal culture. In recent years they have expressed much concern that young people (because of the opening of the reservation to outside influences) are losing interest in learning the traditional healing arts. Although some young men and women continue to learn the ceremonies, it appears that their numbers are indeed declining. With fewer than seven hundred healers and singers remaining active, there is real danger that they and the entire ceremonial system may in fact disappear.[11] Nonetheless, tribal healers continue to make efforts to perpetuate their skills, and the IHS, acknowledging their value, now contributes to this quest by encouraging cross-cultural understanding. As more Navajos come to rely on available and modern government medical services, only time will tell if the long-standing conflict between traditional medicine and western medical practices will end up with a one-sided victory for science. But Navajo culture is too resilient to predict an end to this vital element of tribal life.

NOTES

CHAPTER I

1. The exact date of Navajo arrival in the Southwest is the subject of considerable scholarly debate. Many authorities believe the Navajo did not enter the region until just before the Spanish conquest began in 1540. Revisionists argue that the Athapaskan-speaking Navajo and Apache were on the scene hundreds of years earlier. For comments on Navajo prehistory, see Jack D. Forbes, *Apache, Navajo, and Spaniard* (Norman: University of Oklahoma Press, 1960), xi–xxiii; Edward H. Spicer, *Cycles of Conquest: The Impact of Spain, Mexico, and the United States on the Indians of the Southwest, 1533–1960* (Tucson: University of Arizona Press, 1962), 210–11; Clyde Kluckhohn and Dorothea Leighton, *The Navajo*, rev. ed. (Cambridge: Harvard University Press, 1974), 33; Ruth Underhill, *The Navajos* (Norman: University of Oklahoma Press, 1956), 14–23; David Brugge, "Navajo Prehistory and History to 1850," in *Handbook of North American Indians*, ed. William C. Sturtevant (vol. 10 ed. Alfonso Ortiz)(Washington D.C.: Smithsonian Institution, 1983), 10: 489–98. Also, consult J. Loring Haskell, *Southern Athapaskan Migration, A.D. 200–1750* (Tsaile, Ariz.: Navajo Community College Press, 1987); and Richard J. Perry, *Western Apache Heritage: People of the Mountain Corridor* (Austin: University of Texas Press, 1991).

2. Garrick Bailey and Roberta Glenn Bailey, *A History of the Navajos: The Reservation Years* (Santa Fe: School of American Research, 1986), 12–14; Florence H. Ellis, *Navajo Indians I, An Anthropological Study of the Navajo Indians* (New York: Garland Publishing, 1974), 41.

3. Russell Thornton, *American Indian Holocaust and Survival: A Population History Since 1492* (Norman: University of Oklahoma Press, 1987), 44–47; Alfred W. Crosby, Jr., "Virgin Soil Epidemics as a Factor in the Aboriginal Depopulation in America," *William and Mary Quarterly*, 3d ser., 33 (April 1976): 289–99. David E. Stannard, *American Holocaust: The Conquest of the New World* (New York: Oxford University Press, 1992), 53–54, 57–58.

4. Marshall T. Newman, "Aboriginal New World Epidemiology and Medical Care and the Impact of Old World Disease Imports," *American Journal of Physical Anthropology* 45 (1976): 668–69; Thornton, *American Indian Holocaust*, 103; Ales Hrdlicka, *Tuberculosis among Certain Indian Tribes of the United States*, Bureau of American Ethnology, Bulletin

no. 42 (Washington, D.C.: Government Printing Office, 1909), 1; Jane E. Buikstra, ed., *Prehistoric Tuberculosis in the Americas* (Evanston: Northwestern University Archaeological Program, Scientific Papers no. 5, 1981), 18.

5. Eric Stone, *Medicine among the American Indians* (New York: Hafner Publishing Co., 1962), 22–23; Virgil J. Vogel, *American Indian Medicine* (Norman: University of Oklahoma Press, 1970), 148–61; Ellis, *Navajo Indians I*, 249–50.

6. Hrdlicka, *Tuberculosis among Certain Indian Tribes*, 1.

7. Underhill, *Navajos*, 37–38, 59–60; Brugge, "Navajo Prehistory and History": 493–94; Ellis, *Navajo Indians I*, 253, 267.

8. Brugge, "Navajo Prehistory and History": 491; Daniel T. Reff, *Disease, Depopulation, and Culture in Northwestern New Spain, 1518–1764* (Salt Lake City: University of Utah Press, 1991), 228–29; Lynn R. Bailey, *Indian Slave Trade in the Southwest* (Los Angeles: Westernlore Press, 1966), 73–89.

9. Percy M. Ashburn, *The Ranks of Death: A Medical History of the Conquest of America* (New York: Coward-McCann, 1947), 80–98, 175–90; J. G. Townsend, "Trachoma Control in the Indian Service," National Society for the Prevention of Blindness, Publication 314 (1940): 3; "History of Trachoma," typescript dated January 12, 1942, National Archives, Pacific Southwest Regional Branch, Record Group 75, Records of the Office of Indian Affairs (hereafter cited as NA, PSR), Phoenix Area Office, Box 563; Thornton, *American Indian Holocaust*, 45. Alfred W. Crosby, Jr., *The Columbian Exchange: Biological and Cultural Consequences of 1492* (Westport, Conn.: Greenwood Publishing Co., 1972), 122–60, discusses the varying theories of the origin of syphilis.

10. W. F. M. Arny to E. P. Smith, March 4, 1875, National Archives, RG 75, Records of the Office of Indian Affairs, Microcopy M234, Letters Received by the Office of Indian Affairs, 1824–1880 (hereafter cited as NA, M234), Roll 564; Charles Bent, quoted in William A. Keleher, *Turmoil in New Mexico, 1846–1868*, repr. ed. (Albuquerque: University of New Mexico Press, 1982), 72.

11. Newman, "Aboriginal New World Epidemiology and Medical Care," 670–71.

12. Stephen J. Kunitz, *Disease Change and the Role of Medicine: The Navajo Experience* (Berkeley: University of California Press, 1983), 140–41; Francis H. Elmore, *Ethnobotany of the Navajo* (Albuquerque: University of New Mexico Press, 1944), 96–97; Leland C. Wyman and Stuart K. Harris, *The Ethnobotany of the Kayenta Navajo: An Analysis of the John and Louisa Wetherill Ethnobotanical Collection*, University of New Mexico Publications in Biology, no. 5 (Albuquerque: University of New Mexico Press, 1951), passim. See also Stone, *Medicine among the American Indians*, 32–69; and Vogel, *American Indian Medicine*, passim.

13. Kunitz, *Disease Change and the Role of Medicine*, 119, 140–41.

14. Leland C. Wyman, "Navajo Ceremonial System," in Sturtevant, *Handbook of North American Indians*, 10: 536–38; Kluckhohn and Leighton, *Navajo*, 192–93, 200–202; Karl W. Luckert, "Traditional Navajo Theories of Disease and Healing," *Arizona Medicine* 27 (July 1972): 570–72.

15. John Adair, "Physicians, Medicine Men, and Their Navajo Patients," in *Man's Image of Medicine and Anthropology*, ed. Iago Galdston (New York: International Universities Press, 1963), 242–44; Alexander H. Leighton and Dorothea C. Leighton, *The Navajo Door: An*

Introduction to Navajo Life (Cambridge: Harvard University Press, 1945), 24–25; Leland C. Wyman, "The Religion of the Navajo Indians," in *Forgotten Religions (Including Some Living Primitive Religions)*, ed. Vergilius Ferm (New York: Philosophical Library, 1950), 344–47.

16. Kunitz, *Disease Change and the Role of Medicine*, 132; Charlotte J. Frisbie, *Navajo Medicine Bundles or Jish: Acquisition, Transmission, and Disposition in the Past and Present* (Albuquerque: University of New Mexico Press, 1987), 2–3; Gladys A. Reichard, *Navajo Religion: A Study of Symbolism* (Tucson: University of Arizona Press, 1983), 32–69.

17. John Adair, Kurt W. Deuschle, and Clifford R. Barnett, *The People's Health: Anthropology and Medicine in a Navajo Community*, rev. ed. (Albuquerque: University of New Mexico Press, 1988), 6–7, 162–63; William Morgan, "Navajo Treatment of Sickness: Diagnosticians," *American Anthropologist*, n.s., 33, (July–September 1931): 390–402.

18. Charlotte J. Frisbie, "Temporal Change in Navajo Religion, 1868–1990," *Journal of the Southwest* 34 (Winter 1992): 461; Adair et al., *People's Health*, 163–64; Leighton and Leighton, *Navajo Door*, 27–28. Although not as numerous as men, female healers, or medicine women, have long existed among the Navajo. For information regarding their activities and numbers, see Bobette Perrone, H. Henrietta Stockel, and Victoria Krueger, *Medicine Women, Curanderas, and Women Doctors* (Norman: University of Oklahoma Press, 1989), 29–44; and Charlotte J. Frisbie and Eddie Tso, "The Navajo Ceremonial Practitioners Registry," *Journal of the Southwest* 35 (Spring 1993): 53–92.

19. Wyman, "Religion of the Navajo Indians," 347; Wyman, "Navajo Ceremonial System," 537, 541–43; Vogel, *American Indian Medicine*, 22–23.

20. Wyman, "Navajo Ceremonial System," 541–46, contains a good description of the various Navajo chantways.

21. Adair et al., *People's Health*, 10–11; Robert L. Bergman, "Navajo Health Services and Projects," in Sturtevant, *Handbook of North American Indians*, 10: 672.

22. Richard H. Shryock, *The Development of Modern Medicine: An Interpretation of the Social and Scientific Factors Involved* (New York: Alfred A. Knopf, 1947), 3–16; Henry E. Sigerist, *Landmarks in the History of Hygiene* (London: Oxford University Press, 1956), 1–19. The best overview of early American medical history is Richard H. Shryock, *Medicine and Society in America, 1660–1860* (New York: New York University Press, 1960).

23. Shryock, *Development of Modern Medicine*, 20–21.

24. Martin Kaufman, *American Medical Education: The Formative Years, 1765–1910* (Westport, Conn.: Greenwood Press, 1976), 3–8; William Frederick Norwood, *Medical Education in the United States Before the Civil War* (Philadelphia: University of Pennsylvania Press, 1944; repr., New York: Arno Press, 1971), 3–34.

25. Quoted in Norwood, *Medical Education in the United States*, 22–23. See also Shryock, *Medicine and Society in America*, 8–9, 17.

26. Norwood, *Medical Education in the United States*, 1–8; Paul Starr, *The Social Transformation of American Medicine* (New York: Basic Books, 1982), 40–42; Kaufman, *American Medical Education*, 10–11.

27. Kaufman, *American Medical Education*, 12–13, 36–53; Milton I. Roemer, ed., *Henry E. Sigerist on the Sociology of Medicine* (New York: M. D. Publications, 1960), 165–68; Norwood, *Medical Education in the United States*, 36–56.

28. Quoted in Joseph Kett, *The Formation of the American Medical Profession: The Role of Institutions, 1780–1960* (New Haven: Yale University Press, 1968), vii–viii.

29. A good description of doctoring on the 1840s frontier is contained in Raymond N. Doetsch, *Journey to the Green and Golden Lands: The Epic of Survival on the Wagon Trail* (Port Washington, N.Y.: Kennikat Press, 1976), 44–52. One should also consult Henry E. Sigerist, *American Medicine* (New York: W. W. Norton, 1934); and William G. Rothstein, *American Physicians in the Nineteenth-Century* (Baltimore: Johns Hopkins Press, 1972).

30. Kenneth M. Ludmerer, *Learning to Heal: The Development of American Medical Education* (New York: Basic Books, 1985), 9–11; George W. Adams, *Doctors in Blue: The Medical History of the Union Army in the Civil War* (New York: Henry Schuman, 1952), 194–97, 204–5; Paul E. Steiner, *Physician-Generals in the Civil War: A Study in Nineteenth Mid-Century American Medicine* (Springfield, Ill.: Charles C. Thomas, 1966), 107–8, 148–57. The Civil War produced a tremendous amount of information on medical treatment and sanitation. While much of this focused on battlefield wounds, a goodly amount of study related to disease also appeared. See United States Surgeon-General's Office, *The Medical and Surgical History of the War of the Rebellion (1861–65)* (Washington, D.C.: Government Printing Office, 1870–1888), 3 pts.; and George A. Otis, *A Report of Surgical Cases Treated in the Army of the United States from 1865 to 1871* (Washington, D.C.: Government Printing Office, 1871).

31. Starr, *Social Transformation of American Medicine*, 99. 102–12.

32. Kaufman, *American Medical Education*, 109–24, 161; Ludmerer, *Learning to Heal*, 25–26, 60; Shryock, *Development of Modern Medicine*, 273–303.

33. Kaufman, *American Medical Education*, 120–21.

34. For a general overview of Indian policy during the early national period, the reader should consult Francis P. Prucha, *The Great Father: The United States Government and the American Indian* (Lincoln: University of Nebraska Press, 1984), vol. 1. See also Prucha, *American Indian Policy in the Formative Years: The Indian Trade and Intercourse Acts, 1790–1834* (Cambridge: Harvard University Press, 1962); and Reginald Horsman, *Expansion and American Indian Policy, 1783–1812* (East Lansing: Michigan State University Press, 1967).

35. James Axtell, *The Invasion Within: The Contest of Cultures in Colonial North America* (New York: Oxford University Press, 1985), 10.

36. James Axtell, *Beyond 1492: Encounters in Colonial North America* (New York: Oxford University Press, 1992), 158–61. See also Axtell, *Invasion Within*, 86, 96–97.

37. Alden T. Vaughan, *New England Frontier: Puritans and Indians, 1620–1675* (Boston: Little, Brown and Co., 1965), 84–85; Vogel, *American Indian Medicine*, 40–41.

38. Vaughan, *New England Frontier*, 243–44; William S. Simmons, "Conversion from Indian to Puritan," *New England Quarterly* 52 (June 1979): 208; Margaret Connell Szasz, *Indian Education in the American Colonies, 1607–1783* (Albuquerque: University of New Mexico Press, 1988), 120–21.

39. Vogel, *American Indian Medicine*, 45.

40. Horsman, *Expansion and American Indian Policy*, 53–65; Robert F. Berkhofer, Jr., *Salvation and the Savage: An Analysis of Protestant Missions and American Indian Response* (New York: Atheneum, 1972), 115; Shryock, *Medicine and Society in America*, 48.

41. Herman J. Viola, *Thomas L. McKenney: Architect of America's Early Indian Policy, 1816–1830* (Chicago: Sage Books, 1974), 32–43; Bernard W. Sheehan, *Seeds of Extinction: Jeffersonian Philanthropy and the American Indian* (Chapel Hill: University of North Carolina Press, 1973), 130–32; Jedediah Morse, quoted in Berkhofer, *Salvation and the Savage*, 28.

42. Robert A. Trennert, *Alternative to Extinction: Federal Indian Policy and the Beginnings of the Reservation System, 1846–51* (Philadelphia: Temple University Press, 1975), passim; Robert M. Utley, *The Indian Frontier of the American West, 1846–1890* (Albuquerque: University of New Mexico Press, 1984), 31–63.

43. Kunitz, *Disease Change and the Role of Medicine*, 150.

44. For good overviews of the assimilation philosophy of the postwar period, see Francis P. Prucha, *American Indian Policy in Crisis: Christian Reformers and the Indian, 1865–1900* (Norman: University of Oklahoma Press, 1976); Robert W. Keller, Jr., *American Protestantism and United States Indian Policy, 1869–82* (Lincoln: University of Nebraska Press, 1983); and Loring B. Priest, *Uncle Sam's Stepchildren: The Reformation of United States Indian Policy, 1865–1887* (Lincoln: University of Nebraska Press, 1975).

CHAPTER 2

1. Good overall coverage of the period between 1846 and 1862 is provided by Frank McNitt, *Navajo Wars: Military Campaigns, Slave Raids, and Reprisals* (Albuquerque: University of New Mexico Press, 1972), 95–429. See also Ralph E. Twitchell, *The History of the Military Occupation of New Mexico from 1846–1851* (Denver: Smith-Brooks Company, 1909); Keleher, *Turmoil in New Mexico*, 3–108; Frank D. Reeve, "The Government and the Navajos, 1846–1858," *New Mexico Historical Review* 14 (January 1939): 82–114; Trennert, *Alternative to Extinction*, 94–130; Underhill, *Navajos*, 85–111.

2. James S. Calhoun to William Medill, October 15, 1849, in *Official Correspondence of James S. Calhoun while Indian Agent at Santa Fe and Superintendent of Indian Affairs in New Mexico*, ed. Annie H. Abel (Washington, D.C.: Government Printing Office, 1915), 54–55; Trennert, *Alterative to Extinction*, 128.

3. Keleher, *Turmoil in New Mexico*, 47; *Annual Report, Commissioner of Indian Affairs, 1854* (hereafter cited as *Annual Report, CIA*, and year), 172.

4. McNitt, *Navajo Wars*, 224–25, 286; James H. Simpson, *Navajo Expedition: Journal of a Military Reconnaissance from Santa Fe, New Mexico, to the Navajo Country, Made in 1849 by Lieutenant James H. Simpson*, ed. and annotated by Frank McNitt (Norman: University of Oklahoma Press, 1964), 184–85.

5. Henry L. Dodge to David Meriwether, September 30, 1855, May 16, 1856, NA, M234, Roll 548; Bailey and Bailey, *History of the Navajos*, 21. See also *Santa Fe Weekly Gazette*, September 10, 1853.

6. *Santa Fe Weekly Gazette*, November 19, 1853; Henry L. Kendrick to Meriwether, November 13, 1853, and William Messervy to George Manypenny, March 29, 1854, NA, M234, Roll 247; Kendrick to Meriwether, February 10, 1854, National Archives, Record Group 75, Records of the New Mexico Superintendency, Microcopy T21 (hereafter cited as

NA, T21), Roll 2; *Annual Report, CIA, 1870,* 135. For historical background on smallpox, see E. Wagner Stearn and Allen E. Stearn, *The Effect of Smallpox on the Destiny of the Amerindian* (Boston: Bruce Humphries, 1945), 56–58, 95–96; William Hanna, *Studies in Smallpox and Vaccination* (New York: William Wood and Co., 1913), 52; and Benjamin White, *Smallpox and Vaccination* (Cambridge: Harvard University Press, 1925). A description of the process by which smallpox vaccine was manufactured in the 1870s is contained in Henry A. Martin & Sons to E. A. Hayt, May 2, 1878, NA, M234, Roll 574.

7. Jules Le Carpentier to Captain F. T. Bennett, December 12, 1870, NA, M234, Roll 558. Marc Simmons, *Spanish Government in New Mexico* (Albuquerque: University of New Mexico Press, 1990), 127n., indicates that the Spanish introduced smallpox vaccinations into New Mexico after 1804. Although the Navajo were not vaccinated, they may have learned about it as a preventive measure.

8. Meriwether to Manypenny, May 16, 1856, and James L. Collins to J. W. Denver, October 31, 1857, NA, M234, Roll 548; McNitt, *Navajo Wars,* 300–301, 309.

9. Underhill, *Navajos,* 105–6; McNitt, *Navajo Wars,* 325–57; "Correspondence with the Governor of New Mexico relating to Indian disturbances in that Territory," January 7, 1861, 36th Cong., 2d Sess., Exec. Doc. 24, Serial 1097, 5.

10. McNitt, *Navajo Wars,* 410–29; Frank D. Reeve, "Federal Indian Policy in New Mexico, 1858–1880, Chapter 1," *New Mexico Historical Review* 12 (July 1937): 218–47.

11. Clifford E. Trafzer, *The Kit Carson Campaign: The Last Great Navajo War* (Norman: University of Oklahoma Press, 1982), 56–59; Lynn R. Bailey, *The Long Walk: A History of the Navajo Wars, 1846–68* (Pasadena, Calif.: Westernlore Press, 1978), 149–52.

12. General Orders no. 15, Department of New Mexico, June 15, 1863, quoted in Bailey, *Long Walk,* 157.

13. Christopher Carson to Ben. C. Cutler, January 24, 1864, quoted in Lawrence C. Kelly, *Navajo Roundup: Selected Correspondence of Kit Carson's Expedition against the Navajo, 1863–65* (Boulder, Colo.: Pruett Publishing Company, 1970), 98–101.

14. Carson to Cutler, January 3, 1864, quoted in Kelly, *Navajo Roundup,* 92–93; Trafzer, *Kit Carson Campaign,* 138.

15. Keleher, *Turmoil in New Mexico,* 316; Carson to Cutler, January 24, 1864, quoted in Kelly, *Navajo Roundup,* 98.

16. Carleton to Brig. General Lorenzo Thomas, December 12, 1863, NA, M234, Roll 552; Kelly, *Navajo Roundup,* 115–19; *Santa Fe Weekly Gazette,* March 5, 1864.

17. Ruth Roessel, ed., *Navajo Stories of the Long Walk Period* (Tsaile, Ariz.: Navajo Community College Press, 1973), 83, 118–19, 125, 225–26.

18. Capt. Joseph Berry to Asst. Adj. General, April 7, 1864, quoted in Kelly, *Navajo Roundup,* 115–16; Bailey, *Long Walk,* 168; Keleher, *Turmoil in New Mexico,* 319.

19. Bailey, *Long Walk,* 169–70; Trafzer, *Kit Carson Campaign,* 190–94; Roessel, *Navajo Stories of the Long Walk Period,* 260.

20. Quoted in Gerald Thompson, *The Army and the Navajo: The Bosque Redondo Reservation Experiment, 1863–1868* (Tucson: University of Arizona Press, 1976), 28.

21. Thompson, *Army and the Navajo,* 10–27; Price to Michael Steck, October 21, 1863,

quoted in J. Lee Correll, ed., *Through White Man's Eyes: A Contribution to Navajo History. A Chronological Record of the Navajo People from Earliest Times to the Treaty of June 1, 1868* (Window Rock, Ariz.: Navajo Heritage Center, 1979), 2: 392–93.

22. Carleton to Major Henry D. Wallen, February 25, 1865, and Carleton to Adjutant General Lorenzo Thomas, February 27, 1864, in Joint Special Committee on Indian Affairs, *The Condition of the Indian Tribes* (Washington, D.C.: Government Printing Office, 1867), 158–61.

23. George Gwyther File, National Archives, Record Group 15, Veteran's Records Pension Files, no. 203529; Adjutant General, Muster Rolls, 1847–67, New Mexico Records Center and Archives, Santa Fe. For an example of Gwyther's ideas regarding the Indians, see "An Indian Reservation," *Overland Monthly* 10 (February 1873), 126–29. Gwyther was mustered out of the service in October 1866, but immediately contracted with the army to continue providing medical services. Between 1868 and 1876 he worked at several western military posts. He died in San Francisco on October 6, 1876, after participating in a march between Portland, Oregon, and Fort Colville, Washington Territory.

24. Lorenzo Labadie to Carleton, April 1, 1864, and Major Henry D. Wallen to Asst. Adj. General, April 1, 1864, National Archives, Record Group 94, Office of the Adjutant General, Letters Received, Main Series, Microcopy M619 (hereafter cited as NA, M619), Roll 286.

25. Roessel, *Navajo Stories of the Long Walk Period*, 32, 122, 132, 214–15, 242–43.

26. Wallen to Carleton, April 15, 1864, NA, M619, Roll 236; Joseph Updegraff to Carleton, September 18, 1863, Wallen to Cutler, December 18, 1863, and Carelton to Wallen, December 24, 1863, all quoted in Correll, *Through White Man's Eyes*, 3: 372–73, 445, 457.

27. Thompson, *Army and the Navajo*, 47; Capt. Henry B. Bristol to Asst. Adj. General, May 13, 1864, quoted in Correll, *Through White Man's Eyes*, 4: 169.

28. Crocker to Cutler, September 28, 1864, [Crocker] to Carleton, November 17, 1864, Special Order no. 6, January 14, 1865, and Major W. McCleave Report [August 1865], National Archives, Record Group 393, United States Army Continental Commands, Fort Sumner Records, Letters Sent and Received, 1862–69 (hereafter cited as NA, Fort Sumner Records); Joint Special Committee on Indian Affairs, *Condition of the Indian Tribes*, 338–42.

29. Joint Special Committee on Indian Affairs, *Condition of the Indian Tribes*, 339; Thompson, *Army and the Navajo*, 80–81; Robert Mario Salmon, "The Disease Complaint at Bosque Redondo (1864–68), *The Indian Historian* 9, no. 3 (Summer 1976): 4.

30. Various "Return of Indian Captives held in custody and Fort Sumner" forms, March, July 1865, NA, M234, Roll 552; Carleton to J. R. Doolittle, July 25, 1865, NA, M619, Roll 561; Joint Special Committee on Indian Affairs, *Condition of the Indian Tribes*, 342–43. In February 1865 an epidemic (disease unknown) reportedly killed over a hundred Navajos apparently on their way to the reservation; see [Crocker] to Act. Asst. Surgeon C. L. Mann, February 10, 1865, NA, Fort Sumner Records.

31. Joint Special Committee on Indian Affairs, *Condition of the Indian Tribes*, 338; O. M. Bryan to Medical Director's Office, April 6, 1865, NA, Fort Sumner Records; Proceedings of a Council with Navajoes held by Superintendent A. B. Norton, July 15, 1866, NA, M234, Roll 554.

32. Joint Special Committee on Indian Affairs, *Condition of the Indian Tribes*, 339, 342.

33. Report of Julius K. Graves, Part 8 [1866], NA, M234, Roll 553. Inspector Graves came from Dubuque, Iowa. Judging from the rhetoric of his report, he was a devout Christian.

34. Bristol to Asst. Adj. General, August 6, 1864, in Correll, *Through White Man's Eyes*, 4: 218; Thompson, *Army and the Navajo*, 48; Joint Special Committee on Indian Affairs, *Condition of the Indian Tribes*, 339–40, 342; Carleton to Doolittle, July 25, 1865, NA, M619, Roll 561; Salmon, "Disease Complaint," 3.

35. William J. Brown et al., *Syphilis and Other Venereal Diseases* (Cambridge: Harvard University Press, 1970), 17–25; Gwyther to Medical Director, September 2, 1864, quoted in John Brooke to Lt. Mason Howard, December 19, 1866, NA, M234, Roll 554; Joint Special Committee on Indian Affairs, *Condition of the Indian Tribes*, 356; Second Annual Message of Acting Governor Arny, December 1866, National Archives, Record Group 59, New Mexico Territorial Papers, Microcopy T17, Roll 3. Arny's numbers were apparently taken from the report of Dr. Michael Hillary, published in *Annual Report, CIA, 1866*, 151, which indicates that 235 of 331 cases were syphilis. The exact method of treating syphilis at the Bosque Redondo has not been recorded. Military doctors of that era, however, appear to have favored mercury or iodide of potassium treatments. See United States Surgeon-General's Office, *Medical and Surgical History of the War of the Rebellion*, pt. 3, 1: 891–92.

36. Joint Special Committee on Indian Affairs, *Condition of the Indian Tribes*, 342, 356; Arny Message, December 1866, NA, New Mexico Territorial Papers, T17, Roll 3.

37. Katherine Marie Birmingham Osburn, "The Navajos at the Bosque Redondo: Cooperation, Resistance, and Initiative, 1864–1868," *New Mexico Historical Review* 60 (October 1985): 403–5.

38. [Crocker] to Carleton, November 17, 1864, NA, Fort Sumner Records; Joint Special Committee on Indian Affairs, *Condition of the Indian Tribes*, 358.

39. Joint Special Committee on Indian Affairs, *Condition of the Indian Tribes*, 355, 358; Osburn, "Navajos at the Bosque Redondo," 404–5; Roessel, *Navajo Stories of the Long Walk Period*, 99, 101, 215.

40. Joint Special Committee on Indian Affairs, *Condition of the Indian Tribes*, 339, 342; [Crocker] to Carleton, November 17, 1864, NA, Fort Sumner Records.

41. Joint Special Committee on Indian Affairs, *Condition of the Indian Tribes*, 354; [Crocker] to Carleton, November 17, 1864, NA, Fort Sumner Records.

42. See the general testimony regarding health conditions at the reservation in Joint Special Committee on Indian Affairs, *Condition of the Indian Tribes*, 335–58.

43. Ibid.; Thompson, *Army and the Navajo*, 89–90.

44. Report of Graves, 1866, NA, M234, Roll 553.

45. Not much is known about Hillary other than he served as an assistant surgeon during July 1863 at the Union army hospital in Frederick, Maryland, treating soldiers wounded at Boonesboro. See United States Surgeon-General's Office, *Medical and Surgical History of the War of the Rebellion*, pt. 2, 2: 253. Brooke had a long and distinguished military career. First appointed as assistant surgeon in November 1862, he remained in the West throughout the war. He later saw duty at military hospitals in New York, Delaware, California, Oregon,

Pennsylvania, and Washington, D.C. He retired with the rank of major in 1894. See John Brooke file, NA, RG 15, Veteran's Records Pension Files, WC 554433.

46. Brooke to Howard, December 19, 1866, and Carleton to General Chauncy McKeever, December 27, 1866, NA, M234, Roll 554; Thompson, *Army and the Navajo*, 128–29; Report of Graves, 1866, NA, M234, Roll 553; *Annual Report, CIA, 1866*, 150–51; E. D. Townsend Report, March 1, 1867, NA, M619, Roll 561.

47. Proceedings of Council with Navajos, July 15, 1866, Report on Consultation with eleven Navajo chiefs, September 2, 1867, and Dodd to Norton, April 2, 1876, NA, M234, Roll 554.

48. *Annual Report, CIA, 1866*, 143; Carleton to McKeever, February 2, 1867, and Norton to Taylor, December 26, 1867, NA, M234, Rolls 554, 555; E. D. Townsend Report, March 1, 1867, NA, M619, Roll 651.

49. Dodd to Norton, December 7, 1867, NA, M234, Roll 555; *Annual Report, CIA, 1867*, 190.

50. Charles J. Kappler, ed., *Indian Affairs, Laws and Treaties* (Washington, D.C.: Government Printing Office, 1915), 2: 1015–20; Keleher, *Turmoil in New Mexico*, 464–66; Thompson, *Army and the Navajo*, 154–55; William Haas Moore, *Chiefs, Agents, and Soldiers: Conflict on the Navajo Frontier, 1868–1882* (Albuquerque: University of New Mexico Press, 1994), 22–31.

CHAPTER 3

1. *Annual Report, CIA, 1868*, 162–65; Dodd to Webb, August 6, 1868, NA, M234, Roll 555; Bailey and Bailey, *History of the Navajos*, 26–27; Underhill, *Navajos*, 146–51.

2. *Annual Report, CIA, 1868*, 19.

3. Kappler, *Indian Affairs*, 2: 977–81, 984–89, 998–1003, 1008–11; Prucha, *American Indian Policy in Crisis*, 18–23.

4. John Ward to S. F. Tappan, August 4, 1868, NA, M234, Roll 555; Dodd to Webb, August 15, 1868, *Annual Report, CIA, 1868*, 165; *Santa Fe Daily New Mexican*, September 17, 1868.

5. Bailey and Bailey, *History of the Navajos*, 28–29; *Annual Report, CIA, 1869*, 677–80.

6. Norman J. Bender, *"New Hope for the Indians": The Grant Peace Policy and the Navajos in the 1870s* (Albuquerque: University of New Mexico Press, 1989), 16–17, 21–22; Keller, *American Protestantism and United States Indian Policy*, 18; Underhill, *Navajos*, 154.

7. Bennett to Major William Clinton, September 29, November 18, December 1, 16, 1869, "Estimates of Funds Requested by the Navajo Indian Agency," NA, M234, Roll 556; *Annual Report, CIA, 1869*, 679–80.

8. Bender, *"New Hope for the Indians,"* 14–17; J. M. Schofield to Secretary of the Interior, October 16, 1868, NA, M234, Roll 555; J. M. Roberts to John Lowrie, November 28, 1868, January 20, March 4, 1869, *American Indian Correspondence: The Presbyterian Historical Society Collection of Missionaries' Letters, 1833–1893* (Greenwood Press, microfilm (hereafter cited as AIC), Box B, Vol. 1.

9. *Annual Report, CIA, 1869*, 531; Roberts to Lowrie, January 18, September 13, 1870, AIC, Box B, Vol. 2; Bennett to Clinton, March 9, 1870, and Roberts to Parker, March 18, 1870, NA, M234, Roll 557; Parker to Clinton, March 26, 1870, National Archives, RG 75, Microcopy M21, Letters Sent by the Office of Indian Affairs, 1824–1881 (hereafter cited as NA, M21), Roll 94; Bender, *"New Hope for the Indians,"* 30–32.

10. Bennett to Clinton, August 10, 1870, NA, M234, Roll 557; *Annual Report, CIA, 1870*, 153. For comments on earlier vaccination programs, see Richard White, "The Winning of the West: The Expansion of the Western Sioux in the Eighteenth and Nineteenth Centuries," *Journal of American History* 65 (September 1978): 328–29.

11. Jules Le Carpentier to Clinton, October 10, 1870, NA, M234, Roll 557; Le Carpentier to Commissioner, August 25, October 10, 1872, NA, M234, Roll 559; *Annual Report, CIA, 1870*, 134.

12. Le Carpentier to Bennett, December 12, 1870, NA, M234, Roll 558; Le Carpentier to Superintendent of Indian Affairs, December 19, 1870, NA, M234, Roll 557.

13. Le Carpentier to Bennett, December 12, 1870, NA, M234, Roll 558.

14. *Necrological Reports and Annual Proceedings of Princeton Theological Seminary* (Princeton, N.J.: C. S. Robinson, 1891–1919), 4: 165–66; Luther M. Dimmitt to F. W. Hodge, September 28, 1944, Presbyterian Historical Society Archives, Philadelphia; *Hinton (Oklahoma) Record*, January 11, 1912; Bender, *"New Hope for the Indians,"* 39–40.

15. Menaul to Lowrie, October 31, November 21, December 21, 1870, AIC, Box B, Vol. 2; Nathaniel Pope to Parker, February 22, 24, 1871, James Miller to Pope, October 17, 1871, NA, M234, Roll 558; Bender *"New Hope for the Indians,"* 48, 56. Menaul's first wife, Harriet E. McMechan, perished in Africa, leaving the missionary with two young daughters, who apparently did not come to New Mexico.

16. Roberts to Lowrie, February 20, 1872, AIC, Box C; Bender, *"New Hope for the Indians,"* 54.

17. *Annual Report, CIA, 1872*, 68–70.

18. Bender, *"New Hope for the Indians,"* 54; Miller to Pope, August 27, 1871, NA, T21, Roll 14; Menaul to Miller, February 27, 1872, NA, T21, Roll 16.

19. W. F. Hall to Commissioner, m.d. [August 12, 1873,] NA, M234, Roll 561; Miller to Lowrie, April 10, 1872, AIC, Box L; *Annual Report, Board of Indian Commissioners, 1872* (hereafter cited as *Annual Report, BIC*, and year), 40.

20. Menaul to Miller, March 14, 1872, NA, M234, Roll 559; W. F. M. Arny to Lowrie, December 11, 1873, AIC, Box M; Miller to Lowrie, April 10, 1872, and Menaul to Lowrie, May 4, 1872, AIC, Box L; Menaul to Pope, July 5, 1872, NA, T21, Roll 16.

21. Menaul to Pope, July 5, 1872, NA, T21, Roll 16. Menaul prepared a similar list in September 1873; see L. E. Dudley to E. Smith, October 1, 1873, NA, M234, Roll 561. For a comparison of medical lists at a different agency, see L. E. Dudley (Cimarron Agency) to H. R. Clum, June 24, 1873, NA, M234, Roll 560.

22. *Annual Report, BIC, 1873*, 19–22; *Annual Report, BIC, 1876*, 24–26; Prucha, *American Indian Policy in Crisis*, 41–42.

23. Menaul to Lowrie, June 13, 1872, AIC, Box L; *Annual Report, CIA, 1872*, 296–97, 302–

4; Bender, *"New Hope for the Indians,"* 80. For details on Miller's death and Keam's tenure as temporary agent, see Moore, *Chiefs, Agents, and Soldiers,* 95–113.

24. Menaul to W. F. Hall [January 1873] and List of Medicines needed by John Menaul, Agency Physician, April 16, 1873, NA, T21, Roll 19.

25. "The Indian Service Health Activities," Bulletin 11 (Washington, D.C.: Office of Indian Affairs, 1922); William H. Armstrong, *A Friend to God's Poor: Edward Parmelee Smith* (Athens: University of Georgia Press, 1993), 266–67; Virginia R. Allen, "Agency Physicians to the Southern Plains Indians, 1868–1900," *Bulletin of the History of Medicine* 49 (Fall 1975): 319. See also reference to circular arriving at the Cimarron Agency, June 1873, NA, M234, Roll 560.

26. Hall to Commissioner, n.d. [August 12, 1873] NA, M234, Roll 561.

27. Menaul to Arny, September 1, 1873, AIC, Box M.

28. Lawrence R. Murphy, *William F. M. Arny, Frontier Crusader* (Tucson: University of Arizona Press, 1972), 4–5, 34, 202–6; Bender, *"New Hope for the Indians,"* 99–100; Frank McNitt, *The Indian Traders* (Norman: University of Oklahoma Press, 1962), 144; Moore, *Chiefs, Agents, and Soldiers,* 115–18. Born in 1813, Arny had been a religious crusader and anti-slavery activist in Kansas before securing a federal appointment in 1861 through his Republican party connections. Between 1861 and 1873 he served in various appointed positions in New Mexico, both as territorial secretary (1861–67 and 1872–73) and as an Indian agent at several locations in northern New Mexico.

29. Menaul to Lowrie, June 21, 1873, and Arny to Lowrie, December 11, 1873, AIC, Box M; *Annual Report, CIA, 1873,* 273.

30. Menaul to Lowrie, December 2, 1873, AIC, Box M.

31. Menaul to Arny, January 31, March 31, April 30, May 31, 1874, NA, T21, Roll 22; Menaul to Lowrie, March 18, 1874, AIC, Box M; Arny to L. E. Dudley, May 2, 1874, NA, M234, Roll 562; Arny to E. P. Smith, March 3, 1875, AIC, Box O, Vol. 2.

32. Report of Inspector Daniels, August 20, 1874, National Archives, Record Group 75, Microcopy M1070, Reports of Inspection of the Field Jurisdictions of the Office of Indian Affairs, 1873–1900 (hereafter cited as NA, M1070), Roll 29; Menaul, Yearly Sanitary Report, August 31, 1874, NA, M234, Roll 562.

33. Arny to Lowrie, September 15, 1874, AIC, Box O, Vol. 2. See also a printed version of the letter in *Annual Report, CIA, 1874,* 306–8.

34. Arny to E. P. Smith, October 1, 1874, NA, M234, Roll 562; *Annual Report, CIA, 1874,* 308; Menaul to Lowrie, October 26, December 2, 1874, and March 20, 1875, AIC, Box N; Menaul to Lowrie, January 15, 1876, AIC, Box C; "Report on Employees, Southern Apache Agency, 2nd Quarter, 1875," AIC, Box O, Vol. 2; *Necrological Reports and Annual Proceedings,* 165. Before accepting the Southern Apache position, Menaul apparently returned to Fort Defiance briefly in February 1875, where Arny offered him a job distributing annuity goods. Menaul turned this down, arguing that "his vocation was 'Missionary Work.' " See Arny to Lowrie, February 22, 1875, AIC, Box O, Vol. 2.

35. *Report of the Board of Foreign Missions, Presbyterian Church in the U.S.A., 1873,* 15, quoted in Dimmitt to Hodge, September 28, 1944, Presbyterian Historical Society Archives.

36. Keller, *American Protestantism and United States Indian Policy*, 58–59.

37. Frederick C. Pierce, *Whitney: The Descendants of John Whitney Who Came from London, England, to Watertown, Massachusetts, in 1635* (Chicago: Privately published, 1895), 582; A. A. Walker to Lowrie, April 13, 1877, and Joseph A. Whitney to Lowrie, April 16, 1877, AIC, Box D; Arny to E. P. Smith, September 4, 1873, NA, M234, Roll 560; Arny to Lowrie, February 22, 1875, AIC, Box O, Vol. 2. Although Whitney was not listed as a church member, his family were Presbyterians. There is also some evidence that he was associated with the Fourth Presbyterian Church in Washington, D.C.

38. Arny to E. P. Smith, March 3, 1875, and Monthly Sanitary Reports, February 28, May 31, 1875, AIC, Box O, Vol. 2; Arny to E. P. Smith, June 4, 1875, NA, M234, Roll 564.

39. Claude Quétel, *History of Syphilis* (Cambridge, England: Polity Press, 1990), 3–4. For general histories of this disease, also see Charles C. Dennie, *A History of Syphilis* (Springfield, Ill.: Charles C. Thomas, 1962); and Brown et al., *Syphilis and Other Venereal Diseases*.

40. Arny to E. P. Smith, December 17, 1874, General Pope letter, January 7, 1875, General Sherman to E. D. Townsend, January 13, 1875, AIC, Box O, Vol. 2; *Annual Report, CIA, 1875*, 330–32; *Annual Report, BIC, 1874*, 44–45; Murphy, *William F. M. Arny*, 233.

41. Arny to E. P. Smith, March 4, 1875, NA, M234, Roll 564; Murphy, *William F. M. Arny*, 233–34; *Annual Report, BIC, 1875*, 154–55.

42. Arny to E. P. Smith, April 7, May 31, June 26, 1875, NA, M234, Roll 564.

43. Whitney to Arny, August 19, 1875, Arny to E. P. Smith, September 14, 25, 1875, NA, M234, Roll 564. Good accounts of the incident are contained in Murphy, *William F. M. Arny*, 234–38; Bender, *"New Hope for the Indians,"* 140–43; and McNitt, *Indian Traders*, 156–61.

44. W. Redwood Price to Whitney, September 12, 1875, Arny to E. P. Smith, October 11, 1875, NA, M234, Roll 564. Arny blamed many of his troubles on traders and the military, whom he believed conspired against him. See *Annual Report, BIC, 1875*, 102.

45. Commissioner to Alex Irvine, May 13, 1876, NA, M21, Roll 130; Bender, *"New Hope for the Indians,"* 145–46; Irvine to E. P. Smith, December 6, 1875, NA, M234, Roll 564; Irvine to E. P. Smith, June 6, 1876, NA, M234, Roll 567.

46. Irvine to E. P. Smith, June 6, 1875, NA, M234, Roll 567; Irvine to J. Q. Smith, December 30, 1876, NA, M234, Roll 570; Commissioner to Irvine, May 13, 1876, NA, M21, Roll 130; *Annual Report, CIA, 1877*, 298–99. For the entire fiscal year of 1877, only 843 people received treatment of any kind.

47. S. D. Galpin to Lowrie, April 10, 1877, AIC, Box D; J. N. Whitney to E. A. Hayt, January 31, 1878, NA, M234, Roll 574; Irvine to Commissioner, March 25, 1878 (two letters), NA, M234, Roll 573. Whitney had great political support, including congressmen and General Eliphalet Whittlesey, who had long been connected with the Board of Indian Commissioners. He also had the backing of Dr. Josiah Curtis, head of the Medical and Educational Division. See Curtis to Lowrie, April 9, 1877, AIC, Box D.

48. John E. Pyle to Commissioner, April 15, 1875 (two letters), and Henry A. Martin & Sons to Commissioner, May 2, 1875, NA, M234, Roll 574.

49. Pyle to Commissioner, June 21, 1878, Sherman to Secretary of War, September 9, 1878, Roll 575; George C. Smith to Commissioner, October 16, 1878, NA, M234, Roll 574;

McNitt, *Indian Traders*, 202–3; Bailey and Bailey, *History of the Navajos*, 33–34; Moore, *Chiefs, Agents, and Soldiers*, 185–208.

50. Abraham L. Earle to E. M. Kingsley, January 3, 14, 1879, Galen Eastman to Commissioner, May 1, 10, 22, 24, 1879, NA, M234, Roll 576.

51. Bender, *"New Hope for the Navajos,"* 188–92.

52. Bailey and Bailey, *History of the Navajos*, 36–50, provides a detailed discussion of the growth of the tribal economy. See also *Annual Report, CIA, 1880*, 131.

53. "Treaties, Acts, and Executive Orders," map prepared by Office of Navajo Land Administration, Window Rock, Arizona, 1991.

CHAPTER 4

1. Paul Stuart, *The Indian Office: Growth and Development of an American Institution, 1865–1900* (Ann Arbor: UMI Research Press, 1979), 46–47; Allen, "Agency Physicians to the Southern Plains Indians": 320–21; Henry Heath, quoted in Laurence F. Schmeckebier, *The Office of Indian Affairs: Its History, Activities and Organization* (Baltimore: Johns Hopkins Press, 1927), 72.

2. See the statistical charts published as an appendix to the *Annual Report, CIA, 1881–1889*.

3. McNitt, *Indian Traders*, 60–61, 166; Bender, *"New Hope for the Indians,"* 184; Lansing B. Bloom, ed., "Bourke on the Southwest, VIII," *New Mexico Historical Review* 11 (January 1936): 85; Bourke quoted in Joseph C. Porter, *Paper Medicine Man: John Gregory Bourke and His American West* (Norman: University of Oklahoma Press, 1986), 96–97.

4. Eastman to Commissioner, May 24, 1879, McNett to Commissioner, November 29, 1879, NA, M234, Roll 576; Leo C. Lillie, *Historic Grand Haven and Ottawa County* (Grand Haven, Mich.: n.p., 1931), 316.

5. Monthly Sanitary Reports, Navajo Agency, December 1879 to June 1880, F. T. Bennett to Commissioner, June 25, August 10, 1880, James R. Sutherland to E. J. Brooks, August 28, 1880, NA, M234, Roll 579; Sutherland to Eastman, May 1, 1880, NA, M234, Roll 581.

6. Rothstein, *American Physicians in the Nineteenth-Century*, 205; Richard H. Shryock, *Medicine in America: Historical Essays* (Baltimore: Johns Hopkins University Press, 1966), 156; Allen, "Agency Physicians to the Southern Plains Indians," 319–20.

7. John Little to Commissioner, August 21, 1880, NA, M234, Roll 579.

8. Little to Commissioner, September 16, 1880, NA, M234, Roll 579.

9. Ibid.

10. Charles H. Bowen to Commissioner, September 1880, Bowen to Schurz, October 25, 1880, NA, M234, Roll 579.

11. Bowen to Schurz, October 25, December 11, 1880, NA, M234, Roll 579; Bennett to Commissioner, August 5, 1880, NA, M234, Roll 580. See also *Annual Report, CIA, 1880*, 132.

12. J. M. Haworth, Report of Inspection, Navajo Agency, August 9, 1881, NA, M1070, Roll 27.

13. Ibid; Eastman to Commissioner, November 14, December 31, 1881, January 31, Febru-

ary 15, 28, 1882, NA, PSR, Navajo Agency, Box 3, FD2; *Annual Report, CIA, 1881,* 138. See also "Table Showing Prevailing Diseases among the Indians," *Annual Report, CIA, 1881,* 310.

14. Allen, "Agency Physicians to the Southern Plains Indians," 319; *Annual Report, CIA, 1882,* xlvii–xlviii; Ruth M. Raup, *The Indian Health Program from 1800 to 1955* (Washington, D.C.: U.S. Public Health Service, 1959), 5.

15. *Annual Report, CIA, 1882,* xlviii; "Draft of a bill to create the office of Medical Inspector for the United States Indian Service, January 18, 1882," 47th Cong., 1st sess., Exec. Doc. 59, serial 1987.

16. Ibid.

17. Eastman to Commissioner, June 30, July 31, 1882, NA, PSR, Navajo Agency, Box 3, FD3; Howard, Report of Inspection, October 25, 1882, NA, M1070, Roll 27.

18. Howard, Report of Inspection, October 25, 1882, NA, M1070, Roll 27; *Annual Report, CIA, 1883,* xliii–xliv. Raup, *Indian Health Program,* 3, indicates that the first reservation hospital was built in the early 1880s, yet by the turn of the century only five hospitals or infirmaries were in existence, all serving boarding schools.

19. Eastman to Commissioner, September 1, 1882, *Annual Report, CIA, 1882,* 128; Eastman to Commissioner, September 18, 20, 30, 1882, NA, PSR, Navajo Agency, Box 3, FD3. The listing of medical statistics for the year ending June 30, 1883, *Annual Report, CIA, 1883,* 304–11, shows practically no treatment provided to the Navajo.

20. McNitt, *Indian Traders,* 60–61; Bender, *"New Hope for the Indians,"* 187; Frank D. Reeve, "The Government and the Navajo, 1883–1888," *New Mexico Historical Review* 18 (January 1943): 17–21; D. M. Riordan to Price, December 21, 1882, National Archives, Record Group 75, Records of the Bureau of Indian Affairs, Letters Received, 1881–1907 (hereafter cited as NA, LR), 23443–1882. After leaving the Indian Service, Eastman went to San Francisco, where he entered the hardware business. See *Grand Haven (Michigan) Tribune,* January 19, 1899.

21. Riordan to Price, January 9, 1883, and Riordan to H. M. Teller, January 22, 1883, NA, LR, 1038–1883 and 2051–1883.

22. Riordan to Teller, January 23, 1883, Riordan to Price, January 20, 23, 1883, NA, LR, 2051–1883, 2050–1883, and 2145–1883.

23. G. P. Sampson to J. J. Ingalls, January 3, 1884 [1885], S. F. Neely to J. D. C. Atkins, December 18, 1885, W. V. Coffin to Atkins, December 22, 1885, NA, LR, 748–1885, 30694–1885, and 30929–1885.

24. William Parsons to Atkins, April 23, 1886, and Sampson to Ingalls, January 3, 1884 [1885], NA, LR, 11814–1886 and 748–1885; George R. Pearsons, Report of Inspection, Navajo Agency, November 30, 1885, NA, M1070, Roll 27.

25. Riordan to R. H. Pratt, August 13, September 27, 1883, and Riordan to E. E. Ayer, August 31, 1883, NA, PSR, Navajo Agency, Box 3, LS, FD4; Ruth Underhill, *Here Come the Navajo!* (Washington, D.C.: United States Indian Service, n.d.), 215–16.

26. *Annual Report, CIA, 1883,* 119–23. Riordan remained in northern Arizona following his government service, establishing a lumber and railroad dynasty in Flagstaff. For information on these activities, see Robert A. Trennert, "A Vision of Grandeur: The Arizona Mineral Belt Railroad," *Arizona and the West* 12 (Winter 1970): 345–54.

27. Robert Gardner, Report of Inspection, Navajo Agency, October 15, 1883, NA, M1070, Roll 27; Sampson to Commissioner, January 18, 1884, NA, LR, 18412–1884; *Annual Report, CIA, 1884,* 338–45.

28. *Annual Report, CIA, 1884,* xxxvi.

29. Gregory C. Thompson, "John D. C. Atkins, 1885–88," in *The Commissioners of Indian Affairs, 1824–1977,* ed. Robert M. Kvasnicka and Herman J. Viola (Lincoln: University of Nebraska Press, 1979), 185; *Annual Report, CIA, 1886,* xl–xli; Stuart, *Indian Office,* 48.

30. Neely to Atkins, April 10, 1885, and Sampson to Commissioner, November 25, 1885, NA, LR, 8006–1885 and 28453–1885.

31. Sampson to Commissioner, November 25, 1885, W. V. Coffin to Atkins, December 22, 1885, Sampson to Atkins, January 23, 1886, and Parsons to Atkins, April 28, 1886, NA, LR, 28453–1885, 30694–1885, 4246–1886, and 11814–1886; Pearsons, Report of Inspection, Navajo Agency, November 30, 1885, NA, M1070, Roll 27.

32. Sampson to Samuel S. Patterson, April 10, 1886, and Parsons to Atkins, April 28, 1886, NA, LR, 10926–1886 and 11814–1886.

33. Reeve, "Government and the Navajo, 1883–1888," 44; William A. Olmstead to A. B. Upshaw, December 29, 1886, and Thomas Hill to Atkins, April 25, 1887, NA, LR, 350–1887 and 12363–1887.

34. Olmstead to Upshaw, December 29, 1886, and Charges and Specifications against Dr. Olmstead, May 27, 1887, NA, LR, 350–2887 and 14181–1887; Robert Gardner, Report of Inspection, Navajo Agency, September 26, 1886, NA, M1070, Roll 27.

35. *Annual Report, CIA, 1885,* 154; *Annual Report, CIA, 1886,* 204.

36. Charges against Olmstead, May 27, 1887, NA, LR, 14181–1887.

37. Ibid.; Patterson to Commissioner, August 24, 1887, *Annual Report, CIA, 1887,* 176–77.

38. Charges against Olmstead, May 27, 1887, NA, LR, 14181–1887.

39. Olsmtead to Upshaw, May 5, 1887, and Charges against Olmstead, NA, LR, 13443–1887 and 14181–1887.

40. Ibid.; Olmstead to Commissioner, June 10, 1887, NA, LR, 16476–1887; *Annual Report, CIA, 1887,* 176.

41. W. P. Taulbee to Atkins, June 22, 1887, and J. B. Taulbee to Secretary of the Interior, February 1889, NA, LR, 16064–1887 and 4736–1889; T. D. Marcum, Report of Inspection, Navajo Agency, September 20, 1888, NA, M1070, Roll 27.

42. *Annual Report, CIA, 1888,* 189–90; Robert Gardner, Report of Inspection, Navajo Agency, March 29, 1888, NA, M1070, Roll 27.

43. Gardner, Report of Inspection, Navajo Agency, March 29, 1888, and Marcum, Report of Inspection, Navajo Agency, September 20, 28, 1888, NA, M1070, Roll 27; H. S. Welton to Commissioner, April 29, 1888, J. B. Taulbee to Commissioner, September 3, 1888, and J. B. Taulbee to Secretary of the Interior, February 1889, NA, LR, 11615–1888, 25420–1888, and 4736–1889. The investigation of Patterson's misuse of government supplies apparently came to little. Patterson remained in office for another year. The agency clerk, however, was removed during Welton's visit in April.

44. Frank C. Armstrong, Report of Inspection, Navajo Agency, July 8, 1889, NA, M1070, Roll 27; *Annual Report, CIA, 1889,* 257.

45. C. E. Vandever to Commissioner, February 26, 1889, NA, PSR, Navajo Agency, Box 20, FD12; *Annual Report, CIA, 1889*, 257.

46. Quoted in Raup, *Indian Health Program*, 2–3.

CHAPTER 5

1. *Annual Report, CIA, 1889*, 12–13.

2. Stuart, *Indian Office*, 40–41, 49; *Annual Report, U.S. Civil Service Commissioner, 1891–92* (Washington, D.C.: Government Printing Office, 1893), 221; L. W. White, "Reminiscences of an Indian Physician," *Indians at Work* 3, no. 4 (October 1, 1935): 32.

3. Lisa E. Emmerich, "'To Respect and Love and Seek the Way of White Women': Field Matrons, the Office of Indian Affairs, and Civilization Policy, 1890–1938" (Ph.D. diss., University of Maryland, 1987), passim; Raup, *Indian Health Program*, 5. The concept of field matrons went back several years. See "Letter of the Commissioner of Indian Affairs relative to the employment of matrons at agencies," May 7, 1888, 50th Cong., 1st sess., Senate Exec. Doc. 160, serial 2513.

4. *Annual Report, CIA, 1889*, 12–14; *Annual Report, CIA, 1890*, xxii; *Annual Report, CIA, 1892*, 63.

5. Michael J. Warner, "Protestant Missionary Activity among the Navajo, 1890–1912," *New Mexico Historical Review* 45 (July 1970): 214–15; J. Rockwood Jenkins, *The Good Shepherd Mission to the Navajo* (Phoenix: Privately published, 1954), 2–8. For an overview, see Francis P. Prucha, *American Indian Policy in the United States* (Lincoln: University of Nebraska Press, 1981), 229–51.

6. Robert A. Roessel, Jr., "Navajo History, 1850–1923," in Sturtevant, *Handbook of North American Indians*, 10: 522; Bailey and Bailey, *History of the Navajos*, 165.

7. Underhill, *Navajos*, 226–27.

8. F. F. Dickman, *Kansas Medical Directory for 1881* (Fort Scott, Kans.: Harold Job Printing, 1881), 45; *Third Annual Report of the State Board of Health of the State of Kansas, from January 1, 1887, and ending December 31, 1887* (Topeka: Kansas Publishing House, 1888), 258–59; *The (Benedict, Kansas) Echo*, January 20, 1888; B. W. Perkins to Commissioner, June 13, 1889, and Craig to Perkins, July 19, 1889, NA, LR, 15983–1889, and 19612–1889; *(Wilson County, Kansas) Citizen*, August 2, 1889.

9. White, "Reminiscences of an Indian Physician," 32–33.

10. Arthur W. Tinker, Report of Inspection, Navajo Agency, March 21, 1890, NA, M1070, Roll 27; Vandever to Commissioner, July 31, August 15, 1890, and T. J. Morgan to R. V. Belt, NA, LR, 23926–1890, 25582–1890, and 34634–1890.

11. Tinker, Report of Inspection, Navajo Agency School, March 29, 1890, NA, M1070, Roll 27; *Annual Report, CIA, 1890*, 163; Diane T. Putney, "Fighting the Scourge: American Indian Morbidity and Federal Indian Policy, 1897–1928" (Ph.D. diss., Marquette University, 1980), 62–63.

12. Tinker, Report of Inspection, Navajo Agency School, March 29, 1890, NA, M1070, Roll 27. A new school superintendent, Louis Morgan, was appointed on June 2, 1890. See

William W. Jenkins, Report of Inspection, Navajo Agency School, February 11, 1891, NA, M1070, Roll 27.

13. Robert Gardner, Report of Inspection, Navajo Agency, July 21, 1891, NA, M1070, Roll 27; Tinker, Report of Inspection, Navajo Agency School, June 16, 1892, NA, M1070, Roll 28; *Annual Report, CIA, 1892*, 913–925, 941–947; David Shipley to Commissioner, January 5, 1892, NA, PSR, Navajo Agency, Box 8, FD15.

14. Herbert Welsh to Fanny Schuyler, May 17, 1891, Welsh to Mrs. G. H. Wadleigh, July 8, 1892, *Indian Rights Association, 1885–1901* (Scholarly Resources), microfilm (hereafter cited as IRA Papers), Roll 6, Letterbook 8; Harriet Wadleigh to Welsh, December 2, 1892, IRA Papers, Roll 20, Incoming Correspondence. See Frank Mitchell, *Navajo Blessingway Singer: The Autobiography of Frank Mitchell, 1881–1967*, ed. Charlotte J. Frisbie and David P. McAllester (Tucson: University of Arizona Press, 1978), 50–54, 69–73n., for a Navajo version of the Black Horse affair.

15. Gardner, Report of Inspection, Navajo Agency School, December 23, 1892, NA, M1070, Roll 28; Craig to Shipley, October 17, 1892, J. J. Noah, memorandum, December 29, 1892, That-ta-be-the On-begay, testimony, November 21, 1892, all in NA, LR, 43345–1892.

16. Noah, memorandum, December 29, 1892, and Notes on Council of Chiefs and Headmen, November 25, 1892, NA, LR, 43345–1892; Welsh to Belt, April 3, 1893, IRA Papers, Roll 6, Letterbook 9; Harriet Wadleigh to Welsh, December 2, 1893, Belt to Welsh, April 3, 1893, and Plummer to Commissioner, April 1, 1893, IRA Papers, Roll 20, Incoming Correspondence.

17. J. W. Cadman, Reports of Inspection, Navajo Agency and Navajo Agency School, May 14, 25, 1894, NA, M1070, Roll 28; E. H. Plummer to Commissioner, January 31, 1894, NA, PSR, Navajo Agency, Box 7, FD20; *Annual Report, CIA, 1894*, 101.

18. *Annual Report, CIA, 1892*, 100–102, 210–11; Report of Mary E. Raymond Whyte, January 1 to April 1, 1893, and Mrs. E. W. Simpson to Mrs. M. E. Roberts, June 2, 1893, NA, LR, 14113–1893, and 20654–1893; Welsh to Browning, May 9, 1893, IRA Papers, Roll 6, Letterbook 9.

19. Warner, "Protestant Missionary Activity among the Navajo," 215; *Annual Report, CIA, 1892*, 210–11; Charles F. Messerve to Morgan, April 21, 1890, NA, LR, 20119–1893.

20. *Annual Report, CIA, 1893*, 113; Plummer to Mary Whyte, June 22, 1893, NA, PSR, Navajo Agency, Box 6, FD18; Plummer to Commissioner, May 28, 1894, NA, PSR, Navajo Agency, Box 8, FD22; Report of Mary E. Raymond Whyte, January 1 to April 1, 1893, and Whyte to Plummer, October 7, 1893, NA, LR, 14113–1893 and 41098–1893.

21. Plummer to Commissioner, May 28, 1894, NA, PSR, Navajo Agency, Box 8, FD22; *Annual Report, CIA, 1895*, 120; Simpson to Browning, July 11, 1894, and Report of Mary L. Eldridge, September 30 to December 31, 1894, NA, LR, 26260–1894, and 5327–1895; Constant Williams to Commissioner, January 26, 1895, NA, PSR, Navajo Agency, Box 8, FD23.

22. *Annual Report, CIA, 1893*, 113; *Annual Report, CIA, 1894*, 103.

23. Simpson to Browning, April 29, 1895, Alfred Hardy to Browning, September 21, 1896, Hardy to Miss M. S. Cook, November 20, 1896, Eldridge to W. N. Hailman, May 23, 1898, E. Whittlesey to Commissioner, June 8, 1898, and G. W. Hayzlett to Commissioner, Febru-

ary 21, 1899, NA, LR, 18938–1893, 36279–1896, 45304–1896, 24833–1898, 26016–1898, and 9053–1899; *Annual Report, CIA, 1898*, 123.

24. Quoted in Jenkins, *Good Shepherd Mission*, 10; Plummer to Alfred Harvey, September 19, 1894, NA, PSR, Navajo Agency, Box 8, FD23.

25. Plummer to Kendrick, May 9, 1894, NA, PSR, Navajo Agency, Box 7, FD22.

26. John Mills Kendrick, "Seventeenth Annual Report of the Missionary Bishop of New Mexico and Arizona," *Spirit of Missions* 62 (September 1897): 420; Jenkins, *Good Shepherd Mission*, 10–12; Plummer to D. M. Riordan, October 25, 1894, NA, PSR, Navajo Agency, Box 8, FD23.

27. Jenkins, *Good Shepherd Mission*, 11–12; Thackera letter, quoted in ibid., 12.

28. Plummer to Commissioner, July 18, 1894, NA, PSR, Navajo Agency, Box 7, FD22; Plummer to Kendrick, September 7, 21, October 8, 1894, NA, PSR, Navajo Agency, Box 8, FD23.

29. Plummer to Commissioner, November 11, 1894, and Plummer to Thackera, November 14, 1894, NA, PSR, Navajo Agency, Box 8, FD24; Plummer to Riordan, October 25, 1894, NA, PSR, Navajo Agency, Box 8, FD23; Jenkins, *Good Shepherd Mission*, 14.

30. Jenkins, *Good Shepherd Mission*, 16–21; "Miss Thackera's Hospital for the Navajos," *The Indian's Friend* 10 (March 1898): 7–8.

31. John Lane, Report of Inspection, Navajo Agency, April 30, 1897, NA, M1070, Roll 28.

32. Craig to Plummer, March 31, 1894, and Plummer to Kendrick, May 9, 1894, NA, PSR, Navajo Agency, Box 7, FD21 and FD22; Craig to Plummer, June 30, 1894, NA, PSR, Navajo Agency, Box 25.

33. C. C. Duncan, Report as to Employees, Navajo Agency, December 25, 1894, NA, M1070, Roll 28; Craig to Plummer, June 30, 1894, NA, PSR, Navajo Agency, Box 7, FD22.

34. Plummer to Commissioner, July 30, 1894, NA, PSR, Navajo Agency, Box 7, FD22; *Annual Report, CIA, 1898*, 125; Underhill, *Here Come the Navajo!*, 227.

35. Williams to Commissioner, July 10, 1895, NA, PSR, Navajo Agency, Box 8, FD24; Province McCormick, Report as to Employees, Navajo Agency, May 9, 1896, NA, M1070, Roll 28.

36. Jenkins, *Good Shepherd Mission*, 22–23; Mary Harper to Welsh, April 1, 1892, John Menaul to Welsh, August 17, 1892, IRA Papers, Roll 19, Incoming Correspondence.

37. Jenkins, *Good Shepherd Mission*, 23–24; John Mills Kendrick, "Arizona Navajos," *Spirit of Missions* 64 (February 1899): 62; Kendrick, "Nineteenth Annual Report of the Missionary Bishop of New Mexico and Arizona," *Spirit of Missions* 64 (December 1899): 634; Eliza W. Thackera, "Arizona," *Spirit of Missions* 64 (June 1899): 278.

38. Jenkins, *Good Shepherd Mission*, 24–26.

39. For accounts of the epidemic among the Pueblos, see Richard H. Frost, "The Pueblo Indian Smallpox Epidemic in New Mexico, 1898–1899," *Bulletin of the History of Medicine* 64 (Fall 1990): 417–45; and Robert A. Trennert, "White Man's Medicine vs. Hopi Tradition: The Smallpox Epidemic of 1899," *The Journal of Arizona History* 33 (Winter 1992): 349–66.

40. G. W. Hayzlett to Henry Dodge, January 8, 1899, Hayzlett to Commissioner, January 8, 20, May 8, 1899, and Hayzlett to Charles Burton, August 4, 1899, NA, PSR, Navajo Agency, Box 8, FD26; Eliza W. Thackera, "Small Pox Scare at Fort Defiance," *Spirit of Missions* 64 (August 1899): 407; *Annual Report, CIA, 1899*, 157–59.

41. Hayzlett to Commissioner, October 20, 1899, NA, PSR, Navajo Agency, Box 9, FD27; A. M. Tinker, Report of Inspection, Navajo Agency, June 6, 1900, NA, M1070, Roll 28; "Forty Years Ago," *Navajo Medical News* 8, no. 3 (November 29, 1941): 10–12.

CHAPTER 6

1. Putney, "Fighting the Scourge," ii–iii, 1–8.

2. McConnell to Secretary of the Interior, November 15, 1897, quoted in ibid., 8.

3. Sheila M. Rothman, *Living in the Shadow of Death: Tuberculosis and the Social Experience of Illness in American History* (Baltimore: Johns Hopkins University Press, 1994), 13–14; R. Y. Keers, *Pulmonary Tuberculosis: A Journey Down the Centuries* (London: Bailliere Tindall, 1978), 1–19; F. B. Smith, *The Retreat of Tuberculosis, 1850–1950* (London: Croom Helm, 1988), passim; Rene and Jean Dubos, *The White Plague: Tuberculosis, Man, and Society* (New Brunswick, N.J.: Rutgers University Press, 1987), 3–6, 235; Mark Caldwell, *The Last Crusade: The War on Consumption, 1862–1954* (New York: Atheneum, 1988), 9, 12, 247; Billy M. Jones, *Health-Seekers in the Southwest, 1817–1900* (Norman: University of Oklahoma Press, 1967), 123–25; Albert Reifel, "Tuberculosis among the Indians of the United States," *Diseases of the Chest* 16 (August 1949): 235.

4. A good general description of the disease is presented in Caldwell, *Last Crusade*, 3–10. See also Dubos, *White Plague*, 3–10; Jones, *Health-Seekers in the Southwest*, 123–25. For comments related to the use of chemotherapy treatment, see Kurt Deuschle, "Tuberculosis among the Navajo: Research in Cross-Cultural Technologic Development in Health," *American Review of Respiratory Diseases* 80 (August 1959): 202; Smith, *Retreat of Tuberculosis*, 246–47.

5. Caldwell, *Last Crusade*, 10–12, 76–97; Smith, *Retreat of Tuberculosis*, 97–130; Rothman, *Living in the Shadow of Death*, 179–80; Jones, *Health-Seekers in the Southwest*, 193–97.

6. J. Arthur Myers and Virginia L. Dustin, "Albert Reifel and Tuberculosis among the American Indians," *Hygeria* 25 (April 1947): 272; William A. Jones to Indian Agent, Fort Defiance, November 26, 1901, NA, PSR, Navajo Agency, Box 25; *Annual Report, CIA, 1901*, 182; *Annual Report, CIA, 1904*, 142.

7. Alex Hrdlicka, "Diseases of the Indians, More Especially of the Southwest United States and Northern Mexico," *Washington Medical Annals* 4 (1905–1906): 374, 381–82; Isaac W. Brewer, "Tuberculosis among the Indians of Arizona and New Mexico," *New York Medical Journal* 84 (November 17, 1906): 981–83.

8. *Annual Report, CIA, 1904*, 33–38; *Annual Report, CIA, 1905*, 14–15; Circular no. 127 (August 14, 1905), NA, Record Group 75, Education Circulars; Francis E. Leupp, *The Indian and His Problem* (New York: Charles Scribner's Sons, 1910), 144–46; Putney, "Fighting the Scourge," 78–85.

9. Hrdlicka, *Tuberculosis among Certain Indian Tribes*, 1–7, 29–32.

10. *Annual Report, CIA, 1908*, 16, 23–24; Prucha, *Great Father*, 848–49; Joseph A. Murphy, "The Prevention of Tuberculosis in the Indian Schools," *Journal of Proceedings and Addresses of the National Education Association* 47 (1909): 919–25; Joseph A. Murphy, "Health Problems

of the Indians," *The Annals of the American Academy of Political and Social Science* 37 (March 1911): 104. For a historical look at the Phoenix Indian Sanatorium, see Robert A. Trennert, "The Federal Government and Indian Health in the Southwest: Tuberculosis and the Phoenix East Farm Sanatorium, 1909–1955," *Pacific Historical Review* 65 (February 1996): 61–64.

11. "Contagious and Infectious Disease among the Indians," 62d Congress, 3d sess., Senate Doc. 1038, serial 6365, 26–28, 41, 66–68.

12. For a good description of the disease, see Putney, "Fighting the Scourge," 141–43; Robert A. Trennert, "Indian Sore Eyes: The Federal Campaign to Control Trachoma in the Southwest, 1910–1940," *Journal of the Southwest* 32 (Summer 1990): 121–23; "History of Trachoma," typescript dated January 12, 1947, NA, PRS, Phoenix Area Office, Box 536; and "Contagious and Infectious Disease among the Indians," 16–18.

13. Prucha, *Great Father*, 2: 841–42.

14. Trennert, "Indian Sore Eyes," 123–24; "Trachoma in Certain Indian Schools," 60th Cong., 2d sess., Senate Report no. 1025, serial 5380; *Annual Report, CIA, 1909*, 3; *Annual Report, CIA, 1910*, 10; L. Webster Fox, "The Trachoma Problem among the North American Indians," *Journal of the American Medical Association* 86 (February 6, 1926): 405.

15. C. J. Crandall to Commissioner, March 27, 1909, R. Perry to Commissioner, April 5, 1909, Robert Valentine to M. F. Holland, May 29, 1909, and Ancil Martin to Valentine, October 20, 1909, NA, RG 75, Central Classified Files (hereafter cited as NA, CCF), Phoenix, 22627–1909–721; "Report of Ancil Martin, 1910," NA, RG 75, Microcopy M1011, Superintendent's Annual Narrative and Statistical Reports, 1907–1938 (hereafter cited as NA, M1011), Roll 102.

16. A. E. Marden, "The Trachoma Hospital," *The Native American* (Phoenix) 13 (May 19, 1912): 240; Marden, "Trachoma at Phoenix Indian School—and What Is Being Done for It," *The Native American* 13 (November 16, 1912): 543–44; Fox, "Trachoma Problem among the North American Indians," 406; Helen Sekaquaptewa, quoted in Trennert, "Indian Sore Eyes," 126. Helen's operation was performed at Keams Canyon sometime before 1914, using the grattage procedure.

17. "Report of Ancil Martin, 1910" and "Report of Dr. Martin, July 26, 1913," Phoenix Indian School, NA, M1011, Roll 102; "Contagious and Infectious Disease among the Indians," 20–32; H. J. Warner, "Notes on the Results of Trachoma Work by the Indian Service in Arizona and New Mexico," *Public Health Reports* 44 (November 29, 1929): 2915.

18. Putney, "Fighting the Scourge," 54–62.

19. Ibid., 66–67.

20. Ibid., 67–68; *Annual Report, CIA, 1900*, 13.

21. Putney, "Fighting the Scourge," 69–77.

22. The Hopi reservation had been created by executive order in 1882, at which time it was administered by the Navajo agent. In 1884 lands north of the Hopi reservation and reaching to the San Juan River were added, and in 1900 lands to the west of the Hopi jurisdiction became part of the Navajo reservation. In 1899 the Moqui (Hopi) agency became a separate administrative entity. For specific details, see "Treaties, Acts, and Executive Orders," map, Office of Navajo Land Administration; and Lawrence C. Kelly, *The Navajo Indians and Federal Indian Policy, 1900–1935* (Tucson: University of Arizona Press, 1968), 18–19.

23. Kelly, *Navajo Indians*, 21–27; Bailey and Bailey, *History of the Navajos*, 106–9; *Annual Report, CIA, 1902*, 164–66.

24. *Annual Report, CIA, 1902*, 165; *Annual Report, CIA, 1903*, 135–36. For salary comparisons and dates of appointment, see *Annual Reports, CIA, 1902*, 706; *1903*, 589; and *1904*, 642.

25. *Annual Report, CIA, 1905*, 168.

26. Jenkins, *Good Shepherd Mission*, 31–32, 38, 40.

27. Reuben Perry to William B. Morrow, June 12, 1906, and Perry to Charles G. Dickson, July 22, 1906, NA, PSR, Navajo Agency, Box 10, FD33.

28. S. B. Daire to Master Brothers, November 2, 1906, NA, PSR, Navajo Agency, Box 10, FD35.

29. Peter Paquette to Mark Bauma, March 6, 1909, NA, PSR, Navajo Agency, Box 12, FD45.

30. Deuschle, "Tuberculosis among the Navajo," 200–201; Annie D. Wauneka, "Helping a People to Understand," *American Journal of Nursing* 62 (July 1962): 88–89.

31. Annual Report, Leupp Training School, 1910, NA, M1011, Roll 79; Annual Report, Western Navajo School, 1910, 1911, NA, M1011, Roll 166; Annual Report, Navajo Agency, 1910, NA, M1011, Roll 89.

32. Annual Report, Navajo Agency, 1910, NA, M1011; Annual Report, Leupp Training School, 1910, NA, M1011, Roll 79.

33. Ibid.; Annual Report, Western Navajo School, 1910, NA, M1011, Roll 166.

34. Annual Report, Leupp Training School, 1910, NA, M1011, Roll 79; Annual Report, Navajo Agency, 1910, NA, M1011, Roll 89.

35. Raup, *Indian Health Program*, 7–8, 29; Annual Report, Navajo Agency, 1911, NA, M1011, Roll 89. Prior to 1911 medical activities were financed totally from Miscellaneous Funds. This category continued to make up a large part of the medical budget from 1911 to 1926, after which time appropriations specifically for medical purposes comprised most of the budget.

36. *Annual Report, CIA, 1913*, 145; Annual Report, Navajo Agency, 1912, NA, M1011, Roll 89; Annual Report, Northern Navajo Agency, 1932, NA, M1011, Roll 93.

37. *Annual Report, CIA, 1913*, 18–19; "Contagious and Infectious Disease among the Indians," 11–84; Raup, *Indian Health Program*, 29.

38. *Annual Report, CIA, 1915*, 17, 142; Annual Report, Navajo Agency, 1914, 1915, NA. M1011, Roll 89; Mitchell, *Navajo Blessingway Singer*, 131.

39. Annual Report, Navajo Agency, 1913, 1915, NA, M1011, Roll 89; *The Native American* 17 (May 13, 1916): 177; *Annual Report, CIA, 1916*, 4–7.

40. Annual Report, Navajo Agency, 1915, 1916, NA, M1011, Roll 89; *Annual Report, CIA, 1916*, 6.

41. *Annual Report, CIA, 1916*, 4; Annual Report, Navajo Agency, 1915, 1916, NA, M1011, Roll 89.

42. Mary Sedgwick Conn and Bacil Benjamin Warren, "The Family: Early Days in Wisconsin, Arizona, and All Over," unpublished manuscript, Warren Family Papers, in author's possession; Annual Report, Leupp Agency, NA, M1011, Roll 79; *Annual Report, CIA, 1911*, 6.

43. Conn and Warren, "Family"; Bacil B. Warren to author, September 6, 1993, author's collection; (Tucson) *Arizona Daily Star*, February 25, 1968.

44. Bacil A. Warren, "Report on Epidemic at United States Indian School, Leupp, Arizona, November–December 1914," and Warren to W. E. Van Cleave, March 27, 1915, Warren Family Papers; Murphy to Commissioner, December 22, 1914, Meritt to Janus, May 3, 1915, NA, CCF, Leupp, 128264–1914–731; Annual Report, Leupp Agency, 1914, 1915, NA, M1011, Roll 79. Warren continually worked to enlarge the hospital and secure the "instruments, appliances, cooperation, and the *particular medicines*" he needed. See Warren to Sells, December 31, 1914, NA, CCF, Leupp, 4121–1915–700.

45. Warren to T. K. Adreon, February 8, 1915, Warren to Van Cleave, March 27, 1915, Warren to A. J. Wheeler, September 30, 1915, and Conn and Warren, "Family," Warren Family Papers.

46. Warren to Murphy, April 26, 1914, NA, CCF, 49783–1914–832; Warren to Van Cleave, March 27, 1915, Indian Office Circular no. 1052 (December 2, 1915), Warren to Sells, January 21, 1916, Warren Family Papers.

47. Warren to Van Cleave, March 27, 1915, and Warren to A. J. Wheeler, September 30, 1915, Warren Family Papers.

48. Warren to Sells, August 19, 1915, NA, CCF, Leupp, 92291–1915–721; Annual Report, Leupp Agency, 1915, NA, M1011, Roll 79.

49. Warren to Sells, August 19, 1915, NA, CCF, Leupp, 9221–1915–721; Warren to Van Cleave, March 27, 1915, and Warren to Wheeler, September 30, 1915, Warren Family Papers.

50. Annual Report, Leupp Agency, 1916, NA, M1011, Roll 79; Warren to Commissioner, February 9, 1917, Janus to Commissioner, February 19, 1917, Meritt to Janus, March 1, 1917, NA, CCF, Leupp, 85368–1916–700; George O. Keck to Commissioner, March 20, 1917, NA, CCF, Leupp, 30285–1917–700; P. F. Atkinson to Mrs. B. A. Warren, February 5, 1917, Warren to G. Smith, February 13, 1917, Warren to Commissioner, February 9, 1917, and Warren to [?], March 10, 1917, Warren Family Papers.

51. Annual Report, Leupp Agency, 1916, NA, M1011, Roll 79; Warren to Sells, March 3, 1916, NA, CCF, Leupp, 18033–1916–700; Report of S. A. M. Young on the Leupp Agency and School, July 20–27, 1916, NA, CCF, Leupp, 85368–1916–700; Warren to Keck, March 13, 1917, NA, CCF, Leupp, 30285–1917–700; Bacil B. Warren to author, September 6, 1993, author's collection; *The Native American* 19 (December 28, 1918): 340.

52. *Annual Report, CIA, 1917,* 138; "Government Health Work among the Indians," *The Outlook* 114 (September 27, 1916): 168–69.

53. Annual Report, Leupp Agency, 1916, NA, M1011, Roll 79; Annual Report, Navajo Agency, 1916, ibid., Roll 89.

CHAPTER 7

1. *Annual Report, CIA, 1917,* 16–17; *Annual Report, CIA, 1918,* 38; Raup, *Indian Health Program,* 29.

2. *Annual Report, CIA, 1917,* 17; Annual Report, San Juan Agency, 1917, NA, M1011, Roll

126; Annual Report, Leupp Agency, 1917, NA, M1011, Roll 79; Annual Report, Western Navajo Agency, 1917, NA, M1011, Roll 166.

3. Annual Report, Western Navajo Agency, 1917, NA, M1011, Roll 166; Annual Report, San Juan Agency, 1917, NA, M1011, Roll 126; *Annual Report, CIA, 1918*, 38; George O. Keck to Commissioner, January 18, 1917, NA, CCF, Navajo, 5068–1917–700; W. W. Coon, Report on Supervision of Fort Defiance Navajo Schools, May 1918, NA, CCF, Navajo, 53323–1918–700.

4. Annual Report, San Juan Agency, 1917–1919, NA, M1011, Roll 126; Annual Report, Western Navajo Agency, 1917, NA, M1011, Roll 166; Annual Report, Navajo Agency, 1919, NA, M1011, Roll 89. Information on the actual size of the 1919 Shiprock hospital is vague. The most reasonable figure (forty beds) appears in Robert W. Young, ed. and comp., *The Navajo Yearbook, 1958* (Window Rock, Ariz.: Navajo Agency, 1958), 334.

5. Annual Report, Navajo Agency, 1918, NA, M1011, Roll 89; Annual Report, San Juan Agency, 1918, NA, M1011, Roll 126.

6. Annual Report, Western Navajo Agency, 1918, NA, M1011, Roll 166; Annual Report, Navajo Agency, 1918, NA, M1011, Roll 89; Annual Report, San Juan Agency, 1918, NA, M1011, Roll 126.

7. Annual Report, Navajo Agency, 1918, NA, M1011, Roll 89; Annual Report, San Juan Agency, 1918, NA, M1011, Roll 126; Mitchell, *Navajo Blessingway Singer*, 110, 132.

8. Annual Report, San Juan Agency, 1919, NA, M1011, Roll 126.

9. Bradford Luckingham, *Epidemic in the Southwest, 1918–1919* (El Paso: Texas Western Press, 1984), 1–2; Surgeon General's Report, in *The Native American* 19 (October 19, 1918): 233–35.

10. Luckingham, *Epidemic in the Southwest*, 1–5; *Annual Report, Surgeon General of the Public Health Service, 1919*, 175–79; "Influenza among American Indians," *Public Health Reports* 34 (May 9, 1919): 1008–9. For a good overview of the pandemic, see Alfred W. Crosby, Jr., *Epidemic and Peace, 1918* (Westport, Conn.: Greenwood Press, 1976).

11. *Coconino Sun* (Flagstaff), October 11, 18, 1918; *Arizona Republican* (Phoenix), October 14–16, 1918; C. E. Addams to Surgeon General Gorgas (telegram), October 9, 1918, Arizona State Archives, RG 35, Council on Defense, File 22, Public Health and Medicine.

12. *The Native American* 19 (November 30, 1918): 304.

13. Reagan wrote two articles describing his experiences. The most informative is "The 'Flu' among the Navajos," *Transactions of the Kansas Academy of Science* 30 (1921): 131–38. The second article, "The Influenza and the Navajo," *Proceedings of the Indiana Academy of Science* 29 (1919): 243–47, is less reliable but still informative. For other comments on the epidemic at Tuba City, see C. E. Addams to Governor G. W. P. Hunt, October 22, 1918, Arizona State Archives, RG 35, Council on Defense, File 22; and *Coconino Sun*, October 25, 1918.

14. Reagan, " 'Flu' among the Navajos," 133–37; Annual Report, Western Navajo Agency, 1919, NA, M1011, Roll 166; *Annual Report, CIA, 1919*, 141; *Coconino Sun*, November 1, 1918; *The Native American* 20 (May 3, 1919): 140.

15. Reagan, " 'Flu' among the Navajos," 133–35.

16. Ibid., 135.

17. A large file regarding the epidemic in the vicinity of Fort Defiance is contained

in National Archives File CCF, General Service, 92970–1918–FW/82837–1818–723. Especially notable are Wigglesworth and Hailman to Commissioner, December 31, 1918, and L. L. Culp, Report on the Influenza Epidemic, February 8, 1919. See also *The Native American* 19 (November 30, 1918): 306; *Coconino Sun*, November 22, 1918; *New York Sun*, April 27, 1919; Annual Report, Navajo Agency, 1919, NA, MI011, Roll 89; *Annual Report, CIA, 1919*, 145.

18. Annual Report, Pueblo Bonito Agency, 1919, NA, MI011, Roll 110; Annual Report, San Juan Agency, 1919, NA, MI011, Roll 126; Franc Johnson Newcomb, *Hosteen Klah, Navajo Medicine Man and Sand Painter* (Norman: University of Oklahoma Press, 1964), 145–47.

19. Annual Report, Leupp Agency, 1919, NA, MI011, Roll 79; *Coconino Sun*, November 15, 1918.

20. Reagan, "'Flu' among the Navajos," 135–36; Reagan, "Influenza and the Navajo," 247; Newcomb, *Hosteen Klah*, 146–47; Hilda Faunce, *Desert Wife* (Boston: Little, Brown and Co., 1934), 297, 301. Faunce used the pseudonym "Covered Water" for the Black Mountain Trading Post.

21. *Cincinnati Enquirer*, December 18, 1918; *Rocky Mountain News* (Denver), December 18, 1918; Sells to Culp, January 9, 1919, and Culp, Report on Influenza Epidemic, February 8, 1919, NA, CCF, General Service, 92970–1918–FW/82837–1918–732; William S. Collins, "The Navajo and Hopi Experience with Spanish Influenza" (unpublished graduate paper, Arizona State University, 1993): Bailey and Bailey, *History of the Navajos*, 119–20; Newcomb, *Hosteen Klah*, 146–47. Everyone involved admitted that the number of deaths was difficult to ascertain. Culp attempted to rely solely on firsthand information, yet he too recognized that his conclusions were not totally accurate.

22. The Navajo figures are compiled from statistical reports filed in 1920 from the Navajo, San Juan, Western Navajo, Pueblo Bonito, and Leupp agencies in NA, MI011, rolls 79, 89, 110, 126, 166. They generally agree with the figures for all Indians, which in 1920 were estimated to be 25,000 cases of tuberculosis and 30,000 cases of trachoma. See "The Indian Service Health Activities," Office of Indian Affairs, Bulletin 11 (1922), 4.

Agency	Population	Estimated TB	Estimated Trachoma
W	6,300	580 [9.2%]	150 [2.3%]
SJ	7,000	375 [5.3%]*	875 [11.4%]
PB	2,700	263 [19.4%]	650 [48.1%]
L	1,289	455 [35.2%]	255 [19.7%]
N	11,280	1060 [10.6%]	1550 [12.1%]

*The tuberculosis estimate for the San Juan Agency appears to be misreported and the figure of 375 is based on the author's recalculation.

23. Ibid.

24. Annual Report, San Juan Agency, 1920, NA, MI011, Roll 126; Annual Report, Pueblo Bonito Agency, 1920, NA, MI011, Roll 110.

25. Annual Report, Pueblo Bonito Agency, 1920, NA, M1011, Roll 110; Annual Report, Navajo Agency, 1920, NA, M1011, Roll 89.

26. Sells to J. W. Atwood, April 4, 1919, NA, CCF, Navajo, 64231–1919–816.2; Efficiency Report on A. M. Wigglesworth, February 8, 1919, NA, CCF, General Service, 92970–1918–FW/82837–1919–732; *The Native American* 20 (September 6, 1919): 207; Jenkins, *Good Shepherd Mission*, 41.

27. Sells to Atwood, August 4, 1919, and Atwood to Sells, October 21, 1920, NA, CCF, Navajo, 64231–1919–816.2; *The Native American* 20, (December 13, 1919): 265; Elinor D. Gregg, *The Indians and the Nurse* (Norman: University of Oklahoma Press, 1965), 102–3; Polk Richards to Harry S. Gradle, October 7, 1936, NA, PSR, Phoenix Area Office, Box 536; Jenkins, *Good Shepherd Mission*, 41–42; "Dr. Polk Richards, World-Famous Trachoma Expert, Retires," *Indians at Work* 10, no. 1 (July–September 1942): 24. Richards temporarily left Fort Defiance in 1920, but was back by May 1921. Like Wigglesworth, Richards received a small stipend for his work at the Episcopal hospital.

28. *The Native American* 20 (April 19, 1919): 127, and 22 (June 4, 1921): 138; "The Indian Health Service Activities," Office of Indian Affairs, Bulletin 11 (1922), 4; J. S. Perkins to Commissioner, July 2, 1922, NA, PSR, Phoenix Area Office, Box 487; *Annual Report, CIA, 1921*, 10–11.

29. Perkins to Commissioner, June 6, 1921, June 2, 1922, NA, PSR, Phoenix Area Office, Box 487.

30. Perkins to Commissioner, July 2, 1922, and Charles Burke to Perkins, December 10, 1923, ibid.

31. *Annual Report, CIA, 1921*, 9–10; *Annual Report, CIA, 1922*, 8; Lawrence C. Kelly, "Charles Henry Burke, 1921–29," in Kvasnicka and Viola, *Commissioners of Indian Affairs*, 253–55.

32. Hubert Work to Secretary of the Treasury, April 10, 1924, George Vaux to Secretary of the Interior, May 17, 1924, NA, CCF, Navajo, 25663–1924–700, pt. 1; *Annual Report, CIA, 1924*, 2.

33. Kelly, *Navajo Indians*, 184–85; Peter Iverson, *The Navajo Nation* (Albuquerque, University of New Mexico Press, 1983), 19–22; *The Gallup Independent*, April 23, 1924; *Annual Report, CIA, 1924*, 2; Annual Report, Navajo Agency, NA, M1011, Roll 90; Burke to Paquette, April 4, 1924, NA, CCF, Navajo, 25663–1924–700, pt. 1. The Navajo Tribal Council was created in 1923, primarily to deal with oil leases. As part of this package, the position of Commissioner to the Navajo Indians was established to provide authority over the five agency superintendents.

34. Vaux to Secretary of the Interior, May 17, 1924, and Robert Newberne to Commissioner, June 24, 1924, NA, CCF, Navajo 25663–1924–700, pt. 1; Instructions Concerning the Southwestern Trachoma Campaign, June 12, 1924, NA, PSR, Navajo Agency, Box 30; Annual Report, Navajo Agency, 1924, NA, M1011, Roll 90; *Annual Report, CIA, 1925*, 3; *Annual Report, CIA, 1924*, 2–3.

35. Fox, "Trachoma Problem among the North American Indians," 405–6; Fox to Burk [*sic*], January 28, 1925, NA, CCF, General Service, 93221–1924–734. Putney, "Fighting the Scourge," 232–51, provides an excellent discussion of the Fox treatment program.

36. Paquette to Commissioner, November 15, 1924, NA, PSR, Navajo Agency, Box 30; Annual Report, Navajo Agency, 1924, NA, M1011, Roll 90; Perkins to Commissioner, October 2, 1924, NA, CCF, Navajo, 25663–1924–700, pt. 1.

37. These descriptions come from the captions included with a set of photographs. See "Photographs from Navajo Indian Agency, Showing Trachoma Operations" [August 1924], NA, CCF, Navajo, 25663–1924–700, pt. 2.

38. Ross to Commissioner, August 1, 1924, Burke to Ross, August 12, 1924, and Perkins to Commissioner, August 14, 1924, NA, CCF, Navajo, 25663–1924–700, pt. 1; Burke to Paquette, October 9, 1924, NA, PRS, Navajo Agency, Box 30; "Photographs from Navajo Indian Agency," NA, CCF, Navajo, 25663–1924–700, pt. 2.

39. Putney, "Fighting the Scourge," 237–38; Martin Stevens to H. J. Hagerman, November 22, 1924, Richards to Hagerman, November 22, 1924, NA, CCF, Navajo, 25663–1924–700, pt. 1; Fox to Burk [sic], NA, CCF, General Service, 93221–1924–734.

40. Work to Vaux, February 14, 1925, NA, CCF, General Service, 10101–1925–724; August F. Duclos to Commissioner, April 8, 1925, Claude E. Putnam to Duclos, July 2, 1925, and Richards to Duclos, July 6, 1925, NA, PSR, Navajo Agency, Box 30; H. V. Hailman to Burke, July 14, 1926, NA, PSR, Phoenix Area Office, Box 449. For an overall review of the campaign, see Sidney J. Tillim, "Trachoma among American Indians," National Society for the Prevention of Blindness, Publication 179 (1936): 4–5.

41. Perkins to Commissioner, August 15, 1924, NA, CCF, 25663–1924–700, pt. 1.

42. Perkins to Commissioner, August 3, 1926, NA, PSR, Phoenix Area Office, Box 452; Perkins to Commissioner, July 25, 1927, NA, Special Physicians Reports, Box 7; Hailman to Burke, July 14, 1926, NA, PSR, Phoenix Area Office, Box 449.

43. E. B. Meritt to H. J. Warner, December 14, 1926, Warner to Commissioner, January 17, 1927, NA, PSR, Phoenix Area Office, Box 463; William Campbell Posey, "Trachoma among the Indians of the Southwest," *Journal of the American Medical Association* 88 (May 12, 1927): 1618–19; Warner, "Notes on the Results of Trachoma Work by the Indian Service in Arizona and New Mexico," 2919; Report of the Advisory Committee on Trachoma among the Indians, April 15, 1927, NA, CCF, General Services, 40506–1925–732.

44. Outline of Suggestions for the Control and Treatment of Trachoma among the American Indians [April 1925], prepared by Committee on Trachoma, American Medical Association, NA, CCF, General Service, 78136–1924–732; Report on the Advisory Committee on Trachoma among the Indians, April 15, 1927, NA, CCF, General Service, 40506–1925–732; Posey, "Trachoma among the Indians of the Southwest," 1618–19.

45. Lewis Meriam et al., *The Problem of Indian Administration* (Baltimore: Johns Hopkins Press, 1928), 214; Kelly, *Navajo Indians*, 186. See also Kenneth R. Philp, *John Collier's Crusade for Indian Reform, 1920–1954* (Tucson: University of Arizona Press, 1977), 90–91.

46. Meriam, *Problem of Indian Administration*, 189–345.

47. Ibid., 189–90.

48. Ibid., 205–6, 287–94.

49. Ibid., 274–87.

50. Ibid., 208–16.

51. Ibid., 229–42.

52. Ibid., 259–74.

CHAPTER 8

1. Annual Report, Western Navajo Agency, 1929, NA, M1011, Roll 166; *Annual Report, CIA, 1929*, 2. Federal appropriations for Indian health services increased from 948,000 dollars in 1928 to 4,050,000 dollars in 1932. For a yearly breakdown, see Raup, *Indian Health Program*, 29.

2. Gregg, *Indians and the Nurse*, 120–21; Duclos to H. J. Warner, June 17, 1926, NA, PSR, Phoenix Area Office, Box 463; *Annual Report, Secretary of the Interior* (hereafter cited as *SI*), *1927*, 51.

3. Guthrie, "Health of American Indians," 1198–99; *Annual Report, SI, 1927*, 51.

4. Guthrie, "Health of American Indians," 1198–99; Sandra K. Schackel, " 'The Tales Those Nurses Told!': Public Health Nurses among the Pueblo and Navajo Indians," *New Mexico Historical Review* 65 (April 1990): 225–32.

5. Duclos to Warner, June 17, 1926, NA, PSR, Phoenix Area Office, Box 463; Annual Report, Southern Navajo Agency, 1929, 1930, NA, M1011, Roll 141.

6. H. P. Marble to Duclos, February 6, 1925, Duclos to Marble, February 21, 1925, NA, PSR, Navajo Agency, Box 26. Duclos suggested that Marble might want to see if a vacancy existed at one of the off-reservation sanatoriums, but offered nothing more.

7. Duclos to Commissioner, February 21, 1927, NA, PSR, Phoenix Area Office, Box 463; Duclos to Commissioner, March 11, 1927, NA, PSR, Phoenix Area Office, Box 425.

8. Annual Report, Southern Navajo Agency, 1929, 1930, NA, M1011, Roll 141; Warner to Commissioner, May 2, 1929, NA, PSR, Phoenix Area Office, Box 425.

9. Meriam, *Problem of Indian Administration*, 303–4. A brief history of the Kayenta school and sanatorium was written by the wife of trader John Wetherill and included in the Annual Report of the Kayenta Sanatorium, 1933, NA, M1011, Roll 68.

10. Guthrie to Commissioner, November 9, 1927, and Guthrie to Warner, November 9, 1927, NA, PSR, Phoenix Area Office, Box 463.

11. C. H. Koentz to Guthrie, October 24, 1928, and Koentz to Commissioner, December 5, 1928, NA, PSR, Phoenix Area Office, Box 463.

12. Warner to Commissioner, January 18, 1929, NA, PSR, Phoenix Area Office, Box 462; *Annual Report, SI, 1929*, 3.

13. Koentz to Warner, April 6, 1929, Koentz to Commissioner, April 27, 1929, NA, PSR, Phoenix Area Office, Box 463; Annual Report, Kayenta Sanatorium, 1930, NA, M1011, Roll 68.

14. Koentz to Warner, April 9, 1930, enclosed in Warner to Commissioner, April 28, 1930, NA, PSR, Phoenix Area Office, Box 417.

15. Resolution of the Mayor and Common Council of the City of Winslow, March 13, 1929, NA, PSR, Phoenix Area Office, Box 466.

16. Warner to Don G. Lynwalter, March 29, 1930, NA, PSR, Phoenix Area Office, Box 466; Warner to Commissioner, April 28, 1030, NA, PSR, Phoenix Area Office, Box 417.

17. Edgar K. Miller to Warner, May 3, 1930, Charles Rhoads to Warner (telegram), August 5, 1930, Guthrie Memorandum, November 7, 1931, and Mossman to Guthrie, February 24, 1932, NA, PSR, Phoenix Area Office, Box 466.

18. Guthrie to Mossman, March 1, 1932, and R. L. Jones to L. R. White, November 21, 1933, NA, PSR, Phoenix Area Office, Box 466.

19. Warner to Commissioner, January 17, 1927, NA, PSR, Phoenix Area Office, Box 463; Kelly, *Navajo Indians*, 186.

20. Annual Report, Southern Navajo Agency, 1930, NA, M1011, Roll 141; E. B. Meritt to Burke, December 22, 1927, NA, CCF, Navajo, 25663–1924–700, pt. 2.

21. S. M. Young to Commissioner, March 3, 1928, NA, PSR, Phoenix Area Office, Box 462; Kelly, *Navajo Indians*, 186.

22. William L. Davis to Commissioner, August 17, 1928, NA, PSR, Phoenix Area Office, Box 417; Richards to Warner, October 2, 1928, PSR, Phoenix Area Office, Box 425.

23. Warner to Commissioner, January 18, 1929, NA, PSR, Phoenix Area Office, Box 463; Rhoads to John G. Hunter, July 14, 1930, NA, PSR, Phoenix Area Office, Box 425.

24. Warner to Commissioner, March 25, 1929, NA, PSR, Phoenix Area Office, Box 463; Hunter to Commissioner, August 27, 1929, NA, PSR, Phoenix Area Office, Box 425; Warner to Commissioner, October 31, 1929, NA, PSR, Phoenix Area Office, Box 449.

25. Mossman to Commissioner, January 6, 1931, NA, PSR, Phoenix Area Office, Box 425.

26. Mossman to Commissioner, August 29, 1931, NA, PSR, Phoenix Area Office, Box 532.

27. Guthrie to Mossman, October 15, 1931, ibid.

28. Mossman to Guthrie, November 21, 1931, ibid.

29. Lawrence C. Kelly, "Charles James Rhoads, 1929–33," in Kvasnicka and Viola, *Commissioners of Indian Affairs*, 268–69; J. Henry Scattergood to H. J. Hagerman, July 21, 1932, NA, PSR, Phoenix Area Office, Box 417; Mossman to Commissioner, July 5, 1932, NA, PSR, Phoenix Area Office, Box 532.

30. Mossman to Guthrie, November 21, 1931, NA, PSR, Phoenix Area Office, Box 532; Scattergood to Hagerman, July 31, 1932, NA, PSR, Phoenix Area Office, Box 417.

31. Meriam, *Problem of Indian Administration*, 247–50; Gregg, *Indians and the Nurse*, 120–21; Kelly, "Charles James Rhoads," 268.

32. Gregg, *Indians and the Nurse*, 102–6; Elizabeth Forster and Laura Gilpin, *Denizens of the Desert: A Tale in Word and Picture of Life among the Navajo Indians*, ed. Martha A. Sandweiss (Albuquerque: University of New Mexico Press, 1988), 6–8; Schackel, " 'The Tales Those Nurses Told,' " 241. Duggan went on to work for the Indian Service. In 1930 she was appointed a field nurse working out of the Kayenta Sanatorium. See William B. Hagerty to Mossman, August 2, 1931, NA, PSR, Phoenix Area Office, Box 463.

33. Annual Report, Southern Navajo Agency, 1930, NA, M1011, Roll 141; Schackel, " 'The Tales Those Nurses Told,' " 241.

34. Forster, quoted in Forster and Gilpin, *Denizens of the Desert*, 11.

35. Forster and Gilpin, *Denizens of the Desert*, 12–13; Annual Report, Northern Navajo Agency, 1932, NA, M1011, Roll 93; Schackel, " 'The Tales Those Nurses Told,' " 244–45.

36. Schackel, " 'The Tales Those Nurses Told,' " 245–48.

37. Donald L. Parman, *The Navajos and the New Deal* (New Haven: Yale University Press, 1976), 220–21.

38. Annual Report, Northern Navajo Agency, 1932, NA, M1011, Roll 93; "Survey of Conditions of the Indians in the United States," pt. 18, Navajos in Arizona and New Mexico, 71st Cong., 3d sess. (Washington, D.C.: Government Printing Office, 1932), 9780.

39. Wade Davies, "Missionary Medical Care and the Navajo" (unpublished graduate paper, Arizona State University, 1993), 9–10; Annual Report, Southern Navajo Agency, 1931, NA, M1011, Roll 141; "Survey of Conditions," 9217–18.

40. R. H. Pousma, "Venereal Disease among the Navajo," *Southwestern Medicine* 13 (November 1929): 503–5; "Survey of Conditions," 9213–14.

41. Clarence G. Salsbury, with Paul Hughes, *The Salsbury Story: A Medical Missionary's Lifetime of Public Service* (Tucson: University of Arizona Press, 1969), 111–12, 115, 121, 127–28; Salsbury, "Medical Work in Navajoland," *American Journal of Nursing* 32 (April 1932): 416; Davies, "Missionary Medical Care and the Navajo," 15–16.

42. *Ganado News Bulletin*, March, October, and December 1930; Salsbury, "Medical Work in Navajoland," 415–16; Salsbury, *Salsbury Story*, 152–55.

43. Parman, *Navajos and the New Deal*, 220; Annual Report, Southern Navajo Agency, 1931, NA, M1011, Roll 141; Sidney J. Tillim, "Health among the Navajos," *Southwestern Medicine* 20 (July–November 1936): 390; J. C. Morgan to L. P. Brink, March 10, 1932, Navajo Nation Museum, Window Rock, Ariz., J. C. Morgan File, unclassified letters.

44. Philp, *John Collier's Crusade for Indian Reform*, 84, 103.

45. "Survey of Conditions," 9837, 9186, 9462.

46. Ibid., 9136, 9190, 9264, 9449, 9779–81.

47. Ibid., 9117, 9447–48, 9779.

48. Ibid., 9187–88, 9710–11.

49. Ibid., 9115, 9188, 9307, 9449, 9504–5, 9780.

50. Ibid., 9115, 9710–9711, 9748, 9782.

51. Ibid., 8945, 9217, 9710.

52. Ibid., 9822–27.

53. Ibid., 9341–42.

54. Rhoads to L. R. White, June 17, 1932, NA, PSR, Phoenix Area Office, Box 417; Annual Report, Southern Navajo Agency, 1932, M1011, Roll 141.

55. Annual Report, Southern Navajo Agency, 1932, M1011, Roll 141.

CHAPTER 9

1. Kenneth R. Philp, "John Collier, 1933–45," in Kvasnicka and Viola, *Commissioners of Indian Affairs*, 273–78; Philp, *John Collier's Crusade for Indian Reform*, 1–112; Parman, *Navajos and the New Deal*, 15–16, 25–32.

2. Parman, *Navajos and the New Deal*, 52–56; Ruth Roessel and Broderick H. Johnson,

comps., *Navajo Livestock Reduction: A National Disgrace* (Tsaile, Ariz.: Navajo Community College Press, 1974), 72.

3. David F. Aberle, *The Peyote Religion among the Navajo* (Chicago: Adline, 1966), 52–70; Roessel and Johnson, *Navajo Livestock Reduction*, 22, 33, 146, 152.

4. Roessel and Johnson, *Navajo Livestock Reduction*, 53, 71; Iverson, *Navajo Nation*, 23.

5. Parman, *Navajos and the New Deal*, 217–23.

6. Collier to All Navajo Superintendents, May 23, 1934, *Native Americans and the New Deal: The Office Files of John Collier, 1933–1945* (University Publications of America), microfilm (hereafter cited as Collier Files), Roll 8; "Navajo Developments," *Indians at Work* 2, no. 20 (June 1, 1935): 20–23; Parman, *Navajos and the New Deal*, 222–23; Philp, *John Collier's Crusade for Indian Reform*, 190.

7. "Some Health Problems in the Navajo Area," *Navajo Medical News* 8, no. 3 (November 29, 1941): 13–17.

8. Gregg, *Indians and the Nurse*, 142–43; *The Christian Century*, November 14, 1936, 1459–60.

9. Annual Report, Navajo Agency, 1936, NA, M1011, Roll 90.

10. Ida Bahl, *Nurse among the Navajos* ([Northvale, N.J.]: Shepherd Publishing, 1984), 26–28; Tillim, "Health among the Navajos," 355; J. C. Morgan, "A Voice from an Indian," undated typescript [1936], Navajo Nation Museum, J. C. Morgan File; *The Christian Century*, October 31, 1934, 1379–80, and November 14, 1936, 1459–60.

11. Parman, *Navajo and the New Deal*, 221; *Ganado News Bulletin*, January 1933.

12. *Ganado News Bulletin*, October and November 1938; Salsbury, *Salsbury Story*, 165–71; Parman, *Navajo and the New Deal*, 221. In 1937 the Indian Office suggested that all medical services offered by Sage Memorial Hospital be required to comply with government policies and procedures. See Tentative Program for Public Health Nurses in the Navajo Area, December 13, 1937, NA, PSR, Phoenix Area Office, Box 470.

13. W. W. Peter to Indian Office, April 13, 1935, Collier Files, Roll 8.

14. Ibid.; W. W. Peter, "Navajo Medical Work—Old and New," *Indians at Work* 4, no. 4 (October 1, 1936): 47–48; Annual Report, Navajo Agency, 1936, NA, M1011, Roll 90.

15. John Hunter and M. K. Mirhran to Guthrie, April 4, 1933, Hunter to Commissioner [telegram], August 10, 1933, and Collier to Hunter, September 23, 1933, NA, PSR, Phoenix Area Office, Box 463. The Fort Defiance hospital also failed to receive accreditation for other reasons, one of which may have been the stipulation that postmortem examinations be performed, something the Diné opposed. See "Indian Service Hospitals Gradually Meeting Standards for Acceptance by the American College of Surgeons," *Indians at Work* 5, no. 2 (October 15, 1937): 11–13.

16. Annual Report, Navajo Agency, 1936, NA, M1011, Roll 90; Tillim, "Health among the Navajos," 390, 432–33; Annual Report, Western Navajo Agency, 1935, NA, M1011, Roll 167.

17. Leo Schnur, "Physicians U.S.I.S. Medical Meeting," *Navajo Medical News* 7, no. 4 (November 25, 1940): 8–9; Estella Ford Warner to J. R. McGibony, November 7, 1941, NA, PSR, Phoenix Area Office, Box 463.

18. "The Institute for Training Navajo Nurse-Aids," *Indians at Work* 1, no. 21 (June 15, 1934): 29–30; *Annual Report, SI, 1934*, 89–90.

19. Sally Lucas Jean, "Health Institute," *Indians at Work* 3, no. 4 (October 1, 1935): 14–18; Parman, *Navajos and the New Deal*, 222.

20. J. G. Townsend to S. W. Cartwright, August 4, 1934, NA, PSR, Phoenix Area Office, Box 463; Jean, "Health Institute," 14, 18; *Annual Report, SI, 1934*, 89–90; *Annual Report, SI, 1935*, 131.

21. Edna A. Gerken, "Health Education at Wingate Summer School," *Indians at Work*, 4, no. 4 (October 1, 1936): 27–28; Report on Fort Defiance General Hospital, August 23, 1939, NA, PSR, Phoenix Area Office, Box 463.

22. Philp, *John Collier's Crusade for Indian Reform*, 122.

23. Mollie B. Reebel, "Tenting on Western Navajo," *Indians at Work* 2, no. 17 (April 15, 1935): 29–30; "Drama in the Life of Field Nurses," *Indians at Work* 2, no. 22 (July 1, 1935): 39; Edna G. Gerken, "The Home in Public Health Advancement," *Indians at Work* 3, no. 5 (October 15, 1935): 39–41; W. W. Peter, "What Does a Field Nurse Do?," *Indians at Work* 3, no. 24 (August 1, 1936): 28–29.

24. Peter, "What Does a Field Nurse Do?," 28–29; Reebel, "Tenting on Western Navajo," 29–30. See also "Navajo Mountain Nurse Report," *Indians at Work* 3, no. 4 (October 1, 1935): 37–38.

25. Annual Report, Kayenta Sanatorium, 1934, NA, M1011, Roll 68; Annual Report, Navajo Agency, 1936, NA, M1011, Roll 90; Peter, "What Does a Field Nurse Do?," 29.

26. Leota W. Elliott to Peter, September 6, 1940, NA, PSR, Phoenix Area Office, Box 470.

27. Analysis of Present Nurse Allocations and Recommendations as to Stations and Activities, December 13, 1937, NA, PSR, Phoenix Area Office, Box 470; *Annual Report, SI, 1937*, 236.

28. Tentative Program for Public Health Nursing in the Navajo Area, December 13, 1937, NA, PSR, Phoenix Area Office, Box 470.

29. Elliott to Peter, September 6, 1940, NA, PSR, Phoenix Area Office, Box 470; Peter, Plan for Enlarged Use of Winslow U.S.I.S. Sanatorium, June 11, 1942, NA, PSR, Phoenix Area Office, Box 466.

30. *Annual Report, SI, 1934*, 94; Annual Report, Navajo Agency, 1936, NA, M1011, Roll 90; Geraldine E. Quinn, "Indian Service Nurses Meet," *Navajo Medical News* 7, no. 4 (November 20, 1940): 10–11; Leo Schnur, "Navajos Train Ward Aids to Counteract 'Medicine Men,'" *Modern Hospital* 59, no. 5 (November 1942): 80.

31. Hunter and Mirhan to Guthrie, April 4, 1933, and S. W. Cartwright to Hunter, May 23, 1934, NA, PSR, Phoenix Area Office, Box 463.

32. Peter to L. W. White, October 21, 1935, NA, PSR, Phoenix Area Office, Box 463.

33. Ibid.; Annual Report, Navajo Agency, 1936, NA, M1011, Roll 90.

34. L. W. White, "A Glance at Progress Made in Indian Service Hospitals," *Indians at Work* 4, no. 4 (October 1, 1936): 43–44; *Annual Reports, SI, 1936*, 175.

35. Warner to Hammond, September 14, 1937, NA, PSR, Phoenix Area Office, Box 463; "Indian Service Hospitals Gradually Meeting Standards for Acceptance by the American College of Surgeons," 11–13.

36. *Annual Report, SI, 1938*, 241; Organization—Ft. Defiance Gen. Hospital and Sanatorium as of March 1, 1938, and Memorandum to Commissioner, August 23, 1939, NA, PSR,

Phoenix Area Office, Box 463; Parman, *Navajo and the New Deal*, 226; J. R. McGibony, "Indian Service Hospitals: Their Part in the Indian Health Program," *Indians at Work* 6, no. 6 (February 1939): 38–40; "New Navajo-Hopi Medical Center at Fort Defiance, Arizona, Dedicated," *Indians at Work* 5, no. 12 (August 1938): 6–7; *The Arizona Republic*, June 21, 1938.

37. Robert Martin to Morgan, February 11, 1936, Collier Files, Roll 8; Grace McCray to Collier, July 7, 1938, Collier Files, Roll 9; Estella Warner to McGibony, November 7, 1938, NA, PSR, Phoenix Area Office, Box 463; Annual Report, Navajo Agency, 1936, NA, M1011, Roll 90; Tillim, "Health among the Navajos," 390.

38. John Collier, "Indian Health: Some Questions and Some Possibilities," *Indians at Work* 3, no. 4 (October 1, 1935): 6–8.

39. Jay B. Nash to Commissioner, August 16, 1933, Mossman to Commissioner, August 27, 1933, Guthrie to Mossman, September 1, 1933, Mossman to Guthrie, November 7, 1933, Hunter to Commissioner, January 12, 1934, and Mossman to Townsend, February 16, 1934, NA, PSR, Phoenix Area Office, Box 463.

40. R. M. Tisinger to Mossman, July 2, 1934, Collier to Frank S. Fellows, November 1, 1934, NA, PSR, Phoenix Area Office, Box 417; Notes on Washington Conference, April 6, 1935, NA, PSR, Phoenix Area Office, Box 425.

41. J. G. Townsend, "Answers to Indian Health Questions," *Indians at Work* 3, no. 4 (October 1, 1935): 8–10; Polk Richards, "Trachoma," *Indians at Work* 4, no. 4 (October 1, 1936): 20–21; "Indian Service Trachoma Control" [1941 typescript], in NA, PSR, Phoenix Area Office, Box 536; Tillim, "Trachoma among American Indians," 8–10.

42. Richards to Harry S. Gradle, September 5, October 7, 1936, Gradle to Richards, September 22, 1936, NA, PSR, Phoenix Area Office, Box 536.

43. Harry S. Gradle, "A Plan for the Control and Eventual Eradication of Trachoma on the Reservation of the Navajo Indians" [October 1937], NA, PSR, Phoenix Area Office, Box 536.

44. Richards to Gradle, July 22, 1937, and Lucy W. Adams to Fryer, October 18, 1937, NA, PSR, Phoenix Area Office, Box 536.

45. E. R. Fryer to Commissioner, October 26, 1937, NA, PSR, Phoenix Area Office, Box 536.

46. J. G. Townsend, "Trachoma Control in the Indian Service"; "Indian Service Trachoma Control," 2–4; Townsend, "Trachoma, Dreaded Eye Disease, Being Conquered," *Indians at Work* 7, no. 4 (December 1939): 8–11.

47. Townsend, "Trachoma, Dreaded Eye Disease, Being Conquered," 10; Polk Richards, Wesley G. Forster, and Phillips Thygeson, "Treatment of Trachoma with Sulfanilamide," *Archives of Ophthalmology* 21 (April 1939): 577–80.

48. Gradle to Richards, May 8, 1938, NA, PSR, Phoenix Area Office, Box 536; "Indian Service Trachoma Control," 7–8. For additional information on the effect of sulfanilamide, see L. A. Julienelle, J. F. Lane, and W. P. Whitted, "The Effect of Sulfanilamide on the Course of Trachoma," *American Journal of Ophthalmology* 22 (November 1939): 1244–52; Wesley G. Forster, "Treatment of Trachoma with Sulfanilamide," *American Journal of Ophthalmology* 23 (May 1940): 532–34; John Pfeiffer, "Sulfanilamide: The Story of a Great Medical Discovery," *Harpers* 179 (March 1939), 384–96.

49. Indian Office circular letters no. 92656 (March 2, 1940) and no. 137223 (March 24,

1941), NA, PSR, Phoenix Area Office, Box 536; "Lifting the Shadows," *Indians at Work* 8, no. 9 (May 1941): 11–14.

50. *Annual Report, SI, 1943*, 281; Rosella Senders, "Indian Medical Service Pioneers in Trachoma Treatment," *Indians at Work* 8, no. 5 (January 1941): 32–33; "Dr. Polk Richards, World-Famous Trachoma Expert, Retires," 24. The sulfanilamide treatment produced such overconfidence that the Indian Service stopped looking for the cause of trachoma. As a result, the disease reemerged again in the 1950s. This time new drugs, such as tetracycline, were employed and the disease has been virtually eradicated. See Trennert, "Indian Sore Eyes," 143–44.

51. "Tuberculosis among Indians," *Indians at Work* 3, no. 8 (December 1935): 35; Peter to Commissioner, April 13, 1935, Collier Files, Roll 8; Tillim, "Health among the Navajos," 310–11. See also Esmond R. Long, "A Brief Comparison of Tuberculosis in the White, Indian and Negro Races," *American Review of Tuberculosis* 35 (January 1937): 1–5.

52. Duggan to Commissioner, March 27, 1933, NA, PSR, Phoenix Area Office, Box 463; L. R. Jones to White, November 21, 1933, NA, PSR, Phoenix Area Office, Box 466; Collier, "Indian Health," 6.

53. Annual Reports, Kayenta Sanatorium, 1935, 1936, NA, M1011, Roll 68.

54. Fryer to Commissioner, August 5, 1938, September 23, 1938, and Joseph A. Schwartz to Commissioner, December 27, 1938, NA, PSR, Phoenix Area Office, Box 463.

55. L. R. Jones to E. H. Hammond, February 22, 1934, Peter to William Zeh, February 23, 1935, William G. Lewis to Peter, July 8, 1935, Churchill G. Bell to Commissioner, August 6, 1935, and Lewis to Peter, April 9, 1936, NA, PSR, Phoenix Area Office, Box 466.

56. "New Navajo-Hopi Medical Center at Fort Defiance, Arizona, Dedicated," 7; Organization—Ft. Defiance Gen. Hospital and Sanatorium as of March 1, 1938, and Report on visit to Fort Defiance General Hospital and Sanatorium, August 23, 1939, NA, PSR, Phoenix Area Office, Box 463; Bretislaw Sedlacek and J. A. Schwartz, "Tuberculosis on the Spot," *Navajo Medical News* 7, no. 4 (November 25, 1940): 20–23; Annual Report, Kayenta Sanatorium, 1936, NA, M1011, Roll 68.

57. Collier, "Indian Health," 7; Townsend, "Answers to Indian Health Questions," 9; *Annual Report, SI, 1930*, 238–39; *Annual Report, SI, 1939*, 47; Parman, *Navajo and the New Deal*, 228; Joseph D. Aronson and Carroll E. Palmer, "Experience with BCG Vaccine in the Control of Tuberculosis among North American Indians," *Public Health Reports* 61 (June 7, 1946): 802–20; Myers and Dustin, "Albert Reifel and Tuberculosis among the American Indians," 322. Although reasonably well accepted in Europe and Canada, the American medical community was very skeptical of BCG as an effective tool in the war against TB. For a comprehensive study of the BCG vaccine, see Georgina D. Feldberg, *Disease and Class: Tuberculosis and the Shaping of Modern North American Society* (New Brunswick, N.J.: Rutgers University Press, 1995).

58. Parman, *Navajo and the New Deal*, 228; Wheeler to Commissioner, March 1, 1933, NA, PSR, Phoenix Area Office, Box 465; Townsend, "Answers to Indian Health Questions," 9; "Tuberculosis among Indians," 35; *Annual Report, SI, 1937*, 235. See also comments of H. Corwin Hinshaw et al., "Some Suggested Procedures for the Early Period of Therapeutic Pneumothorax," *American Review of Tuberculosis* 50 (December 1944): 573–74.

59. Parman, *Navajo and the New Deal*, 228–29.

60. Health Education for Guidance of Leaders, June 1936, NA, PSR, Phoenix Indian School, Box 18/32; Annual Report, Phoenix Indian Sanatorium, NA, PSR, Phoenix Area Office, Box 465; "Posters and Primers Implement Development of a New American Language," *Indians at Work* 7, no. 9 (May 1940): 30; Edna A. Gerken, "Development of a Health Education Program: Navajo Indians," *American Journal of Public Health* 30 (August 1940): 915–20.

CHAPTER 10

1. *Annual Report, SI, 1942*, 256; *Annual Report, SI, 1944*, 249; Philp, *John Collier's Crusade for Indian Reform*, 205.

2. "Director of Indian Medical Service," *Indians at Work* 8, no. 7 (March 1941): 22; Rosella Senders, "New Director Appointed for Indian Medical Service," *Indians at Work* 8, no. 10 (June 1941): 9–10.

3. Alison R. Bernstein, *American Indians and World War II: Towards a New Era in Indian Affairs* (Norman: University of Oklahoma Press, 1991), 67–68; Raup, *Indian Health Program*, 8, 13, 29; *Annual Report, SI, 1942*, 256; *Annual Report, SI, 1944*, 249–50; *Annual Report, SI, 1945*, 247.

4. Iverson, *Navajo Nation*, 47–52; Bailey and Bailey, *History of the Navajos*, 197–201.

5. Underhill, *Here Come the Navajo!*, 255; Adair et al., *People's Health*, 10–11, 30; Broderick H. Johnson, ed., *Navajos and World War II* (Tsaile, Ariz.: Navajo Community College Press, 1977), passim.

6. C. G. Salsbury, "Incidence of Certain Diseases among the Navajos," *Arizona Medicine* 4, no. 6 (November 1947): 31; Charles S. McCammon, Frank J. Dufner, and Frances W. Felsman, "Syphilis among the Navajo Indians," *The Journal of Venereal Disease Information* 32, no. 2 (February 1951): 28.

7. Dorothy R. Parker, *Singing an Indian Song: A Biography of D'Arcy McNickle* (Lincoln: University of Nebraska Press, 1992), 91, 97; Stephen G. Thompson, "Ancient Navajo Religion Is Related to Modern Medicine," *Indians at Work* 10, no. 5–8 (Spring 1943): 5–8; Wade M. Davies, "The Changing Navajo–Physician Relationship, World War II to 1950: A History of Health-Care on the Navajo Reservation" (unpublished graduate paper, Arizona State University, 1992), 7–8.

8. Thompson, "Ancient Navajo Religion Is Related to Modern Medicine," 5–6.

9. Parker, *Singing an Indian Song*, 97–98; Leighton and Leighton, *Navajo Door*, 55, 58.

10. Thompson, "Ancient Navajo Religion Is Related to Modern Medicine," 5; Adair et al., *People's Health*, 37.

11. "Indian Hospitals Rank among Nation's Best," *Indians at Work* 9, no. 6 (February 1942): 13–14; J. M. Stuart to Commissioner, November 3, 1943, NA, PSR, Phoenix Area Office, Box 463; *Ganado News Bulletin*, October 1942.

12. Plan for Enlarged Use of Winslow U.S.I.S. Sanatorium, June 11, 1942, NA, PSR, Phoenix Area Office, Box 463; Joel J. McCook to J. M. Stewart, June 7, 1946, NA, PSR, Phoenix Area Office, Box 466.

13. *Annual Report, SI, 1943*, 281; Stewart to Commissioner, November 3, 1943, Ralph B. Snavley to Stewart (excerpts), March 17 and May 12, 1943, NA, PSR, Phoenix Area Office, Box 463.

14. *Annual Report, SI, 1945*, 247; *Annual Report, SI, 1946*, 361; Raup, *Indian Health Program*, 29.

15. Philp, *John Collier's Crusade for Indian Reform*, 211; S. Lyman Tyler, "William A. Brophy, 1945–48," in Kvasnicka and Viola, *Commissioners of Indian Affairs*, 284–85.

16. Davies, "Changing Navajo–Physician Relationship," 7–8; D. J. Hunt to Snavley, October 25, 1946, and Raymond Mundt to Henry Kassel, April 6, 1948, NA, PSR, Window Rock Agency, Box 160.

17. "Statements on Conditions among the Navajo Tribe: Hearings before the Committee on Indian Affairs, House of Representatives," 79th Cong., 2d sess. (Washington, D.C.: Government Printing Office, 1946), 16–18, 28.

18. Ozro T. Woods, "Health among the Navajo Indians," *Journal of the American Medical Association* 135 (December 13, 1947): 981–82.

19. Ibid., 982–83.

20. Kenneth D. Claw to Doctor, December 1, 1947, and Manuelito Begay to Mr. Kassel, March 16, 1948, NA, PSR, Window Rock Agency, Box 190.

21. Flora L. Bailey, "Suggested Techniques for Inducing Navajo Women to Accept Hospitalization During Childbirth and for Implementing Health Education," *American Journal of Public Health* 38 (October 1948): 1418–23.

22. *Annual Report, SI, 1948*, 386; Michel Pijoan and Charles S. McCammon, "The Problem of Medical Care for Navajo Indians," *Journal of the American Medical Association* 140 (July 23, 1949): 1014; Irving Frank, "Treatment of Epidemic Diarrhea on the Navajo Reservation," *Arizona Medicine* 6 (January 1949): 35–36.

23. Lewis J. Moorman, "Health of the Navajo-Hopi Indians: General Report of the American Medical Association Team," *Journal of the American Medical Association* 139 (February 5, 1949): 370–75.

24. Ibid., 371–72, 374; Davies, "Changing Navajo–Physician Relationship," 13–14.

25. Pijoan and McCammon, "Problem of Medical Care for Navajo Indians," 1013–15.

26. Bailey and Bailey, *History of the Navajos*, 232–34; *Annual Report, SI, 1950*, 339; Young, *Navajo Yearbook, 1958*, 31–32.

27. Pijoan and McCammon, "Problem of Medical Care for Navajo Indians," 1015; Rothman, *Living in the Shadow of Death*, 248; *Annual Report, SI, 1949*, 356–57.

28. Reifel, "Tuberculosis among the Indians of the United States," 234–47; Milton I. Levine and Margaret F. Sackett, "Results of BCG Immunization in New York City," *American Review of Tuberculosis* 53 (June 1946): 517–32. For comments on Reifel's early interest in tuberculosis, see Myers and Dustin, "Albert Reifel and Tuberculosis among the American Indians."

29. Moorman, "Health of the Navajo-Hopi Indians," 375; Moorman, "Tuberculosis on the Navajo Reservation," *American Review of Tuberculosis* 61 (April 1950): 586–91.

30. *Annual Report, SI, 1952*, 395; *Annual Report, SI, 1953*, 34; Paul M. Sears, "Tuberculosis and the Navajos," *Colorado Quarterly* 4 (Autumn 1955): 197–98; "The U.S. Lets Navajo

Children Die of Neglect," *The Argonaut* (November 21, 1951), 9–10; Stanley Glaser and Josephine E. Johnston, *Index of Hospitals and Sanatoria with Tuberculosis Beds in the United States and Territories as of April 1, 1953* (Washington, D.C.: Government Printing Office, 1954), 2. By 1953 the Winslow hospital listed fifteen beds for infant cases of tuberculosis, although it remained a general hospital.

31. Deuschle, "Tuberculosis among the Navajo," 201; *Annual Report, SI, 1951*, 354; *Annual Report, SI, 1952*, 398.

32. *Annual Report, SI, 1952*, 398; Rothman, *Living in the Shadow of Death*, 247–48; Adair et al., *People's Health*, 25–26; Deuschle, "Tuberculosis among the Navajo," 202.

33. Sears, "Tuberculosis and the Navajos," 200–202; Wauneka, "Helping a People to Understand," 89–90.

34. Deuschle, "Tuberculosis among the Navajo," 202; Sears, "Tuberculosis and the Navajos," 204; Young, *Navajo Yearbook, 1958*, 342.

35. Bernstein, *American Indians and World War II*, 95; Donald L. Fixico, *Termination and Relocation: Federal Indian Policy, 1945–1960* (Albuquerque: University of New Mexico Press, 1986), 45–54.

36. Raup, *Indian Health Program*, 21–22; Kunitz, *Disease Change and the Role of Medicine*, 150–52.

37. Fixico, *Termination and Relocation*, 52; Wade Madoc Davies, "The United States Public Health Service and the Navajo Nation" (Master's thesis, Arizona State University, 1993), 19–22.

38. Davies, "United States Public Health Service and the Navajo Nation," 22–25; *Annual Report, SI, 1955*, 236.

39. Adair et al., *People's Health*, 24–27; Young, *Navajo Yearbook, 1958*, 31–32.

40. J. Nixon Hadley, "Health Conditions among Navajo Indians," *Public Health Reports* 70 (September 1955): 831–36.

Trachoma ratios were so high because the disease had been all but eliminated in the general population while it remained untreated in some remote reservation areas.

41. Davies, "United States Public Health Service and the Navajo Nation," 27–29; Steven Spencer, "They're Saving Lives in Navajo-Land," *Saturday Evening Post* (April 23, 1955): 94; Sam Yazzie, quoted in Adair et al., *People's Health*, 12.

EPILOGUE

1. A number of good studies have been completed on Navajo health care since 1955. Anyone interested in this topic should first consult Davies, "United States Public Health Service and the Navajo Nation"; Adair et al., *People's Health*; and Kunitz, *Disease Change and the Role of Medicine*. See also Iverson, *Navajo Nation*, 65–67, 154–60, 202–5.

2. Kunitz, *Disease Change and the Role of Medicine*, 153–59; Davies, "United States Public Health Service and the Navajo Nation," 34–36.

3. Kunitz, *Disease Change and the Role of Medicine*, 159; Adair et al., *People's Health*, xxii, 222–34.

4. Rothman, *Living in the Shadow of Death,* 245; Trennert, "Federal Government and Indian Health in the Southwest," 83; Deuschle, "Tuberculosis among the Navajo," 105; Davies, "United States Public Health Service and the Navajo Nation," 41–46. For a breakdown of the major causes of hospitalization between 1955 to 1977, see Kunitz, *Disease Change and the Role of Medicine,* 160.

5. Bailey and Bailey, *History of the Navajos,* 263–77.

6. Iverson, *Navajo Nation,* 65–66; Stephen J. Kunitz and Jerrold E. Levy, "Dances with Doctors: Navajo Encounters with the Indian Health Service," in *Contested Knowledge: Reactions to Western Medicine in the Modern Period,* ed. A. Cunningham and B. Andrews (Manchester: Manchester University Press, forthcoming).

7. Iverson, *Navajo Nation,* 157–58; *The Arizona Republic,* November 6, 1995. The twelve-member IHS board that reviewed research grants was composed mostly of Navajos, but tribal officials felt that it was far too lenient.

8. *The Arizona Republic,* September 15, 1993; Iverson, *Navajo Nation,* 204; Kunitz and Levy, "Dances with Doctors."

9. Davies, "United States Public Health Service and the Navajo Nation," 88–89; Feldberg, *Disease and Class,* 208–14.

10. Davies, "United States Public Health Service and the Navajo Nation," 128–34; *The Arizona Republic,* September 15, 1995. Following the hantavirus outbreak, healers noted that a larger than usual rodent population had developed as the result of recent rains. They provided this information to government doctors, which enabled them to pinpoint the cases.

11. Davies, "United States Public Health Service and the Navajo Nation," 133–34; Frisbie, *Navajo Medicine Bundles,* 273–315, 403–22; Iverson, *Navajo Nation,* 205; *The Arizona Republic,* May 3, September 15, 1993.

BIBLIOGRAPHY

RECORDS OF THE NATIONAL ARCHIVES

COLLECTIONS AT THE MAIN BRANCH, WASHINGTON, D.C.

Record Group 15. Veteran's Records Pension Files
Record Group 75. Records of the Bureau of Indian Affairs
    Letters Received, 1881–1907
    Education Circulars
    Central Classified Files, 1907–1939
Record Group 393. United States Army Commands
    Fort Sumner Records, 1862–1869

COLLECTIONS AT THE PACIFIC SOUTHWEST REGIONAL BRANCH,
LAGUNA NIGUEL, CALIFORNIA.

Record Group 75.
    Navajo Agency Files
    Phoenix Area Office Files
    Window Rock Agency Files

NATIONAL ARCHIVES MICROFILM

Letters Received by the Office of Indian Affairs, 1824–1880 (Microcopy M234)
Letters Sent by the Office of Indian Affairs, 1824–1881 (Microcopy M21)
Records of the New Mexico Superintendency, 1849–1880 (Microcopy T21)
Reports of Inspection of the Field Jurisdictions of the Office of Indian Affairs, 1873–1900
    (Microcopy M21)
Superintendent's Annual Narrative and Statistical Reports, 1907–1938 (Microcopy M1011)
New Mexico Territorial Papers, 1851–1872 (Microcopy T17)
Office of the Adjutant General, Letters Received, Main Series, 1861–1870 (Microcopy
    M619)

MISCELLANEOUS MANUSCRIPT COLLECTIONS

American Indian Correspondence: The Presbyterian Historical Society Collection of Missionaries' Letters, 1833–1893. Microfilm, Greenwood Press.

Arizona State Archives, Phoenix
    Record Group 35, Council on Defense

Indian Rights Association, 1885–1901. Microfilm, Scholarly Resources.

Native Americans and the New Deal: The Office Files of John Collier, 1933–1945. Microfilm, University Publications of America.

Navajo Nation Museum, Window Rock, Arizona
    J. C. Morgan File.

New Mexico Records Center and Archives, Santa Fe
    Adjutant General Muster Files, 1847–1867

Presbyterian Historical Society Archives, Philadelphia

Warren Family Papers (private), Tucson, Arizona

CONGRESSIONAL DOCUMENTS

"Correspondence with the Governor of New Mexico relating to Indian disturbances in that Territory," January 7, 1861, 36th Cong., 2d sess., Exec. Doc. 24, serial 1097.

"Draft of a bill to create the Office of Medical Inspector for the United States Indian Service, January 18, 1882," 47th Cong., 1st sess., Exec. Doc. 59, serial 1987.

"Letter of the Commissioner of Indian Affairs relative to the employment of matrons at agencies," May 7, 1888, 50th Cong., 1st sess., Senate Exec. Doc. 160, serial 2513.

"Trachoma in Certain Indian Schools," 60th Cong., 2d sess., Senate Report no. 1025, serial 5380.

"Contagious and Infectious Disease among the Indians," 62d Cong., 3d sess., Senate Doc. 1038, serial 6365.

"Survey of Conditions of the Indians in the United States," pt. 18, Navajos in Arizona and New Mexico, 71st Cong., 3d sess. Washington, D.C.: Government Printing Office, 1932.

"Statements on Conditions among the Navajo Tribe. Hearings before the Committee on Indian Affairs, House of Representatives," 79th Cong., 2d sess. Washington, D.C.: Government Printing Office, 1946.

MISCELLANEOUS PRINTED DOCUMENTS

Abel, Annie H., ed. *Official Correspondence of James S. Calhoun While Indian Agent at Santa Fe and Superintendent of Indian Affairs in New Mexico.* Washington, D.C.: Government Printing Office, 1915.

Annual Reports of the Board of Indian Commissioners

Annual Reports of the Commissioner of Indian Affairs

Annual Reports of the Secretary of the Interior

Annual Reports of the Surgeon General, Public Health Service

Annual Reports of the U.S. Civil Service Commissioner

"The Indian Service Health Activities," Bulletin 11. Washington, D.C.: Office of Indian
    Affairs, 1922.
Joint Special Committee on Indian Affairs. *The Condition of the Indian Tribes.*
    Washington, D.C.: Government Printing Office, 1867.
Kappler, Charles J., ed. *Indian Affairs, Laws and Treaties.* 2 vols. Washington, D.C.:
    Government Printing Office, 1915.
Otis, George A. *A Report of Surgical Cases Treated in the Army of the United States from 1865
    to 1871.* Washington, D.C.: Government Printing Office, 1871.
*Third Annual Report of the State Board of Health of the State of Kansas, from January 1, 1887,
    and ending December 31, 1887.* Topeka: Kansas Publishing House, 1888.
United States Surgeon-General's Office. *The Medical and Surgical History of the War of the
    Rebellion (1861–1865).* 3 pts. Washington, D.C.: Government Printing Office, 1870–88.

NEWSPAPERS, MAGAZINES, AND NEWSLETTERS
Arizona Daily Star (Tucson)
Arizona Republican (Phoenix)
Arizona Republic (Phoenix)
The Christian Century
Cincinnati Enquirer
Citizen (Wilson County, Kansas)
Coconino Sun (Flagstaff, Arizona)
The Echo (Benedict, Kansas)
The Gallup Independent (Gallup, New Mexico)
Ganado News Bulletin (Ganado, Arizona)
Grand Haven Tribune (Grand Haven, Michigan)
Hinton Record (Hinton, Oklahoma)
The Native American (Phoenix)
The Outlook
Overland Monthly
Rocky Mountain News (Denver)
Santa Fe Daily New Mexican
Santa Fe Weekly Gazette

BOOKS
Aberle, David F. *The Peyote Religion among the Navajo.* Chicago: Adline, 1966.
Adair, John, Kurt W. Deuschle, and Clifford R. Barnett. *The People's Health: Anthropology
    and Medicine in a Navajo Community.* Rev. ed. Albuquerque: University of New
    Mexico Press, 1988.
Adams, George W. *Doctors in Blue: The Medical History of the Union Army in the Civil War.*
    New York: Henry Schuman, 1952.
Armstrong, William H. *A Friend to God's Poor: Edward Parmelee Smith.* Athens: University
    of Georgia Press, 1993.

Ashburn, Percy M. *The Ranks of Death: A Medical History of the Conquest of America.* New York: Coward-McCann, 1947.

Axtell, James. *The Invasion Within: The Contest of Cultures in Colonial North America.* New York: Oxford University Press, 1985.

——. *Beyond 1492: Encounters in Colonial North America.* New York: Oxford University Press, 1992.

Bahl, Ida. *Nurse among the Navajos.* [Northvale, N.J.]: Shepherd Publishing, 1984.

Bailey, Garrick, and Roberta Glenn Bailey. *A History of the Navajos: The Reservation Years.* Santa Fe: School of American Research Press, 1986.

Bailey, Lynn R. *Indian Slave Trade in the Southwest.* Los Angeles: Westernlore Press, 1966.

——. *The Long Walk: A History of the Navajo Wars, 1846–68.* Pasadena, Calif.: Westernlore Press, 1978.

Bender, Norman J. *"New Hope for the Indians": The Grant Peace Policy and the Navajos in the 1870s.* Albuquerque: University of New Mexico Press, 1989.

Berkhofer, Robert F., Jr. *Salvation and the Savage: An Analysis of Protestant Missions and American Indian Response.* New York: Atheneum, 1972.

Bernstein, Alison R. *American Indians and World War II: Towards a New Era in Indian Affairs.* Norman: University of Oklahoma Press, 1991.

Brown, William J., et al. *Syphilis and Other Venereal Diseases.* Cambridge: Harvard University Press, 1970.

Buikstra, Jane E., ed. *Prehistoric Tuberculosis in the Americas.* Evanston: Northwestern University Archaeological Program, Scientific Papers no. 5, 1981.

Caldwell, Mark. *The Last Crusade: The War on Consumption, 1862–1954.* New York: Atheneum, 1988.

Correll, J. Lee, ed. *Through White Man's Eyes: A Contribution to Navajo History. A Chronological Record of the Navajo People from Earliest Times to the Treaty of June 1, 1868.* 6 vols. Window Rock, Ariz.: Navajo Heritage Center, 1979.

Crosby, Alfred W., Jr. *The Columbian Exchange: Biological and Cultural Consequences of 1492.* Westport, Conn.: Greenwood Publishing Co., 1972.

——. *Epidemic and Peace, 1918.* Westport, Conn.: Greenwood Press, 1976.

Dennie, Charles C. *A History of Syphilis.* Springfield, Ill.: Charles C. Thomas, 1962.

Dickman, F. F. *Kansas Medical Directory for 1881.* Fort Scott, Kans.: Harold Job Printing, 1881.

Doetsch, Raymond N. *Journey to the Green and Golden Lands: The Epic of Survival on the Wagon Trail.* Port Washington, N.Y.: Kennikat Press, 1976.

Dubos, Rene, and Jean Dubos. *The White Plague: Tuberculosis, Man and Society.* New Brunswick, N.J.: Rutgers University Press, 1987.

Ellis, Florence H. *Navajo Indians I, An Anthropological Study of the Navajo Indians.* New York: Garland Publishing, 1974.

Elmore, Francis H. *Ethnobotany of the Navajo.* Albuquerque: University of New Mexico Press, 1944.

Faunce, Hilda. *Desert Wife.* Boston: Little, Brown and Co., 1934.

Feldberg, Georgina D. *Disease and Class: Tuberculosis and the Shaping of Modern North American Society*. New Brunswick, N.J.: Rutgers University Press, 1995.

Fixico, Donald L. *Termination and Relocation: Federal Indian Policy, 1945–1960*. Albuquerque: University of New Mexico Press, 1986.

Forbes, Jack D. *Apache, Navajo, and Spaniard*. Norman: University of Oklahoma Press, 1960.

Forster, Elizabeth and Laura Gilpin. *Denizens of the Desert: A Tale in Word and Picture of Life among the Navajo Indians*. Edited by Martha A. Sandweiss. Albuquerque: University of New Mexico Press, 1988.

Frisbie, Charlotte J. *Navajo Medicine Bundles or Jish: Acquisition, Transmission, and Disposition in the Past and Present*. Albuquerque: University of New Mexico Press, 1987.

Glaser, Stanley, and Josephine E. Johnson. *Index of Hospitals and Sanatoria with Tuberculosis Beds in the United States and Territories as of April 1, 1953*. Washington, D.C.: Government Printing Office, 1954.

Gregg, Elinor D. *The Indians and the Nurse*. Norman: University of Oklahoma Press, 1965.

Hanna, William. *Studies in Smallpox and Vaccination*. New York: William Wood and Co., 1913.

Haskell, J. Loring. *Southern Athapaskan Migration, a.d. 200–1750*. Tsaile, Ariz.: Navajo Community College Press, 1987.

Horsman, Reginald. *Expansion and American Indian Policy, 1783–1812*. East Lansing: Michigan State University Press, 1967.

Hrdlicka, Ales. *Tuberculosis among Certain Indian Tribes of the United States*. Bureau of American Ethnology, Bulletin no. 42. Washington, D.C.: Government Printing Office, 1909.

Iverson, Peter. *The Navajo Nation*. Albuquerque: University of New Mexico Press, 1983.

Jenkins, J. Rockwood. *The Good Shepherd Mission to the Navajo*. Phoenix, Ariz.: Privately published, 1954.

Johnson, Broderick H., ed. *Navajos and World War II*. Tsaile, Ariz.: Navajo Community College Press, 1977.

Jones, Billy M. *Health-Seekers in the Southwest, 1817–1900*. Norman: University of Oklahoma Press, 1967.

Kaufman, Martin. *American Medical Education: The Formative Years, 1765–1910*. Westport, Conn.: Greenwood Press, 1976.

Keers, R. Y. *Pulmonary Tuberculosis: A Journey Down the Centuries*. London: Bailliere Tindall, 1978.

Keleher, William A. *Turmoil in New Mexico, 1846–1868*. Repr. ed. Albuquerque: University of New Mexico Press, 1982.

Keller, Robert W., Jr. *American Protestantism and United States Indian Policy, 1869–82*. Lincoln: University of Nebraska Press, 1983.

Kelly, Lawrence C. *The Navajo Indians and Federal Indian Policy, 1900–1935*. Tucson: University of Arizona Press, 1968.

——. *Navajo Roundup: Selected Correspondence of Kit Carson's Expedition against the Navajo, 1863–1865.* Boulder, Colo.: Pruett Publishing Company, 1970.

Kett, Joseph. *The Formation of the American Medical Profession: The Role of Institutions, 1780–1960.* New Haven: Yale University Press, 1968.

Kluckhohn, Clyde, and Dorothea Leighton. *The Navajo.* Rev. ed. Cambridge: Harvard University Press, 1974.

Kunitz, Stephen J. *Disease Change and the Role of Medicine: The Navajo Experience.* Berkeley: University of California Press, 1983.

Kvasnicka, Robert M., and Herman J. Viola, eds. *The Commissioners of Indian Affairs, 1824–1977.* Lincoln: University of Nebraska Press, 1979.

Leighton, Alexander H., and Dorothea C. Leighton. *The Navajo Door: An Introduction to Navajo Life.* Cambridge: Harvard University Press, 1945.

Leupp, Francis E. *The Indian and His Problem.* New York: Charles Scribner's Sons, 1910.

Lillie, Leo C. *Historic Grand Haven and Ottawa County.* Grand Haven, Mich.: n.p., 1931.

Luckingham, Bradford. *Epidemic in the Southwest, 1918–1919.* El Paso: Texas Western Press, 1984.

Ludmerer, Kenneth. *Learning to Heal: The Development of American Medical Education.* New York: Basic Books, 1985.

McNitt, Frank. *The Indian Traders.* Norman: University of Oklahoma Press, 1962.

——. *Navajo Wars: Military Campaigns, Slave Raids, and Reprisals.* Albuquerque: University of New Mexico Press, 1972.

Meriam, Lewis, et al. *The Problem of Indian Administration.* Baltimore: Johns Hopkins Press, 1928.

Mitchell, Frank. *Navajo Blessingway Singer: The Autobiography of Frank Mitchell, 1881–1967.* Edited by Charlotte J. Frisbie and David P. McAllester. Tucson: University of Arizona Press, 1978.

Moore, William Haas. *Chiefs, Agents, and Soldiers: Conflict on the Navajo Frontier, 1868–1882.* Albuquerque: University of New Mexico Press, 1994.

Murphy, Lawrence R. *William F. M. Arny, Frontier Crusader.* Tucson: University of Arizona Press, 1972.

Necrological Reports and Annual Proceedings of Princeton Theological Seminary. 4 vols. Princeton, N.J.: C. S. Robinson, 1891–1919.

Newcomb, Franc J. *Hosteen Klah, Navajo Medicine Man and Sand Painter.* Norman: University of New Mexico Press, 1964.

Norwood, William Frederick. *Medical Education in the United States Before the Civil War.* Philadelphia: University of Pennsylvania Press, 1944; repr., New York: Arno Press, 1971.

Parker, Dorothy. *Singing an Indian Song: A Biography of D'Arcy McNickle.* Lincoln: University of Nebraska Press, 1992.

Parman, Donald L. *The Navajos and the New Deal.* New Haven: Yale University Press, 1976.

Perrone, Bobette, H. Henrietta Stockel, and Victoria Krueger. *Medicine Women, Curanderas, and Women Doctors.* Norman: University of Oklahoma Press, 1989.

Perry, Richard J. *Western Apache Heritage: People of the Mountain Corridor*. Austin: University of Texas Press, 1991.

Philp, Kenneth R. *John Collier's Crusade for Indian Reform, 1920–1954*. Tucson: University of Arizona Press, 1977.

Pierce, Frederick C. *Whitney: The Descendants of John Whitney Who Came from London, England, to Watertown, Massachusetts, in 1635*. Chicago: Privately published, 1895.

Porter, Joseph C. *Paper Medicine Man: John Gregory Bourke and His American West*. Norman: University of Oklahoma Press, 1986.

Priest, Loring B. *Uncle Sam's Stepchildren: The Reformation of United States Indian Policy, 1865–1887*. Lincoln: University of Nebraska Press, 1975.

Prucha, Francis P. *American Indian Policy in Crisis: Christian Reformers and the Indian, 1865–1900*. Norman: University of Oklahoma Press, 1976.

——. *American Indian Policy in the Formative Years: The Indian Trade and Intercourse Acts, 1790–1834*. Cambridge: Harvard University Press, 1962.

——. *American Indian Policy in the United States*. Lincoln: University of Nebraska Press, 1981.

——. *The Great Father: The United States Government and the American Indian*. 2 vols. Lincoln: University of Nebraska Press, 1984.

Quétel, Claude. *History of Syphilis*. Cambridge, England: Polity Press, 1990.

Raup, Ruth M. *The Indian Health Program from 1800 to 1955*. Washington, D.C.: U.S. Public Health Service, 1959.

Reff, Daniel T. *Disease, Depopulation, and Culture in Northwestern New Spain, 1518–1764*. Salt Lake City: University of Utah Press, 1991.

Reichard, Gladys A. *Navajo Religion: A Study of Symbolism*. 2 vols., New York: Pantheon Books, 1950; repr., Tucson: University of Arizona Press, 1983.

Roemer, Milton I., ed. *Henry E. Sigerist on the Sociology of Medicine*. New York: M.D. Publications, 1960.

Roessel, Ruth, ed. *Navajo Stories of the Long Walk Period*. Tsaile, Ariz.: Navajo Community College Press, 1973.

Roessel, Ruth, and Broderick H. Johnson, comps. *Navajo Livestock Reduction: A National Disgrace*. Tsaile, Ariz.: Navajo Community College Press, 1974.

Rothman, Sheila M. *Living in the Shadow of Death: Tuberculosis and the Social Experience of Illness in American History*. Baltimore: Johns Hopkins University Press, 1994.

Rothstein, William G. *American Physicians in the Nineteenth- Century*. Baltimore: Johns Hopkins University Press, 1972.

Salsbury, Clarence G., with Paul Hughes. *The Salsbury Story: A Medical Missionary's Lifetime of Public Service*. Tucson: University of Arizona Press, 1969.

Schmeckebier, Laurence F. *The Office of Indian Affairs: Its History, Activities and Organization*. Baltimore: Johns Hopkins Press, 1927.

Sheehan, Bernard W. *Seeds of Extinction: Jeffersonian Philanthropy and the American Indian*. Chapel Hill: University of North Carolina Press, 1973.

Shryock, Richard H. *The Development of Modern Medicine: An Interpretation of the Social and Scientific Factors Involved*. New York: Alfred A. Knopf, 1947.

——. *Medicine in America: Historical Essays.* Baltimore: Johns Hopkins Press, 1966.

——. *Medicine and Society in America, 1660–1860.* New York: New York University Press, 1960.

Sigerist, Henry E. *American Medicine.* New York: W. W. Norton, 1934.

——. *Henry E. Sigerist on the Sociology of Medicine.* Edited by Milton I. Roemer. New York: M.D. Publications, 1960.

——. *Landmarks in the History of Medicine.* London: Oxford University Press, 1956.

Simmons, Marc. *Spanish Government in New Mexico.* Albuquerque: University of New Mexico Press, 1990.

Simpson, James H. *Navajo Expedition: Journal of a Military Reconnaissance from Santa Fe, New Mexico, to the Navajo Country, Made in 1849 by Lieutenant James H. Simpson.* Edited and annotated by Frank McNitt. Norman: University of Oklahoma Press, 1964.

Smith, F. B. *The Retreat of Tuberculosis, 1850–1950.* London: Croom Helm, 1988.

Spicer, Edward H. *Cycles of Conquest: The Impact of Spain, Mexico, and the United States on the Indians of the Southwest, 1533–1960.* Tucson: University of Arizona Press, 1962.

Stannard, David E. *American Holocaust: The Conquest of the New World.* New York: Oxford University Press, 1992.

Starr, Paul. *The Social Transformation of American Medicine.* New York: Basic Books, 1982.

Stearn, E. Wagner, and Allen E. Stearn. *The Effect of Smallpox on the Destiny of the Amerindian.* Boston: Bruce Humphries, 1945.

Steiner, Paul E. *Physician-Generals in the Civil War: A Study in Nineteenth Mid-Century American Medicine.* Springfield, Ill.: Charles C. Thomas, 1966.

Stone, Eric. *Medicine among the American Indians.* New York: Hafner Publishing Co., 1962.

Stoney, Rev. James. *Lighting the Candle: The Episcopal Church on the Upper Rio Grande.* Santa Fe, N.M.: n.p., 1961.

Stuart, Paul. *The Indian Office: Growth and Development of an American Institution, 1865–1900.* Ann Arbor: UMI Research Press, 1978.

Szasz, Margaret Connell. *Indian Education in the American Colonies, 1607–1783.* Albuquerque: University of New Mexico Press, 1988.

Thompson, Gerald. *The Army and the Navajo: The Bosque Redondo Reservation Experiment, 1863–1868.* Tucson: University of Arizona Press, 1976.

Thornton, Russell. *American Indian Holocaust and Survival: A Population History since 1492.* Norman: University of Oklahoma Press, 1987.

Trafzer, Clifford E. *The Kit Carson Campaign: The Last Great Navajo War.* Norman: University of Oklahoma Press, 1982.

Trennert, Robert A. *Alternative to Extinction: Federal Indian Policy and the Beginnings of the Reservation System, 1846–51.* Philadelphia: Temple University Press, 1975.

Twitchell, Ralph E. *The History of the Military Occupation of New Mexico from 1846–1851.* Denver: Smith-Brooks Company, 1909.

Underhill, Ruth. *Here Come the Navajo!* Washington, D.C.: United States Indian Service, n.d.

——. *The Navajos.* Norman: University of Oklahoma Press, 1956.

Utley, Robert M. *The Indian Frontier of the American West, 1846–1890.* Albuquerque: University of New Mexico Press, 1984.

Vaughan, Alden T. *New England Frontier: Puritans and Indians, 1620–1675.* Boston: Little, Brown and Co., 1965.

Viola, Herman J. *Thomas L. McKenney: Architect of America's Early Indian Policy, 1816–1830.* Chicago: Sage Books, 1974.

Vogel, Virgil J. *American Indian Medicine.* Norman: University of Oklahoma Press, 1970.

White, Benjamin. *Smallpox and Vaccination.* Cambridge: Harvard University Press, 1925.

Wyman, Leland C., and Stuart K. Harris. *The Ethnobotany of the Kayenta Navajo: An Analysis of the John and Louisa Wetherill Ethnobotanical Collection.* University of New Mexico Publications in Biology, no. 5. Albuquerque: University of New Mexico Press, 1951.

Young, Robert W., ed. and comp. *The Navajo Yearbook, 1958.* Window Rock, Ariz.: Navajo Agency, 1958.

ARTICLES

Adair, John. "Physicians, Medicine Men and Their Navajo Patients." In *Man's Image of Medicine and Anthropology,* edited by Iago Galdston, 237–57. New York: International Universities Press, 1963.

Allen, Virginia R. "Agency Physicians to the Southern Plains Indians, 1868–1900." *Bulletin of the History of Medicine* 49 (Fall 1975): 318–30.

Aronson, Joseph D. and Carroll E. Palmer. "Experience with BCG Vaccine in the Control of Tuberculosis among North American Indians." *Public Health Reports* 61 (June 7, 1946): 802–20.

Bailey, Flora L. "Suggested Techniques for Inducing Navajo Women to Accept Hospitalization During Childbirth and for Implementing Health Education." *American Journal of Public Health* 38 (October 1948): 1418–23.

Bergman, Robert L. "Navajo Health Services and Projects." In *Handbook of North American Indians,* edited by William C. Sturtevant, vol. 10, edited by Alfonso Ortiz, 672–78. Washington, D.C.: Smithsonian Institution, 1983.

Bloom, Lansing B., ed. "Bourke on the Southwest, VIII." *New Mexico Historical Review* 11 (January 1936): 77–122.

Brewer, Issac W. "Tuberculosis among Indians of Arizona and New Mexico." *New York Medical Journal* 84 (November 17, 1906): 981–83.

Brugge, David. "Navajo Prehistory and History to 1850." In *Handbook of North American Indians,* edited by William C. Sturtevant, vol. 10, edited by Alfonso Ortiz, 489–501. Washington, D.C.: Smithsonian Institution, 1983.

Collier, John. "Indian Health: Some Questions and Some Possibilities." *Indians at Work* 3, no. 4 (October 1, 1935): 6–8.

Crosby, Alfred W. Jr. "Virgin Soil Epidemics as a Factor in the Aboriginal Depopulation in America." *William and Mary Quarterly,* 3d ser., 33 (April 1976): 289–99.

Deuschle, Kurt W. "Tuberculosis among the Navajo: Research in Cross-Cultural

Technologic Development in Health." *American Review of Respiratory Diseases* 80 (August 1959): 200–206.

"Director of Indian Medical Service." *Indians at Work* 8, no. 7 (March 1941): 22.

"Dr. Polk Richards. World-Famous Trachoma Expert, Retires." *Indians at Work* 10, no. 1 (July–September 1942): 24.

"Drama in the Life of Field Nurses," *Indians at Work* 2, no. 22 (July 1, 1935): 38–39.

Forster, Wesley G. "Treatment of Trachoma with Sulfanilamide." *American Journal of Ophthalmology* 23 (May 1940): 523–24.

"Forty Years Ago." *Navajo Medical News* 8, no. 3 (November 29, 1941): 10–12.

Fox, L. Webster. "The Trachoma Problem among the North American Indians." *Journal of the American Medical Association* 86 (February 6, 1926): 404–8.

Frank, Irving. "Treatment of Epidemic Diarrheas on the Navajo Reservation." *Arizona Medicine* 6 (January 1949): 35–36.

Frisbie, Charlotte J. "Temporal Change in Navajo Religion, 1868–1990." *Journal of the Southwest* 34 (Winter 1992): 457–514.

Frisbie, Charlotte J., and Eddie Tso. "The Navajo Ceremonial Practitioners Registry." *Journal of the Southwest* 35 (Spring 1993): 53–92.

Frost, Richard H. "The Pueblo Indian Smallpox Epidemic in New Mexico, 1898–1899." *Bulletin of the History of Medicine* 64 (Fall 1990): 417–45.

Gerken, Edna A. "Development of a Health Education Program: Navajo Indians." *American Journal of Public Health* 30 (August 1940): 915–20.

——. "Health Education at Wingate Summer School." *Indians at Work* 4, no. 4 (October 1, 1936): 27–28.

——. "The Home in Public Health Advancement." *Indians at Work* 3, no. 5 (October 15, 1935): 39–41.

"Government Health Work among the Indian." *The Outlook* 114 (September 27, 1916): 168–69.

Guthrie, M. C. "Health of American Indians." *Journal of the American Medical Association* 88 (April 9, 1927): 1198–99.

[Gwyther, George]. "An Indian Reservation." *Overland Monthly* 10 (February 1873): 123–34.

Hadley, J. Nixon. "Health Conditions among Navajo Indians." *Public Health Reports* 70 (September 1955): 831–36.

Hinshaw, H. Corwin, et al. "Some Suggested Procedures for the Early Period of Therapeutic Pneumothorax." *American Review of Tuberculosis* 50 (December 1944): 573–74.

Hrdlicka, Ales. "Diseases of the Indians, More Especially of the Southwest United States and Northern Mexico." *Washington Medical Annals* 4 (1905–1906): 372–94.

"Indian Hospitals Rank among Nation's Best." *Indians at Work* 9, no. 6 (February 1942): 13–14.

"Indian Service Hospitals Gradually Meeting Standards for Acceptance by the American College of Surgeons." *Indians at Work* 5, no. 2 (October 15, 1937): 11–13.

"Influenza among American Indians." *Public Health Reports* 34 (May 9, 1919): 1008–9.

"The Institute for Training Navajo Nurse-Aids." *Indians at Work* 1, no. 21 (June 15, 1934): 29–30.

Jean, Sally Lucas. "Health Institute." *Indians at Work* 3, no. 4 (October 1, 1935): 14–18.

Julienelle, L. A., J. F. Lane, and W. P. Whitted. "The Effect of Sulfanilamide on the Course of Trachoma." *American Journal of Ophthalmology* 22 (November 1939): 1244–52.

Kendrick, John Mills. "Arizona Navajos." *Spirit of Missions* 64 (February 1899): 62.

———. "Nineteenth Annual Report of the Missionary Bishop of New Mexico and Arizona." *Spirit of Missions* 64 (December 1899): 633–35.

———. "Seventeenth Annual Report of the Missionary Bishop of New Mexico and Arizona." *Spirit of Missions* 62 (September 1897): 490–92.

Kunitz, Stephen J., and Jerrold E. Levy. "Dances with Doctors: Navajo Encounters with the Indian Health Service." In *Contested Knowledge: Reactions to Western Medicine in the Modern Period*, edited by A. Cunningham and B. Andrews. Manchester: Manchester University Press, forthcoming.

Levine, Milton I, and Margaret F. Sackett. "Results of BCG Immunization in New York City." *American Review of Tuberculosis* 53 (June 1946): 517–32.

"Lifting the Shadows." *Indians at Work* 8, no. 9 (May 1941): 11–14.

Long, Esmond R. "A Brief Comparison of Tuberculosis in the White, Indian and Negro Races." *American Review of Tuberculosis* 35 (January 1937): 1–5.

Luckert, Karl W. "Traditional Navajo Theories of Disease and Healing." *Arizona Medicine* 27 (July 1972): 570–73.

Marden, A. E. "Trachoma at Phoenix Indian School—and What Is Being Done for It." *The Native American* 13 (November 16, 1912): 453–54.

———. "The Trachoma Hospital." *The Native American* 13 (May 19, 1912): 240.

McCammon, Charles S., Frank J. Dufner, and Francis W. Felsman. "Syphilis among the Navajo Indians." *The Journal of Venereal Disease Information* 32 (February 1951): 28–33.

McGibony, J. R. "Indian Service Hospitals: Their Part in the Indian Health Program." *Indians at Work* 6, no. 6 (February 1939): 38–40.

"Miss Thackera's Hospital for the Navajos." *The Indian's Friend* 10 (March 1898): 7–8.

Moorman, Lewis J. "Health of the Navajo-Hopi Indians: General Report of the American Medical Association Team." *Journal of the American Medical Association* 139 (February 5, 1949): 370–76.

———. "Tuberculosis on the Navajo Reservation." *American Review of Tuberculosis* 61 (April 1950): 586–91.

Morgan, William. "Navajo Treatment of Sickness: Diagnosticians." *American Anthropologist*, n.s., 33 (July–September 1931): 390–402.

Murphy, Joseph A. "Health Problems of the Indians." *The Annals of the American Academy of Political and Social Science* 37 (March 1911): 104–9.

———. "The Prevention of Tuberculosis in the Indian Schools." *Journal of Proceedings and Addresses of the National Education Association* 47 (1909): 919–25.

Myers, J. Arthur, and Virginia L. Dustin. "Albert Reifel and Tuberculosis among the American Indians." *Hygeria* 25 (April 1947): 272–73, 318–22.

"Navajo Developments." *Indians at Work* 2, no. 20 (June 1, 1935): 20–23.

"Navajo Mountain Nurse Report." *Indians at Work* 3, no. 4 (October 1, 1935): 37–38.

"New Navajo-Hopi Medical Center at Fort Defiance, Arizona, Dedicated." *Indians at Work* 5, no. 12 (August 1938): 6–7.

Newman, Marshall T. "Aboriginal New World Epidemiology and Medical Care and the Impact of Old World Disease Imports." *American Journal of Physical Anthropology* 45 (1976): 667–72.

Osburn, Katherine Marie Birmingham. "The Navajos at the Bosque Redondo: Cooperation, Resistance and Initiative, 1864–1868." *New Mexico Historical Review* 60 (October 1985): 399–413.

Peter, W. W. "Navajo Medical Work—Old and New." *Indians at Work* 4, no. 4 (October 1, 1936): 47–48.

——. "What Does a Field Nurse Do?" *Indians at Work* 3, no. 24 (August 1, 1936): 28–29.

Pfeiffer, John. "Sulfanilamide: The Story of a Great Medical Discovery." *Harpers* 178 (March 1939): 384–96.

Pijoan, Michel, and Charles S. McCammon. "The Problem of Medical Care for Navajo Indians." *Journal of the American Medical Association* 140 (July 23, 1949): 1013–15.

Posey, William Campbell. "Trachoma among the Indians of the Southwest." *Journal of the American Medical Association* 88 (May 21, 1927): 1618–19.

"Posters and Primers Implement Development of a New American Language." *Indians at Work* 7, no. 9 (May 1940): 30.

Pousma, R. H. "Venereal Disease among the Navajos." *Southwestern Medicine* 13 (November 1929): 503–5.

Quinn, Geraldine E. "Indian Service Nurses Meet." *Navajo Medical News* 7, no. 4 (November 20, 1940): 10–11.

Reagan, Albert B. "The 'Flu' among the Navajos." *Transactions of the Kansas Academy of Science* 30 (1921): 131–38.

——. "The Influenza and the Navajo." *Proceedings of the Indiana Academy of Science* 29 (1919): 243–47.

Reebel, Mollie B. "Tenting on Western Navajo." *Indians at Work* 2, no. 17 (April 15, 1935): 29–30.

Reifel, Albert. "Tuberculosis among the Indians of the United States." *Diseases of the Chest* 16 (August 1949): 234–47.

Reeve, Frank D. "Federal Indian Policy in New Mexico, 1858–1880, Chapter I." *New Mexico Historical Review* 12 (July 1937): 218–47.

——. "The Government and the Navajo, 1846–1858." *New Mexico Historical Review* 14 (January 1939): 82–114.

——. "The Government and the Navajo, 1878–1883." *New Mexico Historical Review* 16 (July 1941): 275–312.

——. "The Government and the Navajo, 1883–1888." *New Mexico Historical Review* 18 (January 1943): 17–51.

Richards, Polk. "Trachoma." *Indians at Work* 4, no. 4 (October 1, 1936): 20–21.

Richards, Polk, Wesley G. Forster, and Phillips Thygeson. "Treatment of Trachoma with Sulfanilamide." *Archives of Ophthalmology* 21 (April 1939): 577–80.

Roessel, Robert A., Jr. "Navajo History, 1850–1923." In *Handbook of North American Indians*, edited by William C. Sturtevant, vol. 10, edited by Alfonso Ortiz, 506–23. Washington, D.C.: Smithsonian Institution, 1983.

Salmon, Roberto Mario. "The Disease Complaint at Bosque Redondo (1864–68)." *The Indian Historian* 9, no. 3 (Summer 1976): 2–7.

Salsbury, Clarence G. "Disease Incidence among the Navajos." *Southwestern Medicine* 21 (July 1927): 230–32.

——. "Incidence of Certain Diseases among the Navajos." *Arizona Medicine* 4, no. 6 (November 1947): 29–31.

——. "Medical Work in Navajoland." *American Journal of Nursing* 32 (April 1932): 415–16.

Schackel, Sandra K. "The Tale Those Nurses Told!: Public Health Nurses among the Pueblo and Navajo Indians." *New Mexico Historical Review* 65 (April 1990): 225–49.

Schnur, Leo. "Navajos Train Ward Aids to Counteract 'Medicine Men,'" *Modern Hospital* 59, no. 5 (November 1942): 80.

——. "Physicians U.S.I.S. Medical Meeting." *Navajo Medical News* 7, no. 4 (November 25, 1940): 8–9.

Sears, Paul M. "Tuberculosis and the Navajos." *Colorado Quarterly* 4 (Autumn 1955): 195–204.

Sedlacek, Bretislaw, and J. A. Schwartz. "Tuberculosis on the Spot." *Navajo Medical News* 7, no. 4 (November 25, 1940): 20–23.

Senders, Rosella. "Indian Medical Service Pioneers in Trachoma Treatment." *Indians at Work* 8, no. 5 (January 1941): 32–33.

——. "New Director Appointed for Indian Medical Service." *Indians at Work* 8, no. 10 (June 1941): 9–10.

Simmons, William S. "Conversion from Indian to Puritan." *New England Quarterly* 52 (June 1979): 197–218.

"Some Health Problems in the Navajo Area." *Navajo Medical News* 8, no. 3 (November 29, 1941): 13–17.

Spencer, Steven. "They're Saving Lives in Navajo-Land." *Saturday Evening Post* (April 23, 1955): 94.

Thackera, Eliza W. "Arizona." *Spirit of Missions* 64 (June 1899): 278.

——. "Small Pox Scare at Fort Defiance." *Spirit of Missions* 64 (August 1899): 407.

Thompson, Stephen G. "Ancient Navajo Religion Is Related to Modern Medicine." *Indians at Work* 10, no. 5–8 (Spring 1943): 5–8.

Tillim, Sidney J. "Health among the Navajos." *Southwestern Medicine* 20 (July–November 1936): 272, 276–77, 310–13, 355, 388–91, 432–33.

——. "Trachoma among American Indians." National Society for the Prevention of Blindness, Publication 179 (1936): 1–11.

Townsend, J. G. "Answers to Indian Health Questions." *Indians at Work* 3, no. 4 (October 1, 1935): 8–10.

———. "Trachoma Control in the Indian Service." National Society for the Prevention of Blindness, Publication 314 (1940): 1–12.

———. "Trachoma, Dreaded Eye Disease, Being Conquered." *Indians at Work* 7, no. 4 (December 1939): 8–11.

Trennert, Robert A. "A Vision of Grandeur: The Arizona Mineral Belt Railroad." *Arizona and the West* 12 (Winter 1970): 339–54.

———. "The Federal Government and Indian Health in the Southwest: Tuberculosis and the Phoenix East Farm Sanatorium, 1909–1955." *Pacific Historical Review* 65 (February 1996): 61–84.

———. "Indian Sore Eyes: The Federal Campaign to Control Trachoma in the Southwest, 1910–1940." *Journal of the Southwest* 32 (Summer 1990): 121–49.

———. "White Man's Medicine vs. Hopi Tradition: The Smallpox Epidemic of 1899." *The Journal of Arizona History* 33 (Winter 1992): 349–66.

"Tuberculosis among Indians." *Indians at Work* 3, no. 8 (December 1935): 35.

"The U.S. Lets Navajo Children Die of Neglect." *The Agronaut* (November 23, 1951): 9–10.

Wallace, Jerry. "How the Episcopal Church Came to Arizona." *The Journal of Arizona History* 6 (Autumn 1965): 101–16.

Warner, H. J. "Notes on the Results of Trachoma Work by the Indian Service in Arizona and New Mexico." *Public Health Reports* 44 (November 29, 1929): 2913–20.

Warner, Michael J. "Protestant Missionary Activity among the Navajo, 1890–1912." *New Mexico Historical Review* 45 (July 1970): 209–32.

Wauneka, Annie D. "Helping a People to Understand." *American Journal of Nursing* 62 (July 1962): 88–90.

White, L. W. "Reminiscences of an Indian Physician." *Indians at Work* 3, no. 4 (October 1, 1935): 32.

———. "A Glance at Progress Made in Indian Service Hospitals." *Indians at Work* 4, no. 4 (October 1, 1936): 43–44.

White, Richard. "The Winning of the West: The Expansion of the Western Sioux in the Eighteenth and Nineteenth Centuries." *Journal of American History* 65 (September 1978): 319–43.

Woods, Ozro T. "Health among the Navajo Indians." *Journal of the American Medical Association* 135 (December 13, 1947): 981–83.

Wyman, Leland C. "Navajo Ceremonial System." In *Handbook of North American Indians*, edited by William C. Sturtevant, vol. 10, edited by Alfonso Ortiz, 536–57. Washington, D.C.: Smithsonian Institution, 1983.

———. "The Religion of the Navajo Indians." In *Forgotten Religions (Including Some Living Primitive Religions)*, edited by Vergilius Ferm, 344–47. New York: Philosophical Library, 1950.

UNPUBLISHED MATERIALS

Collins, William S. "The Navajo and Hopi Experience with Spanish Influenza." Graduate research paper, Arizona State University, 1993.

Davies, Wade M. "The Changing Navajo–Physician Relationship, World War II to 1950: A History of Health-Care on the Navajo Reservation." Graduate research paper, Arizona State University, 1992.

——. "Missionary Medical Care and the Navajo." Graduate research paper, Arizona State University, 1993.

——. "The United States Public Health Service and the Navajo Nation." Master's thesis, Arizona State University, 1993.

Emmerich, Lisa E. "'To Respect and Love and Seek the Way of White Women': Field Matrons, the Office of Indian Affairs, and Civilization Policy, 1890–1938." Ph.D. diss., University of Maryland, 1987.

Office of Navajo Land Administration. "Treaties, Acts, and Executive Orders." Map. Window Rock, Ariz., 1991.

Putney, Diane T. "Fighting the Scourge: American Indian Morbidity and Federal Indian Policy, 1897–1928." Ph.D. diss., Marquette University, 1980.

INDEX